2

2

THE SUTHERLAND BOOK

Edited by Donald Omand:

THE CAITHNESS BOOK, 1972

THE MORAY BOOK, 1976

THE RED DEER HANDBOOK, 1981

THE SUTHERLAND BOOK

Edited by
DONALD OMAND
MA, MSc, FSA(Scot), FRSGS

ESTABLISHED
1899

THE NORTHERN TIMES LIMITED

Published and printed by
The Northern Times Limited,
Golspie, Sutherland, Scotland

ISBN O 9501718 2 4

Acknowledgements

I wish to thank the following people for supplying relevant material and for giving advice on chapter content:

Mr D Balfour, Tarbert, Harris; Mrs E Beaton, Hopeman, Moray; Mr E Rudie, Bettyhill, Sutherland; The Wildlife Research Officer, The Forestry Commission; Mr A Hinde, Conservation Forester, The Forestry Commission; Mr N Campbell, Nature Conservancy Council; Mr A Currie, Nature Conservancy Council; Mr A Baxter Cooper, Consultant Ecologist and Wildlife Manager; Mr J Maclennan, Forester, Sutherland Estates; Mr R Dennis, Royal Society for the Protection of Birds; Mr D Macdonald, Dornoch and Mr L Myatt, Halkirk.

All maps and diagrams were drawn by Method Publishing Company Ltd., Golspie, and due acknowledgement is given to the Ordnance Survey for permission to use maps based on their publications.

Thanks are given to Mr J L Davidson and his staff, Ordnance Survey, Edinburgh and Mr John Macrae and Mr John Barneveld of the Archaeology Field Section (North Scotland) who have been largely responsible for the recording and survey of the antiquities of East Sutherland for the Ordnance Survey.

Figure 3 is based on Crown Copywright *Geological Survey "10-mile" Sheet 1,* with the permission of the Controller of Her Majesty's Stationery Office.

Figure 14 is based on an illustration from Miss A Henshall's *"The Chambered Tombs of Scotland" Vol 1* and Figures 15 and 16 are based on illustrations from the same volume and Vol 2 with permission of the publishers, The Edinburgh University Press.

The Meteorological Office is thanked for supplying the data from which Figures 11, 12 and 13 were prepared.

The Department of Agriculture for Scotland supplied the statistics for Chapter 15.

The Copyright of Chapter 3 *"The Soils"* is held by The Macaulay Institute for Soil Research, Aberdeen. Figures 6, 7 and 10 were based on maps drawn by Mr W S Shirreffs, cartographer in the Department of Soil Survey, The Macaulay Institute.

Figure 21 was based on a map drawn by Miss Sylvia Leek, Department of Archaeology, University of Glasgow.

Mrs J Mowat, Halkirk, Caithness gave valuable secretarial assistance and Mr J Keenan, Golspie undertook the laborious job of compiling the Index.

The Authors

Editor:
DONALD OMAND   Tutor-Organiser, Department of Adult Education and Extra Mural Studies, University of Aberdeen.

Mr K BLOOD	Archaeologist, Ordnance Survey
Mr M BURNETT	Farmer
Mr E COWAN	Professor, Department of History, University of Guelph
Mr D FUTTY	Soil Scientist, The Macaulay Institute for Soil Research, Aberdeen
Mr M GRAY	Reader, Department of Economic History, University of Aberdeen
Miss A HENSHALL	Archaeologist, Edinburgh
Dr J B KENWORTHY	Lecturer, Department of Botany, University of Aberdeen
Mr D MACAULAY	Head of Department of Celtic Studies, University of Aberdeen
Mr E MICHIE	District Officer, Forestry Commission
Dr I PENNIE	Retired Medical Practitioner, Scourie
Mr R W K REID	Archaeologist, Stirling
Mr H ROSS	Broadcaster and Folklorist
Mr S ROSS	Meteorologist by profession and Geologist by inclination
Mr A SMALL	Reader, Department of Geography, University of Dundee
Mr E TALBOT	Lecturer, Department of Archaeology, University of Glasgow
Mr D BRUCE WEIR	Editor of "The Northern Times" 1949-1975
Mr D WITHRINGTON	Senior Lecturer, Department of History, Univeristy of Aberdeen

We record, with regret, that Mr Hugh Ross died in January, 1982 during the course of publication.

Contents

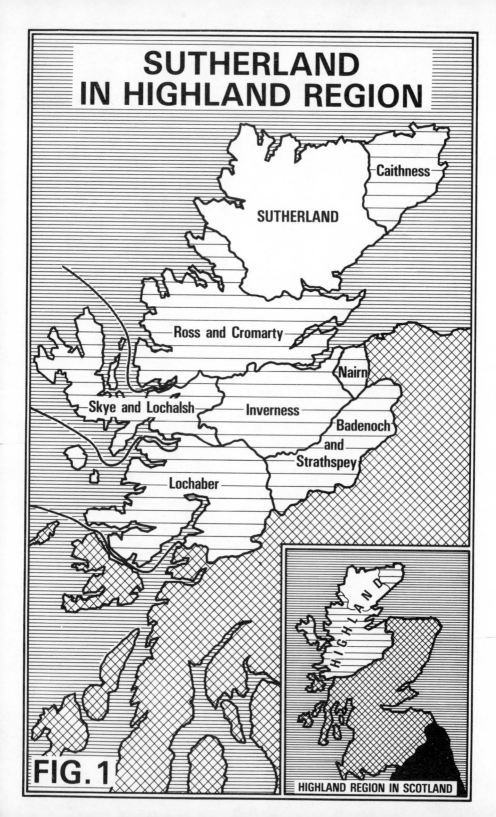

SUTHERLAND
IN HIGHLAND REGION

Caithness

SUTHERLAND

Ross and Cromarty

Nairn

Skye and Lochalsh

Inverness

Badenoch and Strathspey

Lochaber

FIG. 1

HIGHLAND

HIGHLAND REGION IN SCOTLAND

List of Figures

ERRATUM: Please note that Figure 15.3 should read "ACHU" not "ACHN" and Figure 15.4 should read "EMBO" not "EMBOL".

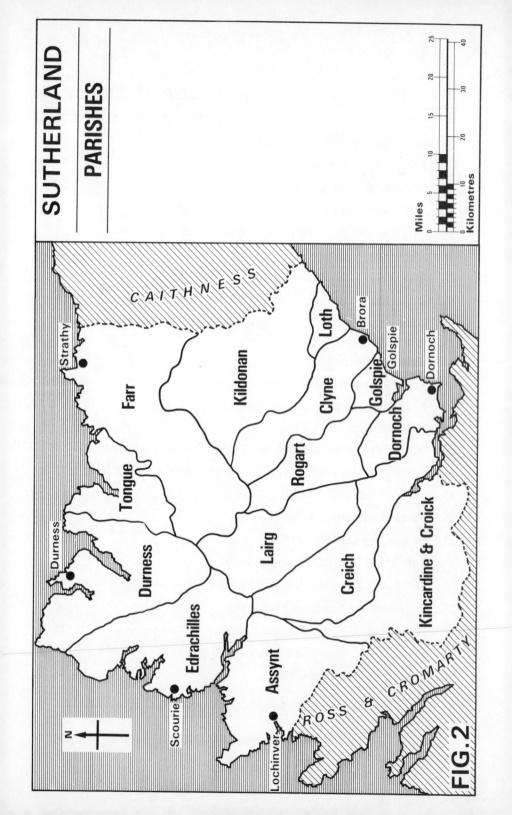

SUTHERLAND

PARISHES

Miles
Kilometres

FIG.2

List of Plates

Permission to reproduce copyright photographs is gratefully acknowledged. The photographers are noted with each individual illustration.

Introduction

Sutherland (Old Norse, "Suthrland" — the Southland), one of the seven crofting counties, with a population of under 13,000 people covers an area of over 5,000 square kilometres (more than 2,000 square miles), giving it the lowest population density of any District in Scotland. Sutherland consists of 13 parishes (Fig. 2) varying in size from the largest, Farr (1,050 square kilometres, 405 square miles) to the smallest, Loth (70 square kilometres, 27 square miles).

In the west of Sutherland there are still true wildernesses and here is found the most spectacular scenery in Britain which offers a landscape of extreme contrast to the eastern lowlands carved out of softer and much younger rocks. In the wild beauty of the west the few tiny settlements nestle by coastal inlets; here, Nature has been generous with scenery and mean with soil. Here, salmon and trout swim in waters unsullied by Man. Glorious beaches and the great tiered bird city of Handa have as yet been spared the ravages of oil pollution.

The north coast is punctured by long sea inlets with Loch Eriboll offering a wide deep sheltered anchorage. This coast is an area of immense botanical interest from the sweet soils of Durness limestone to the sandy terraces of the Naver. Attractive scattered townships sit close by skerry-studded shores.

Within the vast interior Lairg, the only sizeable village, is the focus of road routes. Lairg is the Rome of the North and a great marketing centre for sheep. Here in the heartland of Sutherland is an abundance of sheep, a wealth of peat and a dearth of folk.

Not surprisingly the bulk of Sutherland's population is found in villages (e.g. Bonar Bridge, Dornoch, Golspie, Brora and Helmsdale) along the narrow eastern seaboard fringed by old raised shorelines and more modern shingle/sand constructions. These combine to give attractive beaches for recreation and ideal locations for golf courses with Royal Dornoch one of the finest and one of the earliest known (1616) in Scotland. Traditionally Brora has been the focus of industrial development, but now some east coast eyes are turned seawards towards new wealth under the waves. With the realisation of the promise of a bridge across the Dornoch Firth may come greater optimism for the future and a cut back in Sutherland's long established export — its young folk. Let us hope that this is so and that the sad and bitter irony of *"The Cheviot, the Stag and the black black Oil"* is not wholly fulfilled.

DONALD OMAND, HALKIRK, JUNE 1982.

Part one

NATURAL
ENVIRONMENT

Chapter one

THE GEOLOGY OF SUTHERLAND

INTRODUCTION

The history of geological research in Sutherland is a fascinating story which covers a span of some 150 years.

As the geological surveying of the Highlands progressed it soon became apparent that its structure was extremely complex and that unravelling its development was going to be an immense problem. At this time it was recognised that the rocks in the far north-west of Sutherland were very old, and "In the hope that a detailed study of Wester Sutherland and Ross would throw light on the geological structure of the rest of the Highlands, a beginning was made in the year 1883 in the district of Durness by Messrs. Peach and Horne". With this simple sentence Sir Archibald Geikie, the then Director of the Geological Survey, described the start of a survey which was to become a milestone in geological history.

The publication in 1907 of the results of this work led to a new understanding of large-scale geological processes and won the two geologists international acclaim. Sutherland was established as a classical study area overnight and geologists from all over the world have made pilgrimages to the District ever since. Researches in the area have continued at such a pace that West Sutherland has been mapped and studied in more detail than any other comparable area in the world. Even today with the rapid increase in understanding of the processes of ocean floor spreading and the formation of continental crusts this pace continues unchecked because the rocks of Sutherland have been involved with these processes several times during their history. The endless streams of students being shown over the area as part of their curriculum may well pause to ponder beside the simple memorial overlooking Loch Assynt bearing the now legendary names — Drs. B. N. Peach and J. Horne.

Nor must the rest of the District be overlooked. Many interest-

TABLE 1 – GEOLOGICAL TIME SCALE

ERA	PERIOD		AGE Ma	EVENTS IN SUTHERLAND
KAINOZOIC	QUATERNARY		2	Several ice ages
	TERTIARY			Erosion under semi-tropical conditions
			65	Final opening of the Atlantic
MESOZOIC	CRETACEOUS			Continued erosion overland Deposition in offshore basins
			136	
	JURASSIC			Last transcurrent movements on Great Glen Fault Marine transgression over subsiding Moray Firth and Minch Basins
			190	
	TRIASSIC		225	Continental weathering
PALAEOZOIC	PERMIAN			Moray Firth and Minch Basins begin to subside Central North Sea Rift opens Periodic desert conditions
			280	
	CARBONIFEROUS			Not observed: continued continental weathering of Upper Old Red Sandstone?
			360	
	OLD RED SAND-STONE	Upper	390	Minor vulcanism
		Middle		Movements on transcurrent faults
		Lower	405	Old Red Sandstone Continent. Orcadian Basin. Final collision of continents. Folding.
	SILURIAN		420	Newer granites. Regional metamorphism and migmatites
	ORDOVICIAN		465	Movement on Moine Thrust
	CAMBRIAN		530	Iapetus begins to close Carn Chuinneag intrusion Sedimentation in shelf sea on foreland
PRE-CAMBRIAN*	TORRIDONIAN		600	Upper Torridonian and Moinian
			750	Opening of Iapetus
			1000	Lower Torridonian: continental sedimentation
	LEWISIAN		1800	Laxfordian deformation and metamorphism
			2400	Intrusion of basic dyke swarm Large scale deformation
			2700	
			2800	Existing rocks metamorphosed during Scourian event
	?		?	Formation of early continent from metamorphic and igneous complexes.

* Note that the duration of the Pre-Cambrian era is some eight times the interval between the beginning of the Cambrian Period and the present.

ing studies have been described from the central and northern parts, while in the east the coal-bearing beds at Brora have been exploited since 1529. Less well publicised in this part is the upsurge in interest in this east coastal belt where geologists from most of the oil companies operating in the North Sea have examined the rock structures to understand more fully the processes involved in oil entrapment. Not far offshore is the Beatrice Oil Field, discovered by the systematic researches and exploration of the geologists.

The distribution of the rocks of Sutherland is such that the oldest are exposed in the west and eastwards progressively younger rocks appear. In the Scourie area modern dating methods have shown some rocks to be over 2800 my (million years) old, while on the east coast the youngest are around 140 my. To appreciate fully the significance of the enormous span of geological time which these ages represent, one has to consider events on a time scale where a unit of 1 my is not too large (see Table 1). On this scale processes which to our eye are barely perceptible appear in a different light — e.g. a rate of erosion of 1 mm over a period of 20 years is sufficient to remove the highest mountain in Sutherland in 20 my (1000 m = 3281 ft).

DEVELOPMENT OF THE LANDMASS

The oldest rocks exposed in the north-west of the District are part of the Lewisian Gneiss basement which extends westward to the continental edge and eastward under the Northern Highlands. The rock types and structure indicate that the complex was intensely metamorphosed and deformed over a period of over 1000 my dating from 2800 to 1700 million years ago (Ma). These and rocks of similar age in Greenland and North America are considered to have formed part of one immense supercontinent at that time.

Rifting in this continental crust led to the formation of north-easterly orientated fault-bounded troughs which widened into an ocean known as Iapetus. By 1000 Ma sediments derived from higher ground to the north-west were being deposited on the continental margin and these we see today as the Torridonian rocks. The material being deposited in the ocean we know as the Moinian series. With the Iapetus ocean at its maximum width a marine incursion spread a shallow shelf sea over the margin of the continent now occupied by North-West Sutherland and sediments of Cambrian-Ordovician age were deposited.

The ocean then began to close and the oceanic sediments were compressed and metamorphosed between the advancing plates and finally uplifted into fold mountain systems. The peak of these movements occurred around 495 Ma in the Grampian Highland area and around 420 Ma in Sutherland. By 400 Ma at the close of this cycle known as the Caledonian Orogeny the European Plate had collided with the American-Greenland Plate and the ocean had been eliminated.

From the erosion of the newly formed mountain masses came the sediments that built up the enormous Old Red Sandstone continent and which reached a great thickness in the Orcadian Basin. Later in the Moray Firth a new basin developed, which from the absence of sediments of Carboniferous age, probably dates from the Permian Period as does the mid-North Sea rift system. To the west uplift and erosion continued and the fault-bounded basin of the Minches again subsided. The sandstones deposited in these two basins are of sufficient thickness to indicate that high ground of considerable relief separated them and although there is little indication of the extent of the Northern Highlands in Devonian times, in the Permo-Triassic deposits in the Minches and the Moray Firth the present outline can be found, indicating that this has been a ' positive area ' ever since.

Differential movement between the basins and high ground continued throughout this long period, with movement taking place on various fault systems such as The Minch, The Great Glen and their subsidiaries. This continued during the marine sedimentation of the Jurassic period but had largely ceased by the late Cretaceous.

The formation of the North Atlantic proper did not begin until late Mesozoic or Tertiary times when crustal extensions along rift systems opened into basins floored by oceanic crust. These developed between the Hebrides and Rockall Bank and between Rockall Bank and Greenland, probably on previous lines of weakness. Volcanic outbreaks in the Hebrides associated with the Atlantic margin did not affect areas where the basement was of Lewisian Gneiss and therefore did not occur in Sutherland. This activitiy ceased about 50 Ma and with it the large scale crustal movements in the region.

Again the importance of the correct appreciation of the geological time scale cannot be overstressed — where the opening of the Atlantic at the rate of a few cm per year since c. 65 million years ago has lead to its present dimensions. During this interval erosion of the land surface, which includes the effects of several ice ages in the last million years, has done much to obscure even the recent history of the development of the land we know as Sutherland.

LEWISIAN GNEISS

Along the western coastal part of Sutherland the oldest sedimentary rocks rest on a basement of crystalline metamorphic rocks known as the Lewisian Gneiss. These were recognised by the earliest workers as being of immense age and termed The Fundamental Complex. More recent research has shown that the gneisses developed over a span of more than 1000 my between 2800 and 1700 Ma.

Two divisions are recognised which probably represent the remains of two ancient orogenic episodes widely separated in time. The older group of gneisses which outcrops from Scourie (Plate 1) southwards is known as the Scourian Group and was produced from the metamorphism of an earlier complex by an event which has been dated as taking place between 2800 and 2700 Ma. Further deformation was followed by the intrusion of linear swarms of basic dykes dated as 2400 Ma. The Scourian rocks are separated from a younger group to the north by a narrow zone which runs west-northwest just south of Loch Laxford. This Laxfordian Group of gneisses was affected by a long period of metamorphism and deformation accompanied by the injection of granite sheets. This event has been dated as ceasing around 1800 Ma.

The type of the Scourian gneiss indicates that it developed at depths of 30 to 40 km (19 to 22 miles) near the base of the earth's crust, and some idea of the magnitude of the processes involved can be had when one realizes that by the time the oldest Torridonian sedimentary rocks were being deposited around 1000 Ma, these deep-seated rocks had appeared at the earth's surface. The relatively uniform metamorphism which affected the Scourian Gneiss gave it the characteristic banded and streaky appearance. The bulk of the rock is a grey, rudely foliated pyroxene gneiss with numerous bands and lenticles of basic and occasionally ultrabasic rocks. Many characteristics of the original rocks are still preserved. The basic dykes which traverse the gneiss are very conspicuous in Assynt and form a strongly west-northwesterly orientated swarm. There is also a less abundant group of east-west trending dykes of ultrabasic picrites. Both gneiss and dykes are sheared along pre-

FIG.3

SUTHERLAND
GEOLOGY

Lewisian Gneiss

Lewisian Granite

Moinian

Torridonian

Moine Thrust Zone

Cambrian and Ordovician

Old Red Sandstone

New Red Sandstone
and Mesozoic

Igneous Intrusions

Miles
0   5   10   15   20   25

Kilometres
0   10   20   30   40

N

Cape Wrath
Durness
MOINE THRUST
Point of Stoer
Scourie
Loch Assynt
Lochinver
ROSS & CROMARTY
Oykel Bridge
△Ben Kilbreck
Strathy
Rogart
CAITHNESS
Brora
Golspie
Dornoch

Torridonian crush belts, altering the gneiss to granulitic rocks, the basic dykes to hornblende schists and the ultrabasic dykes to tremolite and talc schists.

The Laxfordian complex is composed of more acid gneisses which have been so modified throughout their development that their origin has been obscured. They may have been formed by the repeated modification of older Scourian gneisses at a higher level in the earth's crust. Near their boundary with the Scourian gneiss in the south the rocks are intensely sheared but northwards this quickly dies out and their structure is dominated by northwest-trending regional folds. Granite and pegmatite veins increase rapidly until they form a zone of granite sheets 2.5 km (1.5 miles) wide stretching across the Loch Laxford region. Farther north the structure is very irregular with the granite veins forming discordant networks. The Laxfordan gneisses have not been so highly metamorphosed as their Scourian neighbours. The bands and lenses of more basic rock are amphibolites which are deformed along with the gneiss.

Geophysical surveys indicate that Scourian type rocks probably underlie the Laxfordian gneisses and also the much younger rocks to the east of the Moine Thrust Zone. The original mapping of the Moinian rocks of Sutherland showed various bodies of hornblendic rocks, acid gneisses etc., included in that group. Recent examination has shown many of these to be Lewisian in origin — some being in the form of thrust slices interleaved with the Moinian rocks.

As well as at the many inland exposures and continuous sections round the coasts, the Scourian gneiss and the basic dykes can readily be examined by the roadsides, particularly from Loch Assynt to Lochinver (Plate 2) and northwards round the coast road and again from Kylesku north to Scourie where there are particularly fine sections in the road cuttings. The Laxfordian gneiss and its granite sheets appear in the road cuttings from Loch Laxford to Rhiconich as well as on the coast. More accessible localities for examining the ultrabasic intrusions occur at Loch an Daimh Mor [158 428]*, near Scourie [157 453] and [145 445] and north of Loch Drumbeg [115 328]. The Lewisian inliers in the Moine are best seen along the north coast between Skerray and Strathy Point as well as in roadside cuttings. Inland the most accessible exposures appear on the north shore of Loch Naver.

* National Grid References are prefixed NC unless otherwise indicated.

TORRIDONIAN SANDSTONE

The Torridonian Sandstone series occurs as discontinuous deposits along the west coast of Sutherland, resting on the old Lewisian foreland, and as small outcrops in the Moine Thrust.

The sandstones rest unconformably on the Lewisian gneiss and the uneven nature of the ground on which they were deposited can be examined along the margins of the outcrops. Fossil hills in the gneiss are well seen along the west and north-west slopes of Quinag where the gneiss rises to about 370 m (1200 ft) above the lower exposures (Fig. 3). The form of the junction on Quinag and on Beinn Garbh can be seen from the roadside on the north shore of Loch Assynt. In the north, on the other hand, the old land surface is almost level, being parallel to the bedding of the overlying sandstone as seen round the base of Fashven. In places the gneiss under the sandstone cover is seen to be deeply decomposed and it has been suggested that this pre-Torridonian weathering points to its being one of the oldest palaeosols in the world. Exposures can be examined on the coast near Sheigra [182 609].

The Torridonian Sandstones are of uniform composition over large areas and appear so fresh and undisturbed that it is difficult to realize that they were deposited as long ago as 750 Ma, which makes them the oldest sedimentary rocks in the British Isles. Throughout the series obscure trace fossils are the only suggestion of life forms during the period.

The oldest rocks of the series in Sutherland are the Stoer Group, outcrops of which occur only in the Stoer Peninsula (becoming more abundant to the south outside the District). They are gently-dipping red sandstones and mudstones containing a marked band of water-deposited volcanic ash, which can be seen on the coast west of Stoer [034 286]. Throughout the remainder of the District all the sandstones belong to the younger Torridon Group. These are largely coarse-grained feldspathic sandstones (arkoses) and grits, with some siltstones. At the base angular breccias are occasionally found and conglomerates and pebbly bands also occur. The material in the breccias is usually Lewisian gneiss of local origin but in some of the pebble deposits occur rocks no longer found in the area, such as chert, jasper and various volcanic rocks. The conglomerates and pebbly deposits can be seen in many localities including the coasts south of Cape Wrath, in the Kyle of Durness, at Sheigra and at the Point of Stoer, while inland they occur round the base of Fashven.

The current bedding indicates that the deposits are in the form of alluvial fans deposited by rivers flowing from a mountainous region which lay to the west or north-west. The uniformity of the deposits over their great thickness suggests that deposition was maintained by block uplifting of the mountain region accompanied by subsidence of the receiving basin — movement taking place in the region of the Minch Fault. The presence of wind-faceted pebbles and the freshness of the feldspar grains suggest that the source land was, at least, semi desert. Detailed itineraries covering many aspects of the Lewisian and Torridonian rocks of the area are included in the Geologists' Association Guide No. 21.

CAMBRIAN AND ORDOVICIAN

By the time the shelf sea of the Cambrian period spread over the continental margin, the Torridonian Sandstone had been slightly tilted, extensively eroded and in some places entirely removed. The waters transgressed across an almost level platform of both Torridonian and Lewisian rocks on which were deposited beds of shallow water sediments. As the sea deepened beds of calcareous mud and later limestones were deposited. In West Sutherland rocks of this series outcrop in a narrow discontinuous band extending from Durness to Elphin.

Some 70 m (230 ft) of non-fossiliferous, rather gritty, white quartzite form the base of the lowest group, the Arenaceous Series. This is followed by a slightly thicker quartzite deposit in which numerous fossil worm burrows are found. These appear as "pipes" at right angles to the bedding planes, giving rise to the name " Pipe Rock " for the unit. Differing types of pipe help to identify five sub-zones and good specimens can be found in the Allt Sgiathaig near Loch Fèoir and near the outlet of Loch na Gainmich.

The arenaceous beds are overlain by the Fucoid Beds, so called because the abundant flattened worm casts along the bedding planes were at one time thought to be the remains of fucoids (sea-weed). These are beds of shales up to 27 m (88 ft) in thickness, ranging from bedded argillite to more massive dolomite. The characteristic fossils of this unit are trilobites (Olenellus). These beds are followed in turn by a thin but persistent quartzite called the Serpulite Grit, 9 m (30 ft) thick, in which occur small fossil tubes originally named Serpulites but now known as Salterella. Good exposures occur near the road at Skiag Bridge.

Next in the succession is the Calcareous Series or Durness

Limestone, which consists of beds of dolomites and limestones varying from massive to well-bedded types. These contain a good fossil
fauna, bands and nodules of chert and a few unfossiliferous sections.
The fossils include Salterella, algae, Cephalopods, Gastropods, Trilobites, Brachiopods and sponges. On the strength of these fossils
the beds have been subdivided into seven units taking their names
from locations in the type area near Durness. The fossils span the
period from Lower Cambrian up to Lower Ordovician. Estimates of
the thickness are difficult to confirm because of incomplete sections
and vary from 450 m (1500 ft) to twice that figure.

It was recognised as long ago as 1859 that these beds had
a close affinity to similar rocks in North America although the
true significance of this has only become apparent in recent years.
The readily identifiable nature of each individual unit in the series
proved vital in the unravelling of the complexities of the Moine
Thrust Zone.

MOINIAN

A glance at the geological map (Fig. 3) shows that by far the
greatest part of Sutherland is made up of rocks of the Moine Series
of metamorphosed sediments. These take their name from A'
Mhoine, the locality in the north-west from where they were first
described.

Geologists have wrestled with the problems of the age, order
of succession and structure of these rocks for over a century and
only in recent years have the various parts of the puzzle shown
signs of fitting together. Evidence now points to their correlation
with the Torridonian Series, being the sediments deposited in the
expanding Iapetus Ocean while the Torridonian sediments were
accumulating on the continental margin. As the ocean basin subsided they formed thick layers of sandstone and shale. Later,
when the closing of the ocean led to the Caledonian Orogeny, they
were transformed into the crystalline metamorphic rocks we see
today. Original sedimentary structures have been preserved in some
of the Moinian rocks, particularly in the south and west. From
these, calculations of the original thickness of the strata can be
made and some estimates put the figure as high at 16 km
(52,500 ft).

The rocks are remarkably uniform in character over large areas.
The more psammitic types (derived from sandstone) are represented
by rocks ranging from flaggy or massive siliceous granulites to

quartz schists, while the pelitic types (derived from shales) are in the form of mica schists. Every gradation between these two types is found, and the intermediate varieties are known as semi-pelitic schists. The whole series is more or less banded, depending on the amount of mica present and as this increases the rocks become more schistose. The colour of the schists is either dark or sliver-grey, depending on whether the dominant mica is biotite or muscovite. Small garnets are common, becoming aboundant in some of the pelitic schists where they can reach more than 2.5 cm (1 in) in size. Calcareous rocks occur as minor members of some groups.

Minor basic intrusions are found in the Moinian rocks of Sutherland. These were probably originally in the form of dykes or sills but are seen to have been folded with the schists and to have been altered to hornblende or chlorite schists, while the larger bodies are now represented by epidiorites and amphibolites. From Figure 3 it will be seen that several large bodies of Lewisian rocks occur in the western half of the Moines of Sutherland. In some places it is difficult to distinguish between rocks of the two groups in the field, but recent advances in chemical analysis methods help to pinpoint the differences, and it is probable that the existence of further areas of Lewisian rocks will be confirmed.

From the many exposures of the Moinian rocks in stream sections and road cuttings it is immediately obvious that they have been intensely folded and often refolded. In all, four sets of fold patterns have been recognised, caused by large-scale deformation during the Caledonian Orogeny, the two earliest groups being major ones. Some of the older Moinian rocks are seen to be interbanded with Lewisian rocks of the basement and these interbanded portions have been repeatedly folded during the earliest Caledonian movements. The second series of folds is of widespread occurrence dating from the peak of the metamorphism, while the other two are later and less well developed. Spectacular columnar or mullion-structure resulting from severe folding in two directions can be seen in the granulites in the River Oykel at Oykel Bridge. Here and there in the Moinian Series thin bands of pebbly conglomerate occur and on Ben Hutig quartz pebbles in these bands have been drawn out into lenticular veinlets and cylindrical rods during the folding.

The rocks bordering granite intrusions such as Carn Chuinneag and Rogart are seen to be penetrated by irregular veins of granite, but away from these, over a very large area of central and North-east Sutherland the Moinian rocks are intimately mixed and interlaminated with sheets and veins of granite and pegmatite to form rocks known as migmatites. This area of migmatization extends from the north coast between Bettyhill and the boundary with Caithness southwards to near the Rogart granite. Over the greater part of this complex granite veins make up more than 35% of the rocks, especially in the Loch Coire area, while the huge granite vein complex of Strath Halladale is mapped as a granite in Fig. 3. This is the area in which "in situ" granitization of sedimentary rocks was first established in Britain.

The area was a centre of high grade regional metamorphism and the distribution of various minerals of high temperature origin (such as sillimanite) in the rocks is used to map the extent of the zone. Age dating of the rocks affected by this great metamorphic event shows a spread of ages from 400 to 430 Ma which represents the period of the main deformation on the closing of the Iapetus Ocean and the Caledonian Orogeny in Sutherland.

This part of the District has for long been one of the least understood areas of the Highlands and much research will be needed before the full sequence of the events which affected it is revealed.

MOINE THRUST ZONE

The Moine Thrust Zone marks the north-west margin of the Caledonian orogenic belt in Scotland, where, on the closing of the Iapetus Ocean, the edge of the mobile oceanic belt was forced to over-ride part of the unmoved continental edge.

In a complex zone 195 km (120 miles) long, extending from Whiten Head in the north southwards to Elphin and continuing through Wester Ross to Skye, rocks from the east are seen to have moved north-westwards, on a series of low angle thrust planes, over the rocks to the west. The main and most easterly fracture is the Moine Thrust which carries the Moine Schists north-westwards over a complex zone of intensely disturbed Cambrian, Torridonian and Lewisian rocks, which themselves have moved on lower thrusts (Fig. 4b).

The area is classic ground in Highland geology and was in the middle of last century the scene of prolonged controversy between many eminent geologists of the period. Their disagreements stemmed largely from their not recognising the type and scale of movements involved. A review of their various theories and a detailed account of the work of Peach, Horne and others on the structure

FIG.4 — CROSS SECTIONS TO ILLUSTRATE THE GEOLOGY OF ASSYNT

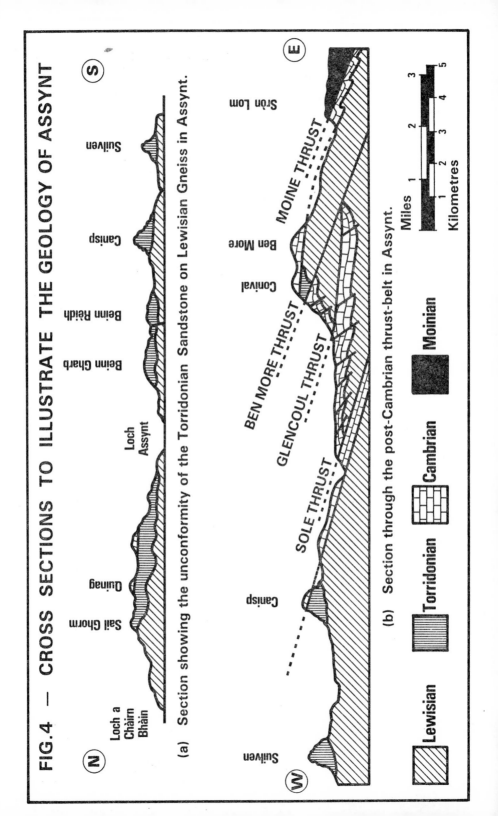

(a) Section showing the unconformity of the Torridonian Sandstone on Lewisian Gneiss in Assynt.

(b) Section through the post-Cambrian thrust-belt in Assynt.

Lewisian Torridonian Cambrian Moinian

of the area are to be found in " *The Northwest Highland Memoir* " published in 1907.

Some of the processes involved in major thrust movements can be more easily understood by referring to the experimental researches undertaken by H. M. Cadell in 1889. To investigate the behaviour of strata when pushed horizontally over an immovable surface he constructed models from layers of materials of different strengths using varying combinations of sand, clay, plaster of Paris etc., and compressed them.

His main findings were that pressure was not transmitted very far into a mass of strata and that rocks behaved like brittle rigid bodies, with the result that the compressed mass found relief along a series of gently inclined minor thrust planes with the slices so formed heaping on top of each other, overlapping like a stack of roofing slates. This is known as ' imbricate structure ' (Fig. 5a). After a certain amount of heaping up, a major thrust plane developed at a low angle, starting from a fold below, and the whole mass rose and rode bodily forward on this plane (Fig. 5b). As this mass moved forward the front part tended to be folded under the advancing ' nose '. Details of the experiments appear in the 1907 Memoir.

In Sutherland the zone seen to be affected by the thrust movements varies in width from 1.5 km to 5 km (1 mile to 3 miles) but expands to some 13 km (8 miles) in Assynt, then rapidly narrows to only a few metres in the cliffs near the District boundary south of Elphin. A few hundred metres into Ross-shire (geology ignores District boundaries) the full succession can be examined at the Knockanrock Viewpoint, and this is a good place ' to get one's eye in ' with the rock types before tackling the more complex zones farther north.

In Assynt the thrust zone was somewhat domed and as erosion proceeded the highest part (the Moine Thrust) was denuded eastwards into a wide semi-circular sweep, while the lowest part continued on the original north-northeast trend. The removal of the upper layers revealed the sheets of rock (nappes) carried forward on the lower thrusts, the complexities of the stratigraphical succession and the deformation of the rocks themselves. Because of this ' window ', this part of the District has become classic ground for the study of this type of crustal fracture.

Ahead of the main thrusts, slices of Cambrian strata are found piled up in imbricate structure (Fig. 5a) which gives a deceptive thickness to these rocks. Good examples can be seen in the burn

FIG.5 — EXPERIMENTAL REPRODUCTION OF THRUST STRUCTURES

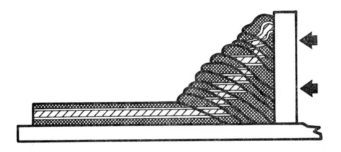

(a) Development of Imbricate Structure (after H. M. Caldell)

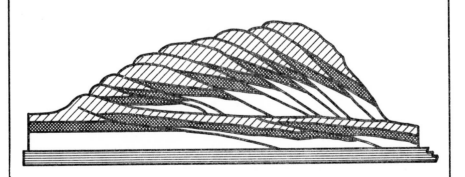

(b) Development of a major thrust-plane (after H. M. Caldell)

400 m (1310 ft) north-west of Auchmore [236 251], and on Liath Bhad south of Loch Glencoul [255 300].

In Assynt, the main thrusts from west to east are the Glencoul Thrust and the Ben More Thrust, which combine in the south to become the Assynt Thrust, and the Moine Thrust (see Fig. 4b). Minor thrusts may become important over short distances. The Glencoul Thrust, seen between the north of Loch na Gainmhich and Loch Glencoul, has brought forward a great slice of Lewisian Gneiss some 450 m (1500 ft) thick, together with an almost complete succession of Cambrian strata. A similar thickness of Lewisian Gneiss has moved forward on the Ben More Thrust above Inchnadamph, carrying with it both Torridonian and Cambrian strata. On both these thrusts the Cambrian rocks are seen to fold over and become inverted at the thrust planes while on the south-west side of Sgonnan Mor inverted Torridonian strata underlie Lewisian Gneiss in an overfold. Along the eastern shore of Loch Eriboll readily accessible sections through the northern thrusts have been described by Soper (1973) at Kempie Bay, on the slopes of Ben Arnabol and on the Creagan Road.

Parts of various nappes have become detached by erosion from their parental masses and are referred to as 'klippen'. Several occur in Assynt, e.g. Beinn nam Cnaimhseag, Beinn an Fhuarain and the ridge between Ledbeg and Cam Loch. Each successive thrust may in turn be overlapped by a higher one and the Moine Thrust overlaps them all. On Faraid Head a klippe of Moinian rocks can be seen resting on the undisturbed foreland 13 km (8 miles) west of the main outcrop. On the Knockan Crag the Moinian rocks are brought forward to the cliff top and the whole thrust zone appears in the cliff face.

Because of the movement along the thrust planes, the rocks at the base of any of the nappes are always highly sheared and frequently this deformation extends through a considerable thickness of rock. The rocks are seen to have been ground down into a very fine-grained, flinty looking, banded rock known as mylonite. The presence of this rock is a certain indicator of shearing deformation. In the Loch Eriboll area some 800 m (2600 ft) of mylonites occur in the Moine nappe and the various types can be examined in the cliffs along the Creagan Road. Moving eastwards from the thrust zone the Moinian rocks affected by the thrusting still show abnormal finely-granular textures and grade slowly eastwards into normal

Moinian types over a distance varying from 5 km to 20 km (3 miles to 12 miles).

Movement on these thrusts probably commenced at the beginning of the closure of the Iapetus Ocean and continued intermittently to the time of continental collision in the Lower Devonian. There is considerable doubt as to the extent of the horizontal movements in the Moine Thrust Zone, but in the north, Moinian rocks can be shown to have moved westwards a minimum of some 16 km (10 miles) while at the southern end the outcrop of the Moinian rocks can be traced continuously for 10 km (6 miles). The scale of the movements involved can be more fully appreciated after studying the detailed cross sections included in the *Northwest Highland Memoir,* and then too can the magnitude of the task undertaken by Peach and Horne. This volume and the guides to the Assynt and Loch Eriboll areas referred to in the Bibliography are essential reading for those wishing to make a closer study of the zone.

IGNEOUS ROCKS

The large mass of Carn Chuinneag, on the southern boundary of the District, is formed of a granite pluton which covers an area of 15 km by 7 km (9.3 miles by 4.2 miles). It is the earliest of the Caledonian granites and was intruded into the Moinian rocks as long ago as 560 Ma, and was subsequently folded with them in the main deformation phase. It is a coarse-grained, gneiss-like granite and contains a large body of amphibolite on its north-west flank, which can be seen in the Diebidale River. Sheets and veins of granite, such as occur in the Garbh Allt, extend into the Moine Schists and these rocks have been thermally altered in a zone some 1.6 km (1 mile) wide round the granite.

Granites of younger age occur at Rogart and Helmsdale, with smaller outcrops at Fearn, Migdale and Grudie. These intrusions have varying proportions of tonalite, granodiorite and adamellite. The Rogart mass, dated at 416 to 424 Ma, was emplaced in the Moinian rocks with a migmatite zone on its northern and eastern flanks. It contains large irregular inclusions of country rocks and can be examined at the roadside in Strath Fleet. Of the others, the Migdale and Fearn masses have marginal zones in which veins of granite have been injected into the schists, but these do not occur at Helmsdale.

Associated with the 'younger' granites are outcrops of unusual rocks of the Ach Uaine Hybrid and Appinite suites. They are mostly basic to ultrabasic types related to the diorites and are found as small bosses, sills and dykes near the granites and also occur through the migmatite zone. They are named after the type locality at Achuaine [NH 624 951], and as the name suggests their outcrops form knolls of vivid green on the otherwise brown moorland.

Related to the granites are the syenites, a group of medium to coarse-grained igenous rocks containing little or no quartz. They are less common than the granites and usually form smaller masses. In Sutherland intrusions of syenite occur at three localities — Loch Borralan, Loch Ailsh and Loch Loyal.

The Loch Borralan (or Cnoc na Sròine) body is made up of a variety of types of syenite and intrudes and thermally alters the Cambrian rocks. It is of 'newer' granite age and was itself affected by the late Caledonian thrust movements. Close by is the smaller Loch Ailsh mass, which also cuts and alters the Cambrian rocks. It has been shattered and mylonitised in places by thrusting and has been carried westwards over Cambrian rocks by the Assynt Thrust Plane. Moinian rocks have, in turn, been borne over part of the syenite by the Moine Thurst Plane. A great number of rock types occur in the two areas including many varieties of syenites and related rocks, some of rare occurrence. Local place names appear amongst the more unusual types e.g. cromalite, assyntite, ledmoreite and borrolanite, and mineralogists are attracted to the area from far and wide.

Farther north, three separate bodies of syenite occur round Loch Loyal, forming Ben Loyal, Cnoc nan Cùilean and Beinn Stumanadh. The Ben Loyal syenite has intensely altered and veined the surrounding country rocks and these schists have been crumpled by the force of the intrusion. Although there is not the same variety of rock types here as in the Assynt intrusions, these syenites are still uncommon enough to be of great interest to geologists.

Throughout Assynt are found extensive suites of minor intrusions, mostly in the form of sills and dykes grouped in or close to the Moine Thrust Zone. They are emplaced along folds in the Lewisian Gneiss, or follow the bedding planes of the Torridonian Sandstones and Cambrian sediments, while some occur in the Moine Schists. Their distribution is related to the geological formations into which they are intruded and this is useful in the interpretation of the structure of the area. As rock types they are closely related to the nearby syenites, often being fine-grained variants of them; again some of these rocks are of **rare occurrence**.

OLD RED SANDSTONE

Huge mountain ranges had been formed during the Grampian and Caledonian orogenies and sediments accumulating from the erosion of these masses slowly formed the enormous Old Red Sandstone continent.

Fault controlled uplift and basin development were again a feature of the cycle and the large inland Orcadian Basin developed, subsiding as it accumulated a great thickness of sediments. The deposition of these beds was drastically modified from time to time by movement on various fault systems. In Sutherland the rocks of this group are seen to have been deposited on top of the crystalline Moinian and other rocks from which they had been eroded.

Three divisions are recognised in the Old Red Sandstone Series and are distinguishable by their lithology and the fossil fauna they contain. The oldest or ' Lower ' division is composed largely of conglomerates, arkosic sandstones with little cross-bedding and minor mudstones. In Sutherland these rocks are largely ' barren ' but the presence of microscopic spores in some of the beds helps to classify them. The ' Middle ' division is composed of flaggy sandstones, mudstones, marls and conglomerates with a little limestone. Strong rhythmic alternations between alluvial and lacustrine lithologies occur, due to fluctuations, probably seasonal, in the water level in the basin. In the rhythmic units are found fossil fish remains by which the successions can be identified — but this is more strongly developed in Caithness. The ' Upper ' division consists mainly of gritty sandstones containing some clay pellets and is almost all of fluvial deposition. The different lithologies and scarce fish remains help distinguish these from earlier beds.

The main outcrop of these rocks occurs along the eastern side of the District where it forms the hilly ground inland from the coast. Conglomerates of the Lower division lie on the Moinian rocks and are in turn overlain by rocks of the Middle division which form the hilltops. The conglomerates are well exposed on Cnoc Odhar and the Mound Rock and the overlap of the flaggy sandstones of the Middle division can be seen on Beinn a' Bhragaidh where they have been quarried. Northwards peat obscures many of the outcrops on the hilltops. Upper Old Red sandstones occur as a strip along the coast in the Embo-Dornoch area and outcrop as flat reefs on the shore.

Small outliers occur among the Moinian rocks farther west. The largest occur at the Ben Griams, where there are three separate exposures, the largest covering some 3 km by 6 km (2 miles by 4 miles). Here a small volcanic plug of andesite cuts the sandstones on Ben Griam More. A smaller oulier of sandstone and conglomerate occurs at Meall Odhar south-west of Loch Coire. On the north coast at the boundary with Caithness, beds of the Middle division extend into Sutherland from the east to as far as Melvich and a small outlier at Baligill shows a fish fauna in line with the Achanarras beds of the Middle Old Red Sandstone of Caithness.

CARBONIFEROUS

From Table 1 it will be seen that rocks of Carboniferous age are not found in Sutherland. It is probable that the scale and extent of the mountains to the south was such that different geographical and climatological regimes existed on opposite sides of the range. However the occurrence of Carboniferous microfossils in the Mesozoic rocks offshore may indicate that some strata may be found overlying the Old Red Sandstone in central parts of the Moray Firth.

PERMIAN AND TRIASSIC

During this period continental erosion and deposition prevailed including long periods of desert or semi-desert conditions. North-south rifting developed in the centre of the North Sea and this was accelerated in the Triassic. Old north-east-trending fault lines were reactivated and subsiding basins developed in the Minches and the Moray Firth.

A group of small outliers of coarse conglomerates with gritty bands is found on the east side of the Kyle of Tongue, extending from Cnoc Craggie to Eilean nan Ron. These and other small outcrops on the coast near Kirtomy have yielded no fossils and although listed in the past as being of Old Red Sandstone age, they are now considered to be of New Red Sandstone age (Permo-Triassic) from their similarity to beds found offshore.

Only limited exposures of Triassic rocks occur on land in Sutherland and these appear as gently sloping beds of calcareous sandstone on the shore south of Dunrobin Castle, overlain by marls and a cherty limestone which is correlated with the Cherty Rock of Stotfield in Moray. The Triassic succession extends seawards into the faulted Moray Firth Basin where it is overlain by younger rocks.

No outcrops occur in West Sutherland but up to 3 km (10000ft) of Triassic strata are known in the Minch Basin where they lie partly on a floor of Torridonian rocks.

JURASSIC

During this period the waters which had extended into the Moray Firth Basin from the central rift area of the North Sea transgressed slowly over the basin margin and the rocks now present are indicative of varying estuarine conditions.

Jurassic rocks are found in a narrow tract of country stretching from Golspie north to the Ord of Caithness, and are faulted down against the older rocks to the west along the Helmsdale fault. The rocks are mostly sandstones, siltstones and shales and the lowest members of the series appear in Dunrobin Bay. The Brora Coal formation is exposed on the shore just south of the rivermouth but the coal itself, which is less than 1 m (3.3 ft) thick, does not outcrop on the shore. This coal seam, which was first mined in 1529, has for long been of geological and economic interest. It is in turn overlain by further beds of sandstones and shales which can be examined in the river and on the shore. These include two units of economic interest, the Brora Brick Clay and the Clynelish Quarry sandstone. The former is composed of rhythmic units grading from bituminous sandy silt to light green clay and the latter is mostly composed of friable yellow sand which in the quarry has a silica cement. Throughout the series the sequence of the beds has been confirmed in the many boreholes which have been sunk in the area, aided by the occurrence of abundant fossils.

Immediately north of Brora there are no exposures of rock but they appear on the coast as a higher series from Kintradwell to the Ord of Caithness. Here occurs a complex succession of boulder beds interbedded with bituminous shales and sandstones, where the boulders are of Old Red Sandstone and the matrix is of Jurassic age. To account for this confused lithology, over the years their origin has been variously described as being due to crushing, coastal erosion, ice-rafting, landslides into fjords and submarine faulting. Present day opinion is that at the time of formation the Helmsdale Fault formed an underwater scarp off which unconsolidated sediment was shed along with blocks and boulders of Old Red Sandstone from channels or ravines cut into the scarp, probably during movement on the fault. The Helmsdale Fault, like the Great Glen Fault, is thought to be transcurrent and the blocks of Old Red Sandstone such as the "fallen sea stack of Portgower", which measures some 30 m x 27 m x 6 m, (100 ft x 90 ft x 20 ft) match types found much farther north in Caithness on the other side of the fault.

These formations have been intensely studied by oil geologists in their effort to understand the sequence of events which occurred in similar formations offshore. Because of the competitive nature of the oil industry, geological data won at great expense is not made public for some time, but sufficient information has come out of the North Sea to give a much better understanding of the processes involved in oil formation and entrapment.

Most geologists now consider that hydrocarbons are produced by the geothermal heating of beds of organic rich sediments, and provided the pressure due to the depth of burial is sufficient to compress the beds, the oil will migrate through permeable strata until it dissipates at the earth's surface. However, under favourable circumstances oil may collect in a reservoir of porous sandstone when trapped under a cap of impermeable rock. Oil entrapment in Jurassic sands is thought to occur almost always in association with block faulting and in the Moray Firth Basin all these requirements are met. The Jurassic shales are present to act as a source rock together with porous sandstones : these are covered by rock of Cretaceous age, and there is the splay of faults associated with the Great Glen Fault system. A successful oil well has been drilled in this basin but there is no information as to prospects in the Minch Basin.

CRETACEOUS

No rocks of this age are found on land in Sutherland, but shales and sandstones of Lower Cretaceous age occur in the Moray Firth Basin overlying the Jurassic series, while the chalk of the Upper Cretaceous is present farther east.

ECONOMIC GEOLOGY

The Jurassic coal of Sutherland was first exploited as long ago as 1529. The Brora mine is thought to be one of the oldest continuously worked coal mines in the world and has had a very chequered history.

Because of its remoteness from centres of industry and the comparatively low quality of the coal, the viability of the mine has been largely dependent on economic factors elsewhere. In its hey-day the presence of the mine led to the development of a considerable amount of industry in the Brora area, including salt pans, spinning and weaving, fishing and distilling, while coal was exported by sea, mainly to the Moray coast. A brick and tile works was opened in the Brora Brick Clays to supply building materials for local use. In 1825 competition from the industrialised south, with its higher quality of coal, forced the mine to close and thereafter all the local industries declined. The mine was reopened subsequently for varied periods but always proved non-competitive. A new lease of life came when substantial new reserves of coal estimated at some 8 million tons were proven in 1966, but by the mid 70's the cost of labour in the District had become governed by oil related industry and closure was again forced. Open cast mining has been considered, but not approved, so the coal must remain in the ground until the price becomes right.

Closely related to the coal deposits is the presence offshore of oil reserves in the Jurassic sands of the Moray Firth Basin, where, from the Beatrice Oil Field, oil will be pumped to the Cromarty Firth.

Another source of fuel in Sutherland is the vast deposits of peat which cover almost a third of the District and have been used for domestic supplies for centuries. No commercial exploitation has been undertaken in spite of some of the individual tracts covering 50 km^2 (19 miles^2). Hill peat makes up the bulk of the deposits but considerable basin peat also occurs.

Stone for building purposes has been quarried at Beinn a' Bhragaidh in the Middle Old Red Sandstone and Jurassic sandstone at Clynelish Quarry, Brora. Quarries have been opened for roadstone and concrete aggregate in various granite and syenite outcrops and there are considerable fluvio-glacial gravel deposits in the lower reaches of the main straths. Mounds of morainic drift for use as road material are plentiful.

Dolomite, which is used by the steel industry and in the making of magnesium metal as well as in agriculture, occurs in bulk around Durness and Loch Eriboll. In former years the lime-rich beds in the Old Red Sandstone at Baligill were used as a source of lime, and the Lewisian limestone at Shinness was also quarried. The Cambrian Fucoid Beds are known to contain an abnormal amount of potassium — averaging 8% — and tens of millions of tons of these rocks are available as a source of potash.

Metallic ores are known to occur in small quantities in Sutherland. The most famous is, of course, the occurrence of gold in Strath Kildonan which led to the Gold Rush of 1869. About 500 miners flocked to the diggings, living in a shanty-town or under canvas (Plate 27). Gold was found in the Kinbrace, Suisgill, Kildonan, Craggan and Torrish Burns as well as in the main Helmsdale River. The gold initially occurred as sparse quantities in the granites and migmatites and was weathered out in the Tertiary Period to be concentrated by stream action. It is found as dust among the stream gravels, and being heavy tends to concentrate at the base of the gravel against the country rock. It is not known for certain how much gold was found but it has been estimated that £12,000 worth was won in the summer of '69.

A small outcrop of granite in Glen Diebidale contains magnetite-rich bands with which is associated cassiterite (tinstone) in small amounts. Molybdenite mineralization of low grade occurs near Lairg, together with small amounts of other ore minerals such as chalcopyrite, galena, fluorite and barytes. An extensive programme of surveying and sampling throughout the District has been undertaken by commercial concerns but it is thought that the minerals which are present are not in sufficient quantity for exploitation.

With the geology of Sutherland embracing such a wide field and being of enormous interest to both amateur and professional, it has not been possible here to do other than give a summary of the main features. For those wishing to go into the subject in more detail, comprehensive bibliographies are to be found in *The Geology of Scotland, The Northern Highlands, the Assynt Guide,* and the *Geologists' Association Guide No. 21.* Geological maps of the area, including a special sheet covering Assynt, can be purchased and photostats of out of print maps are available. There is, however, no better way of learning than " Going to see for yourself ", but please observe the Geological Code of Conduct.

Chapter two

THE LANDSCAPE

THE PRE-GLACIAL LANDSCAPE

Over the span of geological time many factors have combined to produce the contrasting landscape which we see in Sutherland today, but geologists are still uncertain of the stages in its development.

Throughout most of the Tertiary Period, which began some 70 million years ago, the climate was appreciably warmer and moister than that of today and this led to a rapid decay of the rocks. In Sutherland most of the cover of softer sedimentary rocks has been completely eroded away to expose older and harder metamorphic and igneous rocks which make up the bulk of the land surface. It is impossible however to judge accurately the former extent of the vanished deposits but George (1966) suggests that many thousands of feet of material were eroded from the land surface during the Tertiary. Few, if any, recognisable remnants of a land surface dating from that time can be identified with certainty, but in parts of Sutherland, as elsewhere in the Highlands, hill summits reach up to approximately common levels and some researchers claim that these levels are the remnants of old erosion surfaces cutting across a variety of structures. They advocate a history of uplift in successive pulses which has left a series of stepped platforms, much eroded but still recognisable. This stepped profile increases in height from north to south over the District with varying levels being quoted from 90 m (295 ft) to 700 m (2296 ft), but opinions vary as to how many surfaces there are and which are the significant levels. Godard (1965) claims to have found six.

There are two schools of thought as to how such uniform surfaces might develop: one suggests that each marks a plane of

marine erosion on a landmass progressively emerging from the sea,
and the other postulates subaerial denudation and the influence of
slope retreat. With an increasing understanding of the formation
of the fault-controlled sea basins to the east and west of the
District there is growing opinion that what is now " land " has
been so for some considerable period of geological time, and that
the erosion features are non-marine in origin.

ROCK TYPE AND SCENERY

Quite striking relationships between rock type and scenery can
be demonstrated throughout Britain and Sutherland is no exception.

The landscape of Lewisian Gneiss in the west and north-west of
the District is one of processions of rounded domes and ridges
of bare fissured rock and innumerable small lochs. At first glance
it appears to be a chaotic wilderness of rock and water, but when
viewed from above, a greater order in the landscape is discernible.
The patterns of the lochs and streams, valleys and ridges are
markedly aligned in north-eastward and west-northwestward directions, controlled by the trends of old fault lines and igneous dykes.

The relief is generally low and while in the dreary Parph area
of the north-west much of the ground is covered by peat moss,
elsewhere large tracts of the gneiss are starkly devoid of vegetation (Plate 2). The crests and ridges generally reach up to about
120 m to 150 m (400 ft to 500 ft) making a gently sloping erosion
surface and where the gneiss rises higher, the undulating form is
retained. Many of the hills formed of gneiss are capped with a
thin layer of quartzite, so that in spite of reaching 900 m (2950 ft)
on the northern peak of Foinaven overlooking gloomy Strath Dionard,
the highest hilltop of gneiss in the District is Ben Stack, 721 m
(2364 ft).

The contrast between the scenery of the Lewisian gneiss and
that of the overlying Torridonian Sandstone is extremely marked.
The sandstones are formed of gently inclined strata with well-
defined parallel bedding planes and are traversed by numerous
vertical joints and small faults which have been exploited by
weathering to produce terraced escarpments, steep rounded buttresses and impressive vertical faces cut by deep chimneys. The
terraces are bare and boulder-strewn higher up and flanked by rough
scree slopes and stone chutes but at lower levels the slopes become
gentler and grass-covered.

Throughout the District the outcrops are nowhere continuous

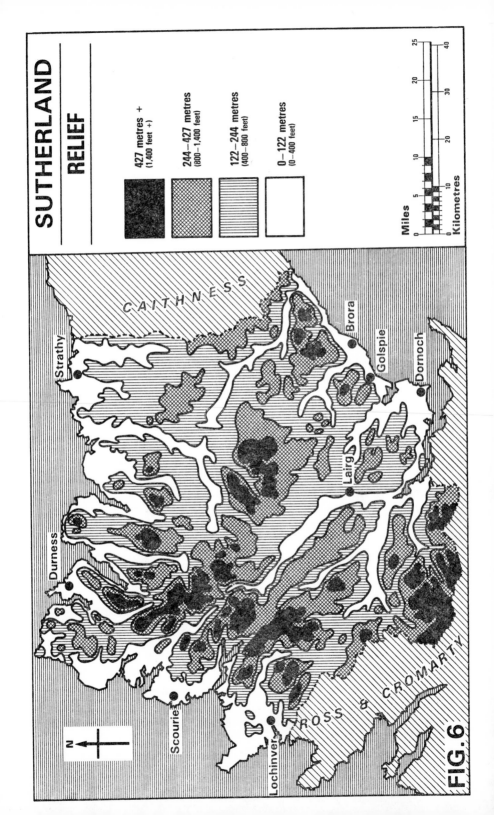

SUTHERLAND

RELIEF

427 metres +
(1,400 feet +)

244–427 metres
(800–1,400 feet)

122–244 metres
(400–800 feet)

0–122 metres
(0–400 feet)

Miles

Kilometres

CAITHNESS

Strathy

Durness

Scourie

Lochinver

Lairg

Brora

Golspie

Dornoch

ROSS & CROMARTY

N

FIG.6

and in the Parph area, though reaching to around 500 m (1640 ft) the hills are flat and unspectacular. In Assynt, however, Suilven 731 m (2399 ft), Canisp 846 m (2779 ft) and Quinag 808 m (2651 ft) stand in splendid isolation on the gneiss and form a unique landscape which is probably the most remarkable in the British Isles. From the cross-section in Figure 4 it can be appreciated how these mountains were shaped by erosion from a formerly continuous cover of sandstone. The huge buttresses of Caisteal Liath, the western peak of Suilven and those of Sail Garbh and Sail Gorm on Quinag show all the Torridonian features to advantage.

Suilven (Plate 4) is one of the most photographed mountains in Britain and although its 2.5 km (1.5 mile) long summit ridge is formed of three peaks, from the east or the west it appears as a solitary pillar.

Many of the Lewisian and Torridonian hills bear small caps of Cambrian Quartzite (see Fig. 4) and where more extensive stretches occur these have the characteristic of long, gently dipping slopes. Good examples of these are the eastern slopes of Canisp and Quinag (Plate 2) and the long ridge to the west of Loch Eriboll. The brown moorland of the quartzite country contrasts sharply with the lush green grasslands which carpet the outcrops of limestone round Durness, Inchnadamph and Elphin.

On the Foinaven and Arkle ranges (Plate 3) where long westward-facing scarps reach heights of 908 m (2980 ft) and 787 m (2580 ft) respectively, there is more spectacular scenery. Huge scree slopes of angular quartzite debris mantle the cliffs (Plate 7) while on the eastern sides deep corries have been carved into the readily shattered quartzite.

In the zone of the Moine Thrust a greater variety of rock scenery occurs and here the steep cliffs and deep corries are most impressive. A long ridge runs south-southeast from Glas Bheinn 776 m (2541 ft) to Conival 987 m (3234 ft), Ben More Assynt 998 m (3273 ft) and then south towards Ben More Lodge. The panorama from these summits on a clear day is particularly fine and there is the spectacular sight of the waterfall of Eas Coulin cascading 200 m (650 ft) into the valley below. The traverse of the entire ridge is a goal which draws mountaineers from far and wide but extreme care is needed in wet or foggy conditions, especially on the connecting ridges between Conival and Ben More, and Ben More and the South Top. Here Strang (1975) advises that what is a pleasant ridge route in summer becomes a serious mountaineering exercise in winter and adds the warning, so true here as elsewhere in the District: "The isolated nature of the area which is virtually devoid of habitation throughout 100 square miles is a factor which should be kept in mind in adverse weather conditions".

Between Loch Eriboll and the Kyle of Tongue is the part of the District known as A 'Mhoine which gave its name to the Moine Schists.

The scenery here is typical of large areas of central Sutherland where the even weathering of large areas of rock of similar composition has produced wide expanses of peaty moorland. The whole of the area of Moinian rocks is by no means low ground and as if to contradict the generalisation, Ben Hope (Plate 6) towers to 927 m (3040 ft) in Strath More and high ground continues south-east through the wild Reay Forest from the direction of Arkle with several hill tops reaching above 700 m (2300 ft) including Ben Hee 873 m (2864 ft). In the heart of Sutherland the peaks of Ben Klibreck (Plate 5) reaching 961 m (3154 ft) and the lower Ben Armine group coincide with the more pelitic groups of schists. On the southern margin of Sutherland the great mass of high ground of the Freevater Forest is also associated with rock of this type. Here a high rolling grassy moorland plateau, representing the highest erosion surface in the District, is cut by deep valleys while scarp lines on the highest ridges rise to the peaks of Seana Braigh 927 m (3040 ft) and Càrn Bàn 845 m (2762 ft).

The few visitors who venture to these hilltops in the interior may be attracted there by their remoteness rather than by the splendid views they offer across the moorlands. Good views may also be had from a few vantage points at road level, in particular the view to Ben Loyal from Loch Badenloch (NC 799332) and to Ben Griam from Lochan Ealach south of Strathy (NC 820650).

Because of its jointing granite weathers into rectangular blocks and finally into a coarse sand, the materials slumping downhill aided by frost action. As a result the profile of granite hills is generally rounded rather than jagged, and this form is demonstrated by the hills round Helmsdale, Rogart, Migdale and the boulder-strewn mass of Carn Chuinneag 838 m (2749 ft) on the southern boundary of the District. The low range of hills of granite veined rock forming the Knockfinn Heights along the boundary with Caithness has been levelled to an erosion surface while as if an exception, tor-capped Ben Loyal (Plate 8), formed of syenite, a rock akin to granite, soars above the lochan-pitted moors south of the Kyle of Tongue. Local guide books refer to it as "The Queen of Mountains" in spite of its modest height of 764 m (2506 ft) and when viewed from the north, there is no doubt as to its regal splendour.

In the sedimentary rocks of Old Red Sandstone age the landscape often reflects the differential erosion of hard and soft bands of rock, resulting in terraced slopes. The isolated stepped-cones of Ben Griam More 590 m (1936 ft) and Ben Griam Beg 580 m (1903 ft) which dominate the interior to the east of the upper Naver, are good examples. These are residual masses of sandstone and coarse conglomerates which are separated from the main mass forming the coastal range of East Sutherland stretching from Glen Loth to The Mound where the highest point is Ben Dhorian 628 m (2060 ft).

The gently sloping coastal plain stretching from Golspie to Helmsdale is formed of sedimentary rocks of Mesozoic age and is separated by a fault from the flanking hills. A fine view of this coast can be had from the readily accessible summit of Beinn a' Bradgaidh just behind Golspie (Plate 31).

Having considered the pre-glacial landscape and the relationship between rock type and relief it is possible to divide Sutherland into five landform regions: the western and eastern hills, the western and central plateaus and the eastern lowlands, as outlined in Figure 7.

DRAINAGE

Any drainage initiated on an evenly stepped landscape in the Tertiary must have been quickly modified as rivers exploited bands of softer and weakened rocks so that today the distribution of ridges and valleys on a relief map of the District shows strong structural trends (Fig. 6). In the north, where fault lines and folds run north-east or north there are long valleys orientated in these directions containing the original or consequent river systems and occasional long lochs. Down these valley sides the smaller tributary or subsequent streams flow at roughly right angles into the consequent systems. Of the main rivers in this part, the Naver is the largest, with the lesser ones, the Halladale, Strathy, Borgie, Kinloch, Hope and Dionard all flowing northwards.

Southwards there is a rapid change to a very strongly orientated north-west to south-east lineation of the drainage pattern brought about by the strike of the rocks and fault crush lines which

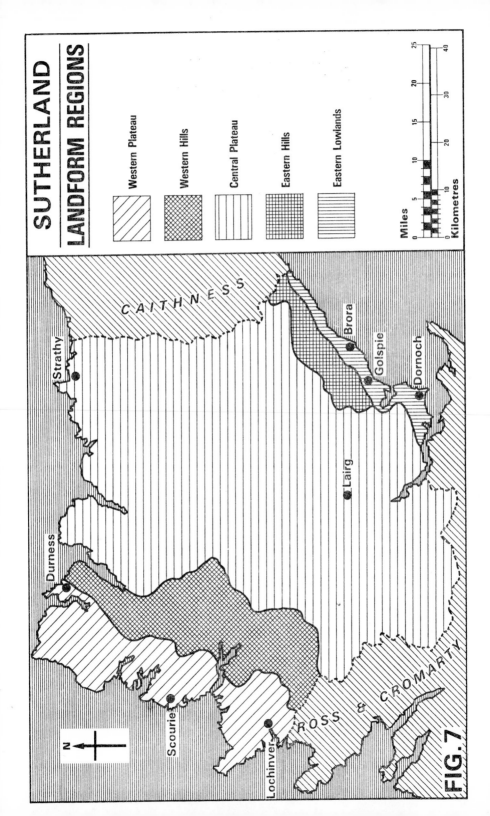

SUTHERLAND
LANDFORM REGIONS

Western Plateau

Western Hills

Central Plateau

Eastern Hills

Eastern Lowlands

Miles

Kilometres

CAITHNESS

Strathy

Brora

Golspie

Dornoch

Durness

Lairg

Scourie

Lochinver

ROSS & CROMARTY

N

FIG. 7

are orientated in that direction. The consequent rivers of the Helmsdale, Fleet, Cassley, Oykel, and Black Water all follow this trend as do a multitude of smaller streams.

The headwaters of some of the northward-flowing streams reach into the region of the south-east trending valleys and there are several instances of one stream capturing the headwaters of another. It seems probable that the Strath More River and the Naver intercepted streams originally flowing east or south-east towards the Helmsdale. On closer inspection many other changes of course can be found where streams have been diverted along minor folds and crush lines: e.g. the River Shin flowing south to join the Oykel.

As the watershed of Sutherland is much closer to the west coast than to the east (Fig. 8), it follows that the westwards flowing rivers (Laxford, Inver and Kirkaig) are much shorter and have more rapid courses than those with an eastern outlet.

LOCHS

The lochs of the District range in size from Loch Shin, which is 29 km (18 miles) long and the largest loch in the North-West Highlands, down to tiny lochans, almost too small to map. On the bare expanses of gneiss in the Scourie and Lochinver areas they are particularly numerous. In the area encircled by the A837 and B869 roads lying to the west of Quinag there are over 300 lochs mapped in an area of approximately 100 km² (39 miles²) and very probably others lurk unmapped amongst the knolls and ridges.

Many of the larger lochs, like the main rivers, lie in valley basins, often where these have been overdeepened by ice action. The largest of the north trending ones are Lochs Hope, Meadie and Loyal and of the north-east trending ones Lochs Naver (Plate 5) and Coire. Lochs Stack, More, Merkland, Shin, Brora and Assynt are the largest of the south-east orientated ones. The North of Scotland Hydro Electric Board have modified the drainage systems round the Shin Basin and raised the level of the loch by a dam at the south-east end (Plate 33).

Farther to the north-east other lochs, such as the group forming Lochs Rimsdale, nan Clar and Badenloch and Lochs an Ruathair and Truderscaig are shallower and lie in drift-dammed hollows, as do many of the smaller lochs on the open moorland. Although on the watershed of the Knockfin Heights tiny lochans in the peat are particularly numerous, no stretch of peat is without some.

On the slopes of the higher mountains can be found good examples of corrie lochs, (see p. 55) lying in small basins which held the last vestiges of the glaciers. They are often dammed behind a small line of morainic debris. Examination of the O.S. maps of Sutherland shows that many of these corrie basins stand at the heads of main valley systems and are the sources of many of the rivers.

DRAINAGE AND CAVES IN THE CAMBRIAN LIMESTONE

Over much of the limestone country, the landscape is dotted with sink holes feeding underground systems where the water drains through a network of slightly widened joints, bedding planes and faults. With the high rainfall many of these channels have been widened to form caves and each year more passages are being discovered by caving societies — cf Ford (1959).

In the Durness area there are many small sinkholes but only two large caves. The famous Smoo Cave (Plate 10) with an entrance 30 m (100 ft) across and 15 m (50 ft) high has what is probably one of the largest cave entrances in Britain. Its position at the end of an 800 m ($\frac{1}{2}$ mile) long geo poses the question whether or not this too was roofed over at one time. In the interior of the cave the Allt Smoo tumbles some 21 m (70 ft) through one of the openings in the roof. Nearby the Balnakeil Gloup extends 55 m (180 ft) into the cliff. It is flooded to a depth of 4 m (13 ft) by the sea and has an open blowhole at the inner end.

Farther south in Assynt the Cambrian Limestone outcrops almost entirely within the thrust zone. The Traligill Valley has the largest number of caves, sinks and risings in the District of which the Cnoc Nan Uamh Cave System is the most extensive, having some 500 m (1600 ft) of passages known. The Allt nan Uamh runs in a deep valley 5 km (3 miles) south-east of Inchnadamph, and for more than 1600 m (1 mile) the stream bed is dry except when in spate, with the water sinking below a small waterfall. Here some 360 m (1200 ft) of underground passages have been explored.

High on the south side of the valley are the Creag nan Uamh Bone Caves, four in number, which form an archaeological site of special interest (see p. 135).

In the Elphin-Knockan area numerous small sink holes and three caves are seen in the high limestone ground near the Moine Thrust Zone.

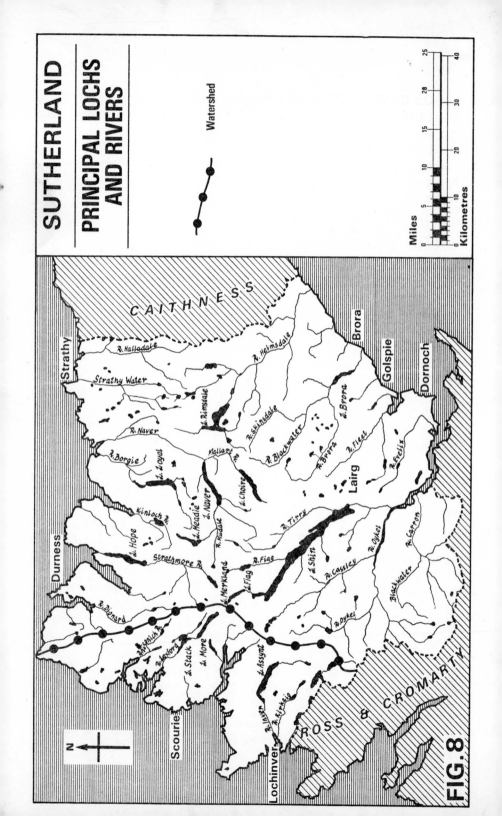

SUTHERLAND

PRINCIPAL LOCHS AND RIVERS

Watershed

Miles
Kilometres

FIG.8

THE COAST

In the west and north-west of Sutherland, where the coastline is formed of Lewisian Gneiss, wave action has produced an extremely varied and complex coast with bays and inlets of every size from small geos to large fjords, studded with small islets and skerries. Many of the bays are very picturesque with their stretches of white sand offering a sharp contrast to the harsh rocky scenery inland. In the remote north the gneiss forms magnificent cliffs near Cape Wrath.

Lochs Inchard (Plate 3), Laxford and Cairnbawn (with its passage through the narrows at Kylesku into Lochs Glencoul and Glendhu) are the largest of the west coast lochs or fjords and have been glacially deepened, penetrating far inland along fault lines. These and a multitude of smaller bays make for sheltered anchorages and Kinlochbervie and Lochinver have become established as busy fishing ports, and small boat cruising in the area is becoming popular.

The sea has sculptured an entirely different coastline from the Torridonian Sandstone. The characteristic coastal scenery of this group is one of superb stretches of soaring cliffs where waves have enlarged the joints in the rocks into caves and where arches, deep geos and sea stacks mark the various stages in the destruction of earlier caves by the Atlantic breakers.

There is fine cliff scenery of this type at Stoer with the 67 m (220 ft) high stack, The Old Man of Stoer (Plate 9), standing close to the cliffs and also on the bird sanctuary of Handa where, on the north-west corner of the island the famous Stack of Handa can be seen standing in a geo 107 m (350 ft) deep. It was here in 1876 that a group of Lewismen, collecting sea birds for salting, passed a rope across the geo and over the top of the stack and one Donald Macdonald crossed hand over fist along the rope to reach its summit. From Sandwood Bay northwards other large sea stacks can be seen and east of Cape Wrath the sandstone cliffs have their ultimate expression along the Clo Mor, where reaching 280 m (920ft) they form the highest sea cliffs on the Mainland of Britain.

Much of the north coast of Sutherland is made up of rocks of the Moine Series. Faulting and folding, trending between north and north-northeast, dictate the grain of the country and a ruggedly serrated coastline with stretches of lofty sea cliffs results. Near Whiten Head these reach 257 m (843ft), second only to Clo Mor in height. There are fine geos, caves and stacks all along this part of the coast but few of the inlets are large and in places some very narrow bays flanked by jagged reefs and backed by high cliffs are used as harbours by local fishermen and there is the unusual sight of an aerial ropeway being used to raise catches, gear and even boats to the cliff tops.

There are three large north coast bays and of these Loch Eriboll has potential as a deep water anchorage in spite of having a shallow threshold, but the Kyles of Durness and Tongue (Plate 6) are both shallow, being largely filled with sand. The former is almost dry at low spring tides and the latter is now crossed by a causeway built just west of Tongue village in 1971.

The coastline of West and North Sutherland is dotted with many sandy bays (Plate 14), backed by areas of blown sand. In the west fluvio-glacial sand deposits are largely absent and the beaches tend to be small, while in the north there is an abundance of this material at the ends of the straths and in the Kyles where sandy beaches are much larger, with more extensive areas of dunes and machair.

The sweet and well-drained soils of these sandy areas provide the only ground suitable for farming in the midst of an otherwise rocky wasteland. Over the years agriculture has declined and the crofts have been given over to grass. In a comprehensive study of these beaches Ritchie and Mather (1969) drew attention to how the tourists were being increasingly attracted to them and they underlined the instability of the dune and machair areas which would readily be damaged by over exploitation, be it overgrazing or by lack of control of caravan and camping sites. The most seriously damaged beaches they found to be those where caravanning was popular and many of the erosion features could be related to the driving of vehicles across the unstable sand surfaces. Pedestrian access to the machair areas seems to cause little erosion, but to invite cars on to this sward, which may have taken centuries to evolve, is to destroy one of the few natural assets in a District largely dependent on tourism. Since the report was published some progress has been made in providing car parking facilities and controlling the numbers of caravans on some of the beaches but the situation remains critical.

The east coast of Sutherland is a complete contrast to its rugged counterparts in the north and west. Long stretches of flat beaches run almost the entire length of the coastline and there are only two major inlets, Loch Fleet and the Dornoch Firth.

The beaches take the form of sandy fringes on gently sloping platforms of sedimentary rock or long curved sandy stretches where the coastal margin cuts the extensive fluvio-glacial deposits at the mouths of the River Brora, Loch Fleet and the Dornoch Firth. With some 50% of the outer coastline being sandy beaches the area is extremely attractive for summer tourists who tend to congregate at the more accessible points, leaving the less obvious beaches empty, making Dornoch probably one of the busiest caravan sites in the Highlands. Smith and Mather (1973) examined the form, stability and potential of these beaches and stressed that though they were relatively stable, the wrong sort of use could destroy this stability. Entering an era of growing pressure by industry, agriculture and tourism for control of the land for expansion, they suggest that planners should channel future developments towards the relatively underdeveloped beaches and away from the already saturated areas round Dornoch — a move that might also take some pressure off the fragile beaches of the north and west.

Loch Fleet (Plate 13) is a shallow tidal estuary at the mouth of Strath Fleet which has been almost completely enclosed by the growth of shingle spits from the north (Plate 9). There is, however, sufficient tidal scour in the 24 m (80ft) deep exit channel at Little Ferry to keep it open. The movement of material southwards in the longshore drift to maintain these spits leads to serious erosion at the golf course just south of Golspie where up to 2 m (6.5ft) of the coastal edge may be lost each year.

The Dornoch Firth (Plate 12) is a much larger inlet which measures over 21 km (13 miles) from Dornoch Point to the narrows at Bonar Bridge. It continues inland from there as the Kyle of Sutherland which receives the waters of the rivers Shin and Oykel. This estuary is tidal as far upstream as Inveroykel, i.e. for a further 16 km (10 miles). The outer Firth is very shallow, being filled with glacial sands and gravels. There are plans to build a bridge across its narrow central point.

GLACIATION

Reading through the previous section should have demonstrated that the principal elements in our landscape were formed in pre-glacial times.

During the Pleistocene glaciations there were several periods

when the Highlands were totally covered in ice to be followed by
ice-free conditions when temperatures were at least as warm as
those of today. The most recent ice age reached its maximum extent in Scotland around 18,000 BP and the subsequent decay of the
ice does not appear to have been interrupted by any major re-
advance with the total deglaciation of Scotland being achieved by
13,500 BP. Our knowledge of Pleistocene events relates primarily
to this, the most recent ice age, because it effectively removed the
evidence of any previous glaciations.

The dating of lake bed deposits in West Sutherland and the
examination of their mineral and pollen content indicates that the
improvement in the climate at the time of deglaciation led to a
steady development of vegetation and soil throughout the District
but that a further climatic deterioration took place about 12,000 BP
which culminated in the break up of vegetation and soil due to low
temperatures between 11,000 and 10,400 BP. At this time some
small glaciers reappeared in the higher corries in Sutherland and
we find the limit of their advance indicated by well-marked
moraines. The largest glacier of this period, flowing down Strath
Oykel from Ben More, reached as far as Loch Ailsh. A rapid ame-
lioration of the climate followed and by 10,000 BP herbaceous grassland was re-established, to be followed by the spread of birch woodland over the next 1000 years.

The main ice collecting area in Sutherland was to the east of
the watershed from where it was free to expand along the major
valleys northwards and south-eastwards. For a time the mountains
of the watershed formed a barrier to its westward advance, but the
form of most of the straths and loch basins running west and north-
west from there indicates that they too have been modified by the
passage of ice.

Glacier ice, moving down valleys, can radically alter their form.
Deep basins may be excavated by ice and in Sutherland all the
major elongated valley lochs occupy such basins, while in the west
over-deepened valleys ultimately became arms of the sea giving
birth to a characteristically west coast fjord landscape. In some
valleys projecting spurs have been cut away leaving former side-
valleys "hanging" on the steepened slopes — e.g. along Strath Brora.

Ice flowing over obtruding rocky knolls smoothes the upstream
and plucks the downstream sides to produce features termed
'roches moutonées'. These are very common in the areas of Lewisian
Gneiss in the west while on the east coast fine examples occur at

Dun Creich, Migdale Rock and by the north shore of Loch Fleet 500 m (600yd) south-east of the Mound.

After the melting of the ice, boulders which were being transported by the glaciers were left on the valley floors and sides. These are known as erratics and if they are of a distinctive rock type they can be useful indicators of the direction of ice movement; e.g. boulders of gneiss and quartzite from west of the Moine Thrust Zone have been found far down the River Cassley. Such rocks are most conspicuous when they appear on ridges or hilltops silhouetted against the skyline: these are known as perched blocks and are very abundant between Laxford Bridge and Rhiconich and along the north coast. A further pointer to ice flow movements is provided by linear scratches (striations) imparted to underlying surfaces by abrasive rock fragments embedded in moving ice. These are best seen on exposures of harder rocks such as the quartzite on the west side of Loch Eriboll and on quartz veins in the Moine Schists, but they have also been found on the conglomerate hills near the Mound.

These indicators point to ice having expanded radially from the highest centre at the peak of the glaciation, but soon after this the maximum ice movement became more and more controlled by the topography with the main valley glaciers being fed from high ground until by the closing stages glaciers had retreated into the high corries.

These corries are the most convincing evidence of glacial erosion in the mountain areas and form deeply scalloped excavations in the slopes. They mostly lie on the sides which face between north and east, where in shadow the snow and ice lingered longest and where the freeze-thaw action which excavated them was at its greatest. The Foinaven range has a huge E-shaped form resulting from two corries having bitten deeply into its eastern flank leaving a cliff to the south of Coire na Lurgainn which rises to over 275 m (900ft). The spine of Arkle curves round a huge amphitheatre consisting of four corries overlooking Loch Easain Uaine. Other fine examples occur on Ben Hope, Ben Hee, Ben Klibreck and on the Ben More range, while the high ground of the Freevater Forest is flanked along its northern margin by a line of corries extending east from Seana Braigh.

Glaciers can contain huge amounts of debris of all sizes from angular boulders to rock flour and with ice decay these materials are dumped on the land as an unsorted mass known as till. It is widespread in Central Sutherland but is found at its thickest in valleys and on the lowlands of the east coast. Till may occur as smooth sheets or it may be deposited as distinct hummocky forms known as moraines, of which good examples occur in almost all the valleys; e.g. in Strath Halladale around Forsinard, Strath Naver between Skaill and Loch Naver, along Strath Brora and in particular by the Blackwater from Balnacoil to Ben Armine Lodge.

Meltwater streams redistributed this loose material as layered mounds and ridges along the valleys and fine sections showing unsorted till overlain by bedded fluvio-glacial deposits occur at Armadale, Strathy and along the south bank of the Golspie Burn. As most of the main valleys in Sutherland were substantially choked with glacial debris, the lower straths became filled with immense spreads of layered sand and gravel into which the developing rivers continued to cut their channels and as these swung back and forth across the valleys more and more material was cleared downstream.

Today we see only remnants of these thick deposits in the form of suites of terraces at the valley sides and the rivers meandering on the flat valley floors. In many cases this floor of fluvio-glacial material and the terraces form the only arable land in a strath but towards the river mouths where the ground becomes very level it is subject to flooding and often this part is used only as meadowland. Many of these features can be seen in the lower reaches of the Naver, Borgie, Strathy, Halladale, Fleet, Oykel and Carron rivers with the Halladale probably offering the largest variety over a short distance.

In time of spate large deltas or fans of sand and gravel can be spread out from the mouths of rivers and streams. When these project into the sea the deposits may be dispersed along the beaches in the longshore drift. Fortunately, some have been preserved in Sutherland e.g. the delta at the mouth of the River Carron is the largest of five projecting into the Dornoch Firth and is 1.6 km (1 mile) across; another spreads from Clynelish to the north of Brora, while at Helmsdale a large one occurs which has been truncated at 27.5 m (90ft). Two fine examples can be seen on the north-east shore of Loch Brora.

Sharply defined sinuous ridges of bedded sand and gravel are found in various parts of Sutherland. These are known as eskers and are deposits from the beds of former meltwater channels which ran in tunnels through or under the ice. The best example occurs to the north-west of Dornoch as a very prominent, heather-covered ridge, about 2.4 km (1.5 miles) long. Others occur close to the A9 road between Brora and Golspie and inland from Brora on the Clynelish Moss. Amongst the mounds and ridges of glacial sands and gravel there are often small lochs lying in rounded hollows. These are known as kettle-holes and are formed when masses of ice which were buried in the glacial debris melted to leave shallow depressions in the surface.

Streams flowing at high speed under pressure below the ice carried a substantial load of rock debris and this had great erosive power, cutting 'meltwater channels' in solid rock as well as in the unconsolidated deposits. These can often be recognised because they now carry only tiny streams or may even be 'dry'. Once recognised these channels are seen to be very common, particularly in the rocky areas of the north between Tongue and Melvich and in Strath Halladale. A number of channels cut in drift are found in Clashmore Wood.

PERIGLACIAL FEATURES

As the higher hills emerged from the wasting ice they were subjected to instense frost shattering, which produced an accumulation of material in the form of mountain top detritus and scree. The granite hills such as Carn Chuinneag are often flanked by large scree slopes and topped by areas of coarse granitic sand while on the hilltops of pelitic schists the rock has disintegrated into small fragments. On some of the more level tops such as Càrn Bàn it is possible to walk for more than 3 km (2 miles) without seeing any outcrops of rock other than these loose fragments which are largely covered by a carpet of moss or grass.

Freeze-thaw processes cause down-hill creep (solifluction) of this loose material even on the gentlest of slopes, leading to the development of varying forms of narrow lobes and terraces separated by small scarps up to 1 m (3ft) high as seen on Càrn Bàn and Arkle. Sorting of material has led to the production of stone polygons (e.g. Beinn an Furain) and of stone stripes (e.g. Ben Armine Plate 16). These phenomena usually occur at heights greater than 300 m (1000ft).

RAISED BEACHES

During the melting stages of the great ice sheet, the land, which had been depressed by the weight of ice, did not rise instantly on the shedding of its load, with the result that sea level rose for varying periods until the land recovered.

This is deduced from the presence of raised beaches which the sea had time to cut into unconsolidated sand and gravel deposits round the coast while it stood at these higher levels. Over the years these beaches had been reported at all levels up to 30 m (100 ft). In Sutherland the position is complicated by the presence, especially along the north coast, of fossil cliff lines cut into solid rock. The comparatively short-lived high glacial seas are unlikely to have had sufficient time to erode such features which appear to be of much greater age. The levels of some of these features coincide roughly with that of the Post-Glacial Beach, cut some 6500 years ago.

These raised beaches can be examined in most of the bays along the north coast but occur along the entire length of the east coast.

Along the north coast Ritchie and Mather (1969) found higher shorelines cut in unconsolidated material at altitudes of 4 m to 5 m (14ft to 16ft), 6.5 m to 8 m (21ft to 27ft) and 13.5 m to 16 m (45ft to 52ft) above sea level. Subsequently Balfour (personal communication, 1978) found evidence in North Sutherland to suggest an arching of the upper marine limit with its highest value 21 m (69ft) in the Kyle of Tongue area, dipping westwards to 15 m (49ft) at Inverhope and eastwards to 12 m (39ft) at Melvich.

The cliff of the Post-Glacial Beach is continuous over long distances (Plate 12) and good examples can be studied at the roadside north of Brora and from the roads round Loch Fleet and south past Embo to the Dornoch Firth. At this sea level, south of Dornoch, the mouth of the River Evelix was diverted by the south-westward growth of shingle spits across its mouth while another complex of storm beach shingle ridges and spits, extending south from Golspie, enclosed Loch Fleet (Fig. 9). Today part of the silt deposits that collected in that estuary have emerged as dry land and form the fertile farmlands between the shingle ridges and the railway. Nearby new storm beach ridges and spits are seen forming at the present sea level.

In his classic work on these east coast beaches, Ogilvie (1923) mapped raised beaches round Loch Fleet at 4.5 m, 7.5 m and 15 m (15ft, 25ft and 50ft) as shown in Figure 9. He also showed higher remnants at 21 m and 24 m (70ft and 80ft). He mapped the so called "50ft" beach round Loch Fleet as being continuous, but expressed grave doubts as to whether the similar features in the Dornoch Firth were not in fact dissected glacial outwash aprons. Bowing perhaps to accepted opinion he included them as beaches. The

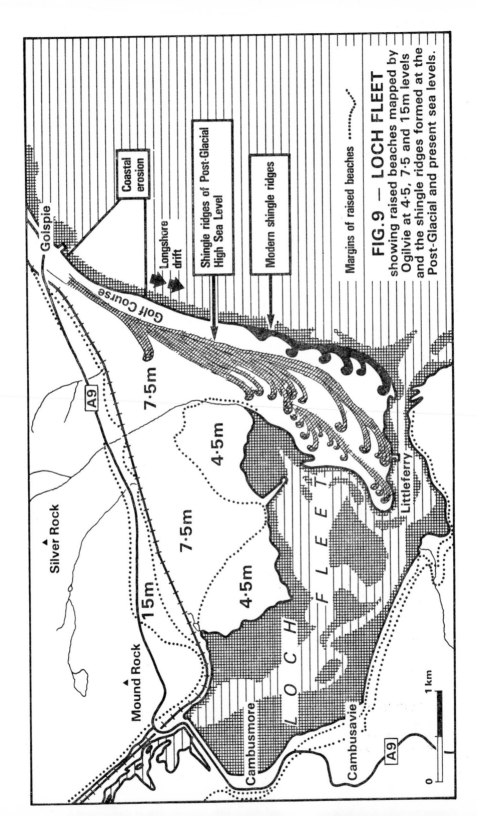

FIG. 9 — LOCH FLEET

showing raised beaches mapped by Ogilvie at 4·5, 7·5 and 15m levels and the shingle ridges formed at the Post-Glacial and present sea levels.

Margins of raised beaches ·········

Coastal erosion

Longshore drift

Shingle ridges of Post-Glacial High Sea Level

Modern shingle ridges

Golspie

Golf Course

Silver Rock

Mound Rock

A9

7·5m

4·5m

7·5m

4·5m

15m

L O C H   F L E E T

Littleferry

Cambusmore

Cambusavie

A9

0   1 km

highest " beach " remnant appears at 29 m (95ft) at Strathsteven to the south of Brora while at Helmsdale there is the large delta at 27.5 m (90ft).

These higher " beaches " cannot be traced northwards into Caithness and there is the growing possibility that some of the features which at a quick glance appear to be raised beach deposits may well be fluvio-glacial in origin.

This diversity of coastal form: relict raised shorelines, remote white beaches and ancient forbidding cliffs along with spectacular mountains, dreary moorlands, rushing rivers and innumerable lochans, combine to give Sutherland an unforgettable landscape.

Landscape features and sections in various deposits are listed below (National Grid references are all NC unless otherwise stated).

SEA STACKS

Stack of Handa	133487	Am Bodach	249736
Old Man of Stoer	014351	Clo Kearvaig	292737
Am Buachaille	202652	An Stac	526687
A' Chailleach	249736	Clach Mhòr na Faraid	398712

NATURAL ARCHES

Eilean nan Ron	644654	Strathy Point	827694
Eilean nan Ron	643661	Uamh Cailliche Peireag	276203
Rabbit Islands	611645		

CAVES

Smoo	419672	Cnoc nan Uamh	276206
Balnakeil Gloup	381688	Creag nan Uamh	
Uamh Dhadhaidh	455644	Bone Caves	269170
Uamh Freisgill	487657	Uamh an Tartair	217092
Coldbackie	606604		

SWALLOW HOLES

Glenbain Hole	265218	Allt nan Uamh	275173
Gleann Dhu Holes	277207	Uamh an Tartair	217092

WATERFALLS

Eas Coulin	280277	Shin Falls	NH 576994
Maldie Burn	251341	Cassley Falls	468028
Falls of Kirkaig	112178		

TOMBOLO
Ard Neakie	446597

WEATHERED ROCK
Gable Burn, Achentoul (granite)	907376	Allt A Mhuilinn, Strath Brora (schist)	841140

TILL
Golspie Burn	838009	Strath Halladale	907642
Dunrobin Glen	804044		

TILL (in Moraines)
Syre	701417	Loch Rimsdale	724399

FLUVIO-GLACIAL FEATURES
Dornoch	NH 789909	Clynelish Moss	878049
	NH 780903	Melvich	892635
Lochan Duinte, Strath Naver	715585	Strath Halladale	903596

KETTLE HOLE LOCHS
Camore	NH 780907
	NH 777900

MELTWATER CHANNELS
Swordly Burn	Armadale Bay
Kirtomy Bay	

ROCHES MOUTONEE
Loch Fleet	782980

RAISED BEACHES
Almost continuous from Dornoch links round coast northwards to Helmsdale. They are prominent in embayments along the north coast.

SHINGLE RIDGES
Scourie Bay	155449	Ferry Links	NH 817960
Cuthill Links	NH 750877		

ROADSIDE VIEWPOINTS
Struie Hill	NH 653857	Kyle of Tongue	579605
Migdale	NH 639924	Loch Eriboll	453603
Strath Halladale	905598	Loch Inchard	236599
Brora	910060	Loch Laxford	210476

Chapter three

THE SOILS

Soils develop as a result of the interaction of chemical, physical and biological processes which take place in mineral material at the surface of the land. These soil-forming processes can include weathering, addition of organic matter at the surface and its incorporation with the upper mineral material, leaching, movement of clay particles by water, podzolization (the removal of iron and aluminium compounds from the surface horizon) and gleying (the reduction of ferric iron to ferrous forms under conditions of waterlogging).

The soil-forming processes differentiate the material into layers, termed soil horizons, roughly parallel to the ground surface. A vertical section through these horizons, from the surface either to relatively unaltered parent material at about 1 m to 1.5 m (39 in to 59 in) or to solid rock in the case of shallower soils, constitutes the soil profile. The soil profile is the basis on which soils are described, identified and classified.

The nature and intensity of the soil-forming processes depend on a number of factors, namely parent material, climate, relief, vegetation, time and Man's agricultural activities.

SOIL FORMING FACTORS

Parent Material
Parent material is the mineral material in which the soil profile is developed, and its properties which most affect soil formation are the texture, i.e. the relative proportions of sand, silt and clay-sized particles, and its mineralogical composition.

Most of the soils in Sutherland are developed on the drift deposits associated with the Pleistocene glaciation, the commonest parent material being a stony till of coarse or moderately coarse texture derived from acid rocks and inherently low in bases such as calcium, magnesium and potassium. Other parent materials comprise fluvioglacial and raised beach sand and gravel deposits, colluvial material, alluvium, frost-shattered material and windblown sand. Most of the soils in Sutherland are thus inherently stony, coarse or moderately coarse-textured and acid.

The only calcareous parent materials occurring in the District are the Durness Limestone and some of the windblown sand (where it contains shell fragments), so calcareous soils have rather a restricted distribution.

The presence of an indurated layer about 20 cm to 40 cm (8 in to 16 in) thick is a common feature in many of the soils developed on the till. This layer is extremely firm, compact, brittle and often has a coarse platy structure with ochreous staining or mottling on the surfaces of the plates. Other features of the indurated layer are the presence of fine pores and fine material lining stone cavities or capping stones. The degree of induration is commonly greatest at the top, decreasing with depth down the soil profile. The top of the indurated layer is usually about 20 cm to 40 cm (8 in to 16 in) below the top of the mineral material. The indurated layer has been considered by some workers to be a fossil permafrost layer formed at a time when periglacial conditions prevailed, and hence a parent material feature inherited by the soil. However, others believe it to be a product of soil-forming processes.

Climate

The main elements of climate which affect soil formation are rainfall and temperature. Not all the rainfall is involved in soil formation because some is lost by immediate run-off and some by evaporation and transpiration. The amount lost by run-off depends on the slope and permeability of the surface, and the intensity of the rainfall. That lost by evapo-transpiration is related to temperature, the loss at lower temperatures being much less than at higher temperatures. Consequently, leaching is more intensive in areas of low summer temperatures and moderate to high rainfall such as in Sutherland, because a relatively higher proportion of the water passes through the soil, and so the soils more quickly become acid. A surface layer of raw organic matter is more readily accumulated on acid soils and this in turn leads to the process of podzolization and the development of peat.

Relief

Slope affects the soil-water regime. Rain water runs off steep slopes more quickly than off gentle slopes, so the better drained soils tend to occur on the more steeply sloping ground and soils with poorer drainage on the flatter land.

An important feature of the Sutherland soils is that with the exception of peat, few soils are continuous over large areas. Instead, there are a number of well-defined soil patterns, each one related to a specific type of topography, so that within each topographic unit a small number of soils constantly recurs. For example, a common soil pattern in areas of moundy moraines comprises peaty podzols on the mounds and peaty gleys or peat in the wetter hollows between the mounds.

Vegetation

Vegetation is dependent on factors such as climate and soil and is not considered to be an independent variable. It does, however, affect the soil, particularly in regard to the humus form developed. Broad-leaved woodland and grassland vegetation are usually associated with moder or mull humus forms in which the organic matter is intimately mixed with the mineral material, and coniferous forest and heath with mor or peaty forms where the organic matter forms a distinctly separate layer. The build-up of raw humus at the surface encourages the process of podzolization of the material below. The marked relationship between soil and vegetation is commented on later in the chapter when individual soil types are discussed.

Time

Soil profiles take time to develop, so the length of time that soil-forming processes have been operating is an important factor in determining the degree of profile development. The Pleistocene glaciation (see Chapter 2) destroyed all pre-existing soils and provided new materials on which many of the present-day soils have developed. Most of Sutherland's soils consequently began to develop at the end of the Ice Age. Soils developed on the younger materials — alluvium and windblown sand — have weakly developed profiles.

Man

Man's agricultural activities can change the natural soil profile in a number of ways. By draining and ditching, the soil-water regime is affected and the drainage status of the soil changed. Ploughing modifies the upper horizons of the natural profile and by mixing and the

1. Scourie Bay and Village   *(J. Campbell)*
2. Lochinver with Quinag   *(Aerofilms)*

3. Loch Inchard showing right to left Ben Stack, Arkle and Foinaven
(D. Robertson)

4. Suilven *(B. Brooker)*

5. Loch Naver and Ben Klibreck   *(J. Selby)*

6. Kyle of Tongue with Ben Hope   *(J. Campbell)*

7. Arkle   *(J. Campbell)*

8. (left) Ben Loyal   *(J. Campbell)*

9. (right) The Old Man O' Stoer   *(J. Selby)*

addition of organic matter creates new ones. Adding lime and ferti-
lizers largely counteracts the effect of leaching and raises the nut-
rient status of the soils.

Man's effect on the soils of Sutherland can be seen mainly in
the farming land in the east of the District and in the crofting land
around the coasts and in the straths. In some cases it is very difficult to assess what the original soil profile would have looked like,
although in others it is very evident that the cultivated soil has been
produced from a podzol or peaty podzol.

SOIL CLASSIFICATION

Soils are identified and classified according to the nature and arrangement of the horizons which make up the soil profile. For con-
venience in describing profiles a conventional letter-symbol is allo-
cated to each horizon in such a way that analogous horizons of similar profiles receive the same symbol. Soil profiles consist basically
of A, B and C horizons. The A horizon is the upper mineral horizon
and the horizon of maximum biological activity. It generally contains organic matter. The B horizon is an intermediate horizon between the A and the C horizons and is characterized either by a
relatively high content of iron and aluminium compounds or by a
well-developed structure, or by bright colours. The C horizon is the
relatively unweathered parent material. Each horizon can be subdivided, e.g. A1, A2, or receive another letter to make the designation more specific, eg. A2g indicates an A2 horizon in which gleying is a prominent feature. In cultivated soils the surface horizon,
or plough-layer, is normally designated the S horizon.

The system of classification used here is basically the one used
by the Soil Survey of Scotland.

The most common soil in Sutherland is probably peat, followed
by peaty podzols and peaty gleys. However, a wide range of other
soil types is represented, including rendzinas, brown forest soils,
humus-iron podzols, noncalcareous gleys and oroarctic soils. In addition a number of miscellaneous soil types occur, such as alluvial
soils, rankers, lithosols and regosols. The general distribution of the
soils is shown in Figure 10.

RENDZINAS

Rendzinas are shallow freely drained soils developed on calcareous
rocks. In Sutherland rendzinas occur on the knolls and ridges of
the Durness Limestone at Durness, Eriboll, Inchnadamph and
Elphin. The soils support a base-rich grassland.

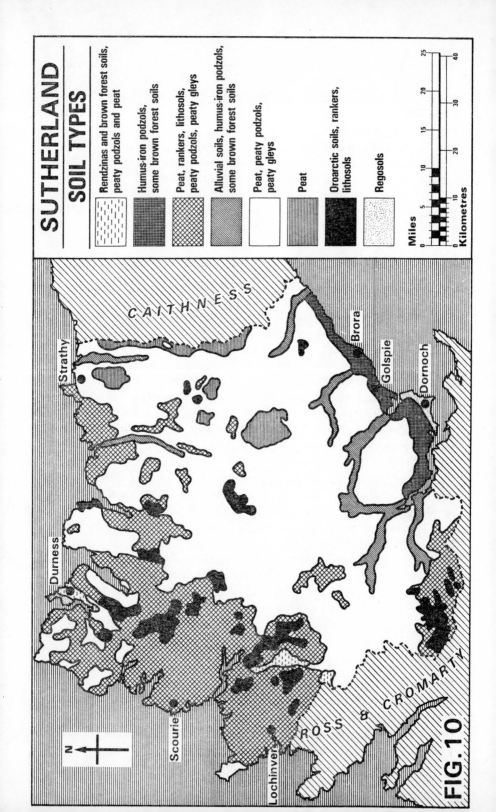

SUTHERLAND
SOIL TYPES

Rendzinas and brown forest soils, peaty podzols and peat

Humus-iron podzols, some brown forest soils

Peat, rankers, lithosols, peaty podzols, peaty gleys

Alluvial soils, humus-iron podzols, some brown forest soils

Peat, peaty podzols, peaty gleys

Peat

Oroarctic soils, rankers, lithosols

Regosols

Miles

Kilometres

CAITHNESS

Strathy

Brora

Golspie

Dornoch

Durness

Scourie

Lochinver

ROSS & CROMARTY

N

FIG. 10

The soil profile consists of a dark brown A horizon between 10 cm and 25 cm (4 in and 10 in) thick overying a C horizon of either hard rock or limestone rubble. The A horizon has a loam texture, a moderately well developed structure, and contains either few or no stones. The pH values of these soils are usually high (>6.5) or medium (5-6.5) in the A horizon and high in the C horizon.

BROWN FOREST SOILS

Brown forest soils are moderately acid soils with free or imperfect drainage. In Sutherland they are mainly restricted to the lower parts of the straths, where they are developed on colluvial material on moderate to steep slopes under either acid grassland with bracken or birch woodland. They have a scattered distribution. The most extensive area of the brown forest soils is in the Rogart district and consists of the steep rocky slopes overlooking Strath Fleet and the lower slopes of the valleys lying to the north of the Strath. Here, the soils are developed on till and colluvial material derived mainly from the rocks of the Rogart igneous complex. Brown forest soils on colluvial material derived from Moinian rocks occur on the steep rocky slopes of Strath Naver between Bettyhill and Skelpick, and at Inchnadamph similar soils are developed on the limestone colluvium on the steep slopes of the limestone escarpment. Brown forest soils, closely associated with humus-iron podzols, are sometimes developed on moundy moraine, as in Strath Brora and on the slopes of the lower part of the Blackwater valley.

The brown forest soils have coarse or moderately coarse textures and are stony, except those developed on the limestone parent materials which have a medium texture. The soil profile consists of a dark brown A horizon, a brown or strong brown B horizon and a paler C horizon. Induration in the lower part of the B horizon or in the C horizon is common, particularly in the soils on moraines or on the more gentle slopes. Soil profiles, with the exception of those on the moraines, are often shallow, with rock present within 1 m (39 in) of the surface.

The pH values of the brown forest soils are usually around pH 4.5 in the A horizon increasing to pH 5 or more in the C horizon.

HUMUS-IRON PODZOLS

Humus-iron podzols are strongly acid, freely and imperfectly drained soils which show morphological and chemical evidence of transloca-

tion of iron and aluminium compounds. They occur mainly in the
drier eastern part of the District in the belt of country lying between Bonar Bridge and Helmsdale and extending inland up Straths
Carron, Oykel, Fleet, Brora and Kildonan, but are also found in
Strath Naver, in the lower part of Strath Halladale, and at Strathy.
The humus-iron podzols are particularly associated with the fluvio-
glacial sand and gravel deposits, although they are also developed
on the stony coarse or moderately coarse-textured till which, in the
valleys, often occurs in the form of moundy moraines. The vegetation is usually dry heath or acid grassland-birchwood.

The soil profile is characterized by a surface layer of raw humus
overlying a bleached A2 horizon depleted in iron and aluminium
compounds. Below the A2 horizon there is a very dark brown or
black A/B horizon of organic deposition around mineral particles.
This horizon is sometimes cemented with organic matter. The B2
horizon has bright colours. The B3 horizon is paler and, in the case
of the soils developed on till, is indurated. Induration is much less
common in the soils developed on fluvioglacial materials. In the C
horizon the colours are those of the parent material.

The pH values in the humus-iron podzols increases from pH4
or less at the surface to pH5.5 or so at the bottom of the profile.

PEATY PODZOLS

Peaty podzols are strongly acid soils characterized by a layer of
peaty humus at the surface and a thin iron pan below a bleached
A2 horizon. The soils are freely drained below the iron pan but
usually poorly drained above it. They are widespread and common
throughout almost the whole of Sutherland. The peaty podzols are
developed on the coarse and moderately coarse-textured stony till
derived from acid rocks and they occur on a variety of slopes ranging from gentle to steep, and in areas of moundy moraines. They are
also developed on fluvioglacial sand and gravel deposits along the
valley of the River Strathy, south of Armadale. The vegetation is
usually moist or wet heather moor.

The soil profile of a peaty podzol developed on the till consists
of a surface layer of peaty humus (less than 50 cm (20 in) thick)
overlying a dark brown organic-stained A2g horizon. The iron pan,
about 1.5 mm (1/16 in) thick, is often wavy but continuous and is
impermeable to water, so the horizons above it are often gleyed. It
is also impenetrable to plant roots and very often a root mat has
formed on the upper surface of the pan. The iron pan generally over-

lies a yellowish brown or strong brown indurated B horizon, although reddish brown colours prevail in soils developed on till derived from the Old Red Sandstone rocks. The C horizon is paler and induration weaker or absent. Less commonly there is a bright-coloured friable B2 horizon between the iron pan and a paler indurated B3 horizon. Profiles of peaty podzols can be readily examined in many of the numerous roadside quarries and cuttings in moraines throughout the District.

Peaty podzols developed on the fluvioglacial materials commonly have a black A/B horizon, similar to that of the humus-iron podzols, present above the iron pan, and gleying in the A2 horizon is usually less pronounced. The B2 horizon has a strong brown colour and is cemented with iron oxides, while the horizons below are paler and the material usually very loose.

The peaty podzols have low pH values in the upper part of the profile and medium pH values in the lower part.

CULTIVATED PODZOLS

Cultivated podzols comprise a variable group of freely and imperfectly drained soils in which an S horizon overlies horizons more characteristic of podzol profiles. These soils have been formed by the cultivation of the natural podzol profiles and are associated with arable and crofting land. Sites no longer cultivated now support acid grassland. The soils are developed on the coarse or moderately coarse-textured stony till. The profile comprises a dark brown S horizon overlying a strong brown or brown B2 horizon in which mottling is sometimes present. The B3 horizon is usually yellowish brown and indurated and the C horizon paler. Sometimes the B2 horizon is absent and the S horizon overlies the indurated B3 horizon.

PEATY GLEYS

Peaty gleys are poorly (and very poorly) drained soils which have a surface horizon of raw peaty humus. They are widespread throughout Sutherland, and support wet heather moorland vegetation.

The peaty gleys are developed on the stony coarse or moderately coarse-textured till. There are two main types of peaty gley, the normal peaty gley and the peaty fragogley, a peaty gley with an indurated layer.

The profile of the normal peaty gley comprises a surface horizon of peaty humus overlying a dark organic-stained A2g horizon very similar to that found in the peaty podzol profiles. Below, a pale brown, greyish brown or grey B2g horizon overlies paler B3g and Cg horizons. The B horizons in particular are characterized by the presence of ochreous and grey mottling.

In the peaty fragogley profile the A2g horizon overlies a pale brown or greyish brown indurated B3(g) horizon characterized by platy structure in which ochreous mottling is often present on the faces of the individual plates. Induration is generally absent in the C horizon.

Noncalcareous Gleys

Noncalcareous gleys are poorly drained mineral soils with no free calcium present in the upper part of the profile, and little or no development of a peaty surface horizon. These soils are uncommon in Sutherland and restricted to a few small areas of old crofting land. They have been found at Scottarie in Strath Brora, at West Langwell, and in Strath Carnaig developed on till of moderately coarse texture, and in Glen Loth on reddish till of moderately fine texture derived from Old Red Sandstone mudstones. The vegetation on the noncalcareous gleys is usually pasture with rushes.

The soil profile consists of a dark greyish brown A horizon overlying greyish brown or reddish brown mottled B and C horizons.

Peat

Peat, a surface accumulation of plant material, is classified as an organic soil. Its formation takes place under conditions of excess surface moisture, low temperatures, and high acidity, factors which inhibit the decomposition of plant remains by causing a reduction in the rate of microbiological activity. In this account peat is defined as having an organic content of more than 60% and a thickness of more than 50 cm (20 in).

Peat is probably the most common soil in Sutherland. It has been estimated (Jowsey, 1973) to cover nearly 33% of the former County of Sutherland. Most of it is the blanket peat type, so called because it forms a blanket over the landscape. Much of it exceeds a thickness of 1 m (39 in). Large continuous tracts of peat occur to the east of Strath Naver, along the Sutherland/Caithness boundary, and at the head of Strath Skinsdale. Large areas of peat broken by isolated moraine mounds or rock ridges are common throughout much of the central, western and northern parts of the District. Blanket peat usually occurs on level or gently sloping ground, but it is also present on steeper slopes, particularly on the hills of east

Sutherland and on the Ben Armine range where it extends upwards almost to the summits of the hills.

In the Lewisian gneiss country of West Sutherland peat occurs in the hollows and channels between the rock knolls.

OROARCTIC SOILS

Oroarctic soils are developed at higher altitudes where, because of the harshness of the climate, the rate at which soil-forming processes take place is greatly reduced. In particular, biological activity and chemical weathering are slow, although as a result of the high rainfall the rate of leaching is fast. Freeze-thaw cycles due to low winter temperatures are an important process in the development of the soil profile and acount for the loose open nature of the soil. Because they are developed on mountain-top detritus, oroarctic soils are usually very stony.

Oroarctic soils in Sutherland are present from about 400 m to 550 m (1300 ft to 1800 ft) upwards on the flatter exposed summits of the higher hills and they commonly support a vegetation dominated either by *Rhacomitrium,* wind-cut *Calluna* or *Nardus.* The soil profiles are variable in the degree of development. Characteristically they consist of a surface horizon of black humus, a dark humose stony A horizon containing bleached mineral grains and rock particles, and a black A/B horizon in which the mineral material is coated with organic matter. Below, a brown or strong brown B2 horizon overlies a paler C horizon. The degree of development of the B2 horizon is variable.

ALLUVIAL SOILS

Alluvial soils are soils developed on alluvium. In Sutherland they occur on the level and gently sloping terraces of alluvium which are particularly extensive in Strath Naver, Strath Halladale and in Straths Carron, Oykel, Fleet, Brora and Kidonan. Alluvial soils can be found in small patches along many of the smaller rivers and streams in the area, and in addition are developed on alluvial fans such as occur near Loch Brora. The alluvial soils usually support acid grassland although some are cultivated.

The alluvium is mostly coarse textured, varying from stony gravelly to sandy stone-free material. Many of the soils have weakly developed profiles consisting of an A or S horizon overlying relatively unaltered parent material, while in others a B horizon, characterized by a bright colour, is present. The soils are predominantly freely drained, although imperfectly and poorly drained alluvial soils often occur as smaller patches in areas of freely drained soils.

RANKERS

Rankers are shallow soils developed on acid rock outcrops and stabilized screes. They are mainly associated with the rocky land-scape of North and West Sutherland but also occur on some parts of the areas underlain by the Rogart igneous complex and the Old Red Sandstone rocks.

Profiles developed on rock usually consist simply of a surface layer of peaty humus overlying the rock, although a thin layer of bleached mineral material is sometimes present between organic matter and rock. Rankers developed on stabilized screes have a similar surface layer of peaty humus overlying a dark-coloured horizon of organic matter and stones, below which there is a C hori-zon of scree material. Sometimes an incipient B horizon of weathered stones occurs below the A horizon, a feature particularly noticeable in the rankers developed on scree derived from the sandstones of Old Red Sandstone age.

LITHOSOLS

Lithosols are free draining raw soils with little or no profile development formed on very stony parent materials. They are asso-ciated with the rocky landscapes of the west and north of Suther-land and are particularly extensive on the Cambrian quartzite hills of the north-west where they are formed on active screes and moun-tain-top detritus. A very thin A horizon is sometimes present at the surface.

REGOSOLS

Soils developed on the windblown sand deposits which occur at the head of many of the bays on the north and west coasts, and as a narrow intermittent strip along the east coast, are here grouped together under the general heading of regosols. The most extensive areas of these soils are at Balnakeil Bay and in the Dornoch district. In general, the sand deposits of the north and west coasts contain varying amounts of comminuted shell fragments and are therefore calcareous, whereas those of the east coast are predominantly non-calcareous. The windblown sand occurs in the form of active and stabilized dunes, usually laid down on gently sloping smooth sur-faces, but near Bettyhill it has been deposited on the steep slopes of the headland of Druim Chuibhe.

The soils have varying degrees of profile development but for the most part they have weakly developed profiles. The main factor affecting the degree of profile development is the length of time the sand deposit has remained stable and undisturbed. The longer that leaching and weathering processes operate on the deposit, and organic matter is incorporated at the surface, the greater is the degree of profile development.

The soils on the active dunes rarely show much evidence of profile development other than a very thin A horizon at the surface. Frequently, however, thin A horizons occur as dark bands in the deposit, indicating periods of relative stability during the build-up of the deposit, when a vegetation cover was able to form. These soils usually support marram vegetation.

On the more stable sites, which usually occur inland of the active dunes, soil profiles are characterized by a dark A horizon consisting of sand and organic matter overlying either a pale C horizon of raw sand or, where profile development is more advanced, a brown B horizon. Weakly podzolized soils, in which a thin bleached layer is present, sometimes occur on the oldest stable sites under a heath vegetation. The majority of the soils support a grassland vegetation.

Soils with moderately well-developed profiles on shelly sand are more precisely named brown calcareous soils, and are characterized by a high content of calcium and high pH values throughout the profile. A high pH at the surface probably indicates that loss of calcium by leaching is balanced by the addition of windblown shelly sand.

Chapter four

CLIMATE

The mountains in the west and south of Sutherland form a barrier over which the prevailing south-west winds must pass and this largely dictates the form of the climate of the District.

When these moist winds from the Atlantic are forced to rise over this barrier, the result is a persistent blanket of cloud and heavy rainfall. In contrast, having shed much of its moisture, the air descending to the lee of the mountains is dried and warmed — a process known as the föhn effect. This gives eastern coastal parts of Sutherland a much better climate than the west, with the most favoured area being the extreme south-east corner where the shelter is greatest.

Because of the scarcity of climatological records for the District, in discussing the various aspects of the climate in the following paragraphs, use has had to be made of estimates based on short term data for varying periods and also of data from outside the District boundary.

RAINFALL

The contrasts between the climate in the east of Sutherland and that in the west are well outlined in Figure 11 where the map of the annual averages of rainfall closely resembles the contour map of the District.

Over the mountainous parts of the west the average rainfall is in excess of 3000 mm (118 in) per year in some places making that area one of the wettest in Scotland. To the east values fall away steadily to just less than 750 mm (30 in) per year near Dornoch. A little outside the south-eastern District boundary is the area with the lowest rainfall in the Highlands, at Tarbat Ness where only 600 mm (24 in) per year are recorded on average.

From Table 3 it can be seen that the wettest month in the north-west is October while in most other parts the peak period is

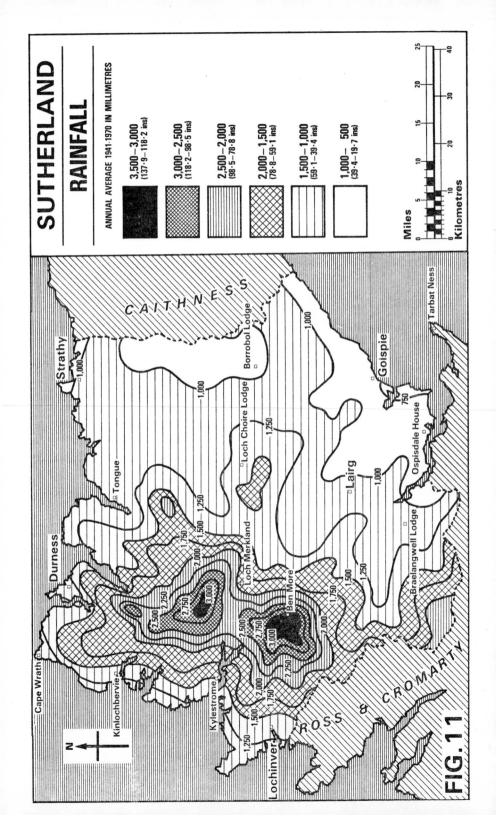

SUTHERLAND
RAINFALL

ANNUAL AVERAGE 1941-1970 IN MILLIMETRES

- 3,500—3,000 (137·9—118·2 ins)
- 3,000—2,500 (118·2—98·5 ins)
- 2,500—2,000 (98·5—78·8 ins)
- 2,000—1,500 (78·8—59·1 ins)
- 1,500—1,000 (59·1—39·4 ins)
- 1,000—500 (39·4—19·7 ins)

Miles
Kilometres

FIG. 11

TABLE 3 – MONTHLY AND ANNUAL AVERAGES OF RAINFALL (MILLIMETRES) FOR STATIONS IN SUTHERLAND 1941 – 1970

STATION	HEIGHT Metres	HEIGHT Feet	JAN	FEB	MAR	APR	MAY	JUN	JUL	AUG	SEP	OCT	NOV	DEC	YEAR
CAPE WRATH*	112	367	109	84	78	72	61	81	90	98	111	132	118	122	1156
KINLOCHBERVIE	55	181	118	91	84	78	66	88	97	106	120	143	127	131	1249
KYLESTROME	30	98	140	108	100	92	78	104	115	126	142	169	151	157	1482
LOCHINVER	6	20	125	106	87	89	67	72	78	87	111	138	128	154	1242
KNOCKAN ROCK	244	800	215	182	150	153	116	124	134	149	192	238	220	265	2138
DURNESS	32	105	116	90	83	77	65	87	96	105	119	141	126	130	1235
LOCH MERKLAND	118	386	191	162	133	136	103	110	119	132	171	211	196	235	1899
BEN MORE (East Slope)	525	1265	329	278	229	234	177	190	205	228	294	364	336	405	3269
GLEANN BEAG	335	1099	226	192	159	162	127	129	141	160	199	247	230	282	2254
TONGUE	6	20	102	82	71	59	61	65	76	91	94	103	116	113	1033
LOCH CHOIRE LODGE	175	572	138	110	95	79	82	87	102	122	127	138	155	151	1386
LAIRG	101	332	102	82	68	73	83	79	91	110	91	105	106	116	1106
BRAELANGWELL LODGE	55	180	106	85	71	76	86	82	95	115	95	110	110	120	1151
STRATHY	38	125	101	81	70	58	60	64	75	90	93	101	114	111	1018
BORROBOL LODGE	104	340	92	75	60	60	75	62	78	91	93	100	101	97	984
GOLSPIE	31	102	68	54	47	50	60	58	69	82	66	75	73	78	780
OSPISDALE HOUSE*	30	98	75	60	50	54	61	58	67	81	67	78	78	85	814

*Averages for these stations are for the full 30-year period. Others are estimated from shorter term records.

November or December. However, in the south-east (e.g. Golspie) this peak shifts to August which is in line with the summer maximum shown by the well-sheltered inner Moray Firth area. At Lairg, Braelangwell Lodge and Ospisdale House this trend is borne out by a high subsidiary maximum value in August.

Because the prevailing south-west to west winds blow for considerable periods at a stretch rainfall in the west tends to be prolonged and heavy, particularly in autumn and early winter. In 1794 the Rev. Wm. Mackenzie commenting on the climate of Assynt wrote, " The rain continues not only for hours but often for days; nay, for weeks, especially if the wind perseveres for a long time to blow from the west. A smart easterly wind arising and continuing for a space of 24 hours will perfectly abate the waters, carry off all superfluous rain from the surface and moisture from the air." He was thus well aware of the importance of wind direction in relation to local weather.

The driest month in the west is May, when there is usually a spell with east to south-east winds. In central parts April is the driest month while in the south-east the minimum moves towards March — again in line with the inner Moray Firth values. Some annual rainfall averages (converted to the nearest inch) for other parts of the United Kingdom are shown for comparison with those for Sutherland.

TABLE 2

Some Annual Rainfall Averages in Britain

Aberdeen	...	830 mm (33 in)	Edinburgh	...	660 mm (26 in)
Manchester	...	818 mm (32 in)	Perth ...	...	780 mm (31 in)
Glasgow	...	1043 mm (41 in)	Kew ...	...	598 mm (24 in)

Table 3 shows the average rainfall and it must be remembered that a wide scatter of values goes to make up an average. For example, in October, 1970, at Cassley Diversion Weir 682 mm (27 in) of rain were recorded, 2.3 times the monthly average and a figure almost equal to the annual rainfall at Golspie. At the same station in April, 1974, only 10.5 mm (0.4 in) fell instead of the average of 145 mm (5.5 in). This is a reminder that extreme values must be looked at as well as the mean values when assessing the likelihood of flooding or drought in any particular area.

All the rain falling in the west does not run to waste as the North of Scotland Hydro Electric Board produces considerable amounts of electricity by using the water from a complex of catchment systems centering on Loch Shin (Plate 33).

TEMPERATURE

The fact that Sutherland is bounded on three sides by the sea has a considerable effect on the climate and in particular on the temperature.

On average the sea temperature reaches a maximum of some 13° C (55° F) in August all round the coast, so that in summer any breeze from the sea will have a cooling effect on coastal districts. As winter approaches the sea cools slowly and does not reach its coldest until March, when in west coast waters the average temperature would be around 6° C (43° F), but in the Moray Firth it would fall to 4° C (39° F). This means that the prevailing westerly winds of autumn and early winter are still comparatively mild and even in mid-winter very cold northerly outbreaks are modified to some extent by passing over the warmer sea. The sea also warms very slowly so that in spring and early summer, while temperatures in the southern parts of the United Kingdom are rising from their winter levels, any winds blowing from these warmer regions are considerably cooled by their passage over the cold waters and the advent of spring is delayed in the north. The effect is very noticeable on the east coast of Sutherland, where during May, June and July it produces persistent banks of sea fog and low cloud (haar) whenever east or south-east winds blow.

Records of temperatures from within Sutherland are limited to those from Cape Wrath, Strathy and Lairg, but Inverpolly and Tarbat Ness are close enough to the District boundary for some of their data to be relevant. Annual and monthly averages and extremes of temperatures are shown in Tables 4a, b and c.

Making allowance for the differences in elevation, summer daily-mean temperatures in the south-east are about a degree higher than those in the north-west while in winter temperatures in western coastal districts are higher than those farther east, with the coldest part being the inland area to the east of the mountains (Figs. 12.1 and 12.2). For coastal parts of South-East Sutherland mean winter daily temperatures would be closer to those at Tarbat Ness rather than those at Lairg.

Mean annual maximum temperatures in the District are highest in inland parts away from the cooling effects of sea breezes (Fig. 12.3) and it is of interest here to note that the extreme maximum temperatures at Strathy, Lairg and Inverpolly were recorded during a single hot spell in August, 1975. The lowest mean annual minimum temperatures also occur in the central parts of the District (Fig.

TABLE 4A – AVERAGES OF DAILY MEAN TEMPERATURES IN DEGREES CELSIUS

	JAN	FEB	MAR	APR	MAY	JUN	JUL	AUG	SEP	OCT	NOV	DEC	YEAR
CAPE WRATH	4.3	3.9	5.1	6.3	8.3	10.7	11.8	12.3	11.3	9.5	6.7	5.3	8.0
STRATHY	2.5	2.5	4.5	6.5	8.9	11.8	12.8	12.7	11.4	8.9	5.3	3.6	7.6
INVERPOLLY	4.4	3.5	5.3	6.8	9.9	12.5	12.9	13.5	11.7	9.5	5.5	4.9	8.4
LAIRG	1.1	1.7	4.1	6.5	8.9	12.3	12.7	12.7	11.4	8.1	3.9	1.9	7.1
TARBAT NESS	3.2	3.5	5.1	7.1	9.3	12.1	13.7	13.4	12.1	9.6	6.0	4.2	8.3

The averages for Cape Wrath and Strathy are for the period 1941–1970 with some breaks.
Those for Inverpolly are 1963–1975, for Lairg 1957–1975 and for Tarbat Ness 1949–1970.

TABLE 4B – AVERAGE MONTHLY MAXIMUM AND MINIMUM TEMPERATURES IN DEGREES CELSIUS

	JAN	FEB	MAR	APR	MAY	JUN	JUL	AUG	SEP	OCT	NOV	DEC	YEAR
CAPE WRATH													
Maximum	10.6	10.1	12.6	14.0	16.9	20.3	19.4	20.6	18.5	16.7	12.6	11.3	22.8
Minimum	-2.2	-2.2	-1.8	-0.8	1.5	5.1	7.4	7.5	5.5	2.3	0.4	-1.1	-3.7
STRATHY													
Maximum	10.4	10.3	14.5	16.5	20.3	23.7	22.9	22.6	20.7	18.0	12.8	11.4	25.4
Minimum	-7.3	-8.1	-5.9	-3.7	-0.9	1.6	3.9	3.5	2.2	-1.0	-3.7	-5.2	-10.2
INVERPOLLY													
Maximum	12.2	10.6	13.1	15.8	19.6	22.1	21.8	22.6	18.9	17.7	13.3	13.0	24.3
Minimum	-4.9	-5.7	-3.1	-1.9	-1.5	4.4	4.8	4.4	3.7	0.5	-2.8	-4.2	-8.5
LAIRG													
Maximum	10.0	10.6	13.6	16.7	20.4	23.5	23.0	22.8	20.2	17.4	12.4	11.0	24.7
Minimum	-11.3	-11.3	-7.2	-5.7	-1.9	0.9	2.7	1.1	0.4	-1.9	-6.4	-9.0	-14.1

TABLE 4C – ABSOLUTE MONTHLY MAXIMUM AND MINIMUM TEMPERATURES IN DEGREES CELSIUS

	JAN	FEB	MAR	APR	MAY	JUN	JUL	AUG	SEP	OCT	NOV	DEC	YEAR
CAPE WRATH													
Maximum	15.0	13.9	20.6	16.7	22.8	25.6	26.1	27.2	22.8	22.8	16.7	17.2	27.2
Minimum	−5.0	−6.9	−5.0	−6.0	−0.8	−0.6	5.6	5.6	1.7	−0.6	−3.0	−4.5	−6.9
STRATHY													
Maximum	12.8	15.0	21.7	21.1	26.7	27.8	30.0	30.0*	25.0	23.3	17.2	14.4	30.0
Minimum	−14.4	−15.0	−14.4	−7.2	−3.9	−1.7	1.1	−1.1	−1.1	−7.2	−11.7	−13.3	−15.0
INVERPOLLY													
Maximum	15.8	13.9	18.8	19.6	22.2	26.7	26.7	29.7	21.1	20.2	15.0	16.7	29.7
Minimum	−11.7	−8.3	−6.1	−3.9	−1.7	0.6	2.7	2.8	−0.6	−1.9	−5.6	−8.3	−11.7
LAIRG													
Maximum	13.3	15.6	19.4	19.4	25.0	26.7	26.1	27.5	23.9	22.2	15.5	12.8	27.5
Minimum	−19.4	−18.3	−16.7	−7.2	−5.0	−1.7	0.5	−0.5	−2.2	−5.6	−10.0	−17.8	−19.4

*In August 1975 a temperature of 30.6 degrees was recorded at Strathy.

12.4) where light winds, cold air drainage and frost-hollow effects are widespread in winter with the probable temperature ranges as in the tabulations for Lairg. Here on average there are 89 days per year with air frost compared with 63 at Strathy, 47 at Inverpolly and 24 at Cape Wrath (Fig. 12.5). While air frost is unlikely in the summer months in the west, only July is free from air frost at Strathy and Lairg. Ground frost, twice as common as air frost, can occur in any month at most sites.

The exposure and elevation of any site are of vital importance to agriculture. Air temperatures fall with increasing elevation at a rate of 1° C (2.1° F) per 100 m [3° C (6.4° F) per 1000 ft] so that the growing season is shorter on the higher ground. South-facing slopes benefit from additional warmth while frost and snow linger longer in the shade on north-facing slopes with resulting lower soil temperatures. The net result is that the climate firmly imposes an upper limit to arable farming.

WIND

Away from the south-east of the District and from the shelter of the straths, Sutherland is by and large windy and with the shortage of sheltering belts of woodland, this is quickly noticed by visitors used to the more gentle climes of Southern Britain. The cooling effects of strong winds can mar what might otherwise be a pleasant sunny day and on damp days in winter and spring produce very " raw " conditions. What shelter belts have been planted are greatly appreciated by man and beast.

Continuous recordings of windspeed and direction from within the District are limited to those from Shin Power Station, but records from Wick, Dounreay and Stornoway can be of assistance in building up a general picture of the wind regime (Fig. 13).

Over Scotland as a whole the prevailing wind is south-westerly but in its passage across North Scotland this direction is modified by the shape of the landmass to favour south to south-east as shown at Dounreay and Wick. There is, however, a strong secondary maximum between west and north-west at both these stations. Winds of strong or gale-force (>22 kt) blow on average for 8% of the time at Wick but for 14% of the time at Dounreay. Eastern coastal parts of Sutherland probably have annual wind regimes similar to that at Wick, while towards the north coast wind speeds would increase to the values shown by Dounreay. Westwards, a further increase takes place and at Cape Wrath, where observations at six-hourly intervals

FIG.12 — ISOTHERMS AND 'DAYS OF SNOW' DISTRIBUTION IN NORTHERN SCOTLAND

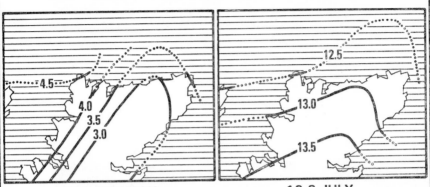

12.1 JANUARY　　　　**12.2 JULY**

Mean daily temperatures for 1941–1970 reduced to mean sea level 0.6°C/100m.

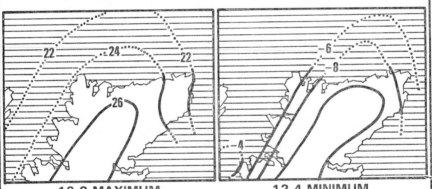

12.3 MAXIMUM　　　　**12.4 MINIMUM**

Mean annual maximum and minimum temperatures for 1941–1970 reduced to mean sea level by 1.0°C/100m and 0.5°C/100m respectively.

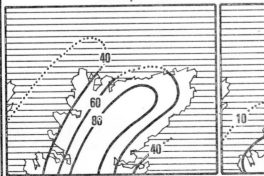

12.5 Mean number of days per year with minimum temperature less than 0°C 1956–1970

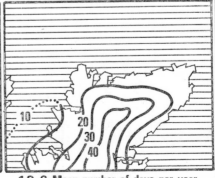

12.6 Mean number of days per year with snow lying at 0900 GMT 1941–1970

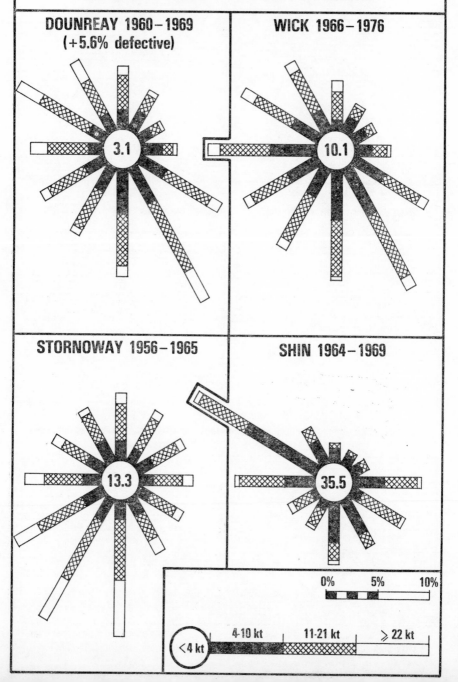

FIG.13 — ANNUAL % FREQUENCIES OF WIND DIRECTION AND SPEED

DOUNREAY 1960–1969
(+5.6% defective)

3.1

WICK 1966–1976

10.1

STORNOWAY 1956–1965

13.3

SHIN 1964–1969

35.5

0%   5%   10%

<4 kt   4-10 kt   11-21 kt   ⩾ 22 kt

show south-west as the favoured direction, gales occur on 38 days per year, a similar figure to that at Stornoway which has winds of strong or gale force blowing for 21% of the time. This indicates that the winds at unsheltered sites in the north-west and west of the District might have wind patterns similar to those at Stornoway.

Data from Shin (Fig. 13) show the marked tendency for winds to blow along the length of the valley and for windspeeds from other directions to be reduced. The incidence of light winds is extremely high, with 35.5% of wind speeds being less than 4 kt. Winds blowing across the valley tend to be very gusty, but strong winds (22 to 33 kt) occur on average only on 7 days per year and gales on 3 days per year. Records from other valley sites in the Highlands produce similar distributions, so that the Shin wind pattern can be taken as being typical of many of the long straths in Sutherland.

Although in Figure 13 the highest wind frequency is shown to occur in the south-east quadrant at Wick and Dounreay the strongest winds are usually recorded from between west and north-west. At Stornoway and Shin the highest speeds usually occur between south-west and west. Over the periods in question the maximum wind recorded at Wick was from the south-west with a speed of 58 kt gusting to 89 kt, at Dounreay north-westerly 69 kt with gusts greater than 97 kt, at Shin westerly 48 kt with gusts to 77 kt and at Stornoway southerly 68 kt with gusts of 98 kt.

Parallels which can be drawn from observations in other parts of the Highlands would be the marked increase in wind speed over the higher hills and the extreme gustiness on ridges and lee slopes of mountains. From the shelter of the valleys it is often difficult to judge the severity of conditions on the high ground. In some situations sudden downslope surges of wind can penetrate into the normally sheltered straths or sea lochs giving exceptionally severe squalls.

SNOW

In winter cold north to north-east winds are often accompanied by snow and in any one year usually no part of the District escapes without a fall of some kind, although amounts and distribution are extremely variable.

Figure 12.6 shows the average number of days per year with snow lying and covering more than half the ground. Inland parts, being higher and farther from the modifying influence of the sea, have considerably more days with snow than places near the coast.

The lower values near the west coast are due to the sea there being some 2° C to 3° C (4.2° F to 6.4° F) warmer than that in the east, where in severe winters ice may be seen on the shallower waters of the Dornoch Firth. Snow can be expected to fall in any month save July and August but lying snow is on average only significant from November to April at lower levels.

When winds are very strong there is less time for polar air to be warmed by its passage over the sea and substantial snowfall may occur. During most winters many roads are blocked by drifting snow under such conditions, but even with light snowfall the drifting of lying snow can be a problem.

Very infrequently exceptionally severe and prolonged winter storms affect Sutherland leading to widespread disruption throughout the District. During the storms of January and February, 1955, and in the same period in 1978 almost all roads and railways were blocked by drifts, some reaching 6 m to 9 m (20 ft to 30 ft) in height; power and telephone lines were brought down by heavy coatings of ice and communities were totally isolated. Losses among livestock were immense, particularly of sheep, and sadly human lives were also lost. With events reaching "disaster" proportions, only the mounting of extensive rescue and supply missions by air prevented much greater losses.

Like frost, lying snow persists longer on the north-facing slopes, while the sun helps thaw deposits elsewhere. Persistent warm rain can thaw lying snow faster than any other medium, and historical records list some of the rare heavy snowfall periods being followed by heavy rain. The rapid thaws resulted in catastrophic flooding in some of the river valleys, in particular Strath Carron and the Kyle of Sutherland. With the comparative infrequency of these events it is difficult to judge to what extent the risk has been modified where hydro-electric schemes have been built.

Fog

Sutherland enjoys comparatively clean air, being far from sources of industrial pollution and winter fogs of the type so frequent in southern Britain are unknown. In fact, apart from the river valleys, radiation fog is rare in the District.

The east coast, where the sea is colder, is particularly prone to banks of sea for or "haar" being brought onshore by east to south-east winds in the summer months, and here it may persist for several days at a time. During the day higher temperatures inland may " burn off " the fog or break up the cloud, but near the coast it persists to return inland as temperatures fall overnight. This tends to make the early mornings the foggiest period under these conditions. At Wick, where fog occurs on average on some 45 days per year, May to August is the foggiest period and July with an average of seven days with fog is the foggiest month. These figures are probably typical of the east coast of Sutherland but a southwards decrease in the frequency would be expected.

The low cloud which develops in moist and rain-bearing winds envelops much of the higher ground for long periods and is particularly persistent over the western hills. This " hill fog " effectively cuts down the sunshine reducing the temperature and this, together with the increased humidity, has a marked effect on vegetation growth in these areas, as is demonstrated in the following chapter.

Chapter five

PLANT LIFE

In his introduction to the book "Mountain Flowers" (1956), John Raven states, "Even in so small an area as the British Isles, there is still much to be done. Vast tracts of country, notably in the Western Highlands of Scotland, still await thorough botanical exploration." Twenty years later, John Anthony's *Flora of Sutherland* was published giving a comprehensive account of plants found in Sutherland, but owing to the remoteness of much of the District, many locations for individual species must be yet undiscovered. Of the 1700 species of flowering plants and ferns found in the British Isles, over 900 occur in Sutherland. Of course, there are major groups of plants, fungi, lichens, algae, mosses and liverworts, which do not attract so much attention and their record in Sutherland is very poorly known.

The rare and the beautiful are not always difficult to find in Sutherland, for what is rare in many parts of Britain is often common in the far north. This is especially true of mountain plants which descend to sea level on the north coast. Purple saxifrage (*Saxifraga oppositifolia*) grows close to roads in many places, on rocks facing the sea, and it is only a short step to the machair or limestone to see mountain avens (*Dryas octopetala*) within 30 m (100 ft) of sea level. The purple oxytropis (*Oxytropis halleri*) has a peculiar distribution, confined to areas around Bettyhill, where in places it is a noticeable feature of machair and clifftop vegetation. Otherwise this plant is known from fewer than six sites in Britain, all of these in Scotland. A plant that most visitors to Sutherland would want to see is the diminutive, mealy-leaved Scottish primrose (*Primula scotica*, Plate 18). All along the cliffs at Strathy, the seaward slopes at Torrisdale, and many other places on the North coast as far west as Cape Wrath this plant is found locally in abundance. Apart from being a delight in itself, it has a rare distinction; an endemic plant, confined in its distribution to Scotland and even there to Sutherland, Caithness and the Orkney Isles. Often associated with the Scottish primrose in the short cliff-top turf and flowering at the same time of year is the delicate spring squill (*Scilla verna*). The distribution of this plant is quite different, extending from Shetland to Cornwall in isolated patches along the western seaboard. Rarity is not always due to climatic requirements although the pale butterwort (*Pinguicula lusitanica*) with its purple-marked leaves does seem to have a distinctly western distribution, both in Sutherland and throughout Britain. Grazing has been blamed for the relative rarity of species like the royal fern (*Osmunda regalis*), often confined to islands in lochs or other inaccessible places where sheep cannot go. Orchids, found in damp meadows, and woodland plants such as one-flowered wintergreen (*Moneses uniflora*) are often threatened by man's activity in drainage and felling. Twinflower (*Linnaea borealis*) named after the great Swedish botanist Linnaeus is a rare plant of pine woods and was reported near Golspie in 1888. It was rediscovered by John Anthony in 1960. In the past when pine woods were more extensive in Sutherland this plant was probably widespread. The Scottish primrose is a good example of those plants threatened by tourists and, sad to say, botanists who in the past have felt they needed to dig it up for their garden. However, the chances of transplanting this beautiful plant are extremely small and germination from seed is also quite difficult.

There is no one way to look at the plant life of Sutherland. Individual plants do not usually occur in isolation but are members of a vegetation type, or plant community: heath, forest or aquatic vegetation. The presence or absence of such vegetation types depends upon a combination of environmental factors. For any climatic zone water and nutrients usually place limits upon plant growth and distribution. It is a very specialised group of plants which can exist in the dry nutrient-poor conditions of sand dunes and quite a different group from that associated with the wet nutrient-poor soils of blanket bog. Other vegetation types rely upon, or tolerate (it is not always clear), aquatic salt-inundated or highly calcareous situations, the latter arising from Durness limestone or shell sand. While much of the vegetation in the District depends upon rain water for its main source of inorganic nutrition, especially in blanket bog and acid lochans, nutrition from the soil is also a major factor in plant growth.

In general terms, soils can be stable or unstable, acid or neutral to alkaline in reaction and based upon organic or inorganic debris.

Areas with unstable soils such as screes and sand dunes have associated with them plants adapted to those conditions. Marram grass (*Ammophila arenaria*) is able to grow up through moving sand dunes, thereby stabilising them for other plants to invade. Yet marram grass is susceptible to trampling by humans with the result that dunes can become unstable or suffer from blowouts. In many places, these soils are further stabilised by species such as dwarf willow (*Salix repens*), which can form mats over considerable areas, thus binding the sand. As well as being a dry habitat the soil surface undergoes wild fluctuations in temperature. The same is true of the quartzite screes of the western mountains of Sutherland.

A much richer series of vegetation types is associated with stable soils. The most important of these soils are the podsol, brown earth, rendzina and peat. Podzols with their grey leached layer, cap of dark humus and red stained iron-pan are extremely common, found under heathland and beneath conifer plantations. They develop wherever acid humus has formed over nutrient-poor geological strata in the cold wet conditions. These soils, and the even more acid peats, are now covered with heather moor, cotton grass and sedges. When a layer of peat has developed, as in some hollows, the tree-stump remains of old forests can be found. Where geological strata are richer in plant nutrients or more easily weathered, where glacial debris has been washed down the straths, and especially on low ground, a richer, deeper, unstratified soil, the brown earth, supports woodland, grassland or cultivated crops. In most places this woodland is dominated by birch but there are oak woods in the east and hazel scrub in places. Many more species are able to grow on this neutral to alkaline soil than on the acid podsols. This feature is often most striking on high mountains such as Ben Hope where an outcrop of epidiorite and hornblende schist gives the peak a much more interesting flora than the adjacent Ben Loyal. In limestone areas down from Durness to Inchnadamph an alkaline soil, chalky brown in colour, called a rendzina, develops on low ground. This is particularly well seen at Heilam Ferry by the old lime-kilns and at Inchnadamph near the junction of the Lochinver/Kylesku road. In both areas mountain avens is a common species and close examination of the mosses reveals that the moss *Ctenidium molluscum* with its glossy, golden green, strongly-curved leaves is also present.

Climate, with its many facets, plays a considerable part in the determination of plant communities in Sutherland. Of the 18 Scottish climatic sub-types in the classification of Birse and Dry

(1970) 15 are present in Sutherland, the very warmest being absent. Perhaps the most obvious feature is that woodland is so scarce, especially in the west and the tree line extends to only 300 m (1000 ft) on Ben Loyal. Birch forest forms this tree-line, which in many cases might be extended slightly in the absence of burning and grazing.

A consequence of the westerly airflow over Scotland is that the climate becomes more oceanic in a north-westerly direction and continental towards the south-east, resulting in a lowering of the treeline and associated altitudinal vegetation zones in the far north of Scotland. As a result many high altitude plants of the Cairngorms are found at low altitudes in Northern Sutherland. This accounts for the large arctic-alpine element in the flora occurring down to sea-level. The growing season is reduced by increasing altitude and this effect becomes greater near the coast. Cnoc an Fhreiceadain (the watch hill) at Tongue rises over 300 m (1000 ft) from the sea on the northern exposed side. Scrub vegetation is confined to the lower slopes whereas on the sheltered south side of the hill, birch wood rises to 200 m (650 ft). Measurements on the heath bed-straw (*Galium saxatile*) from this hill show considerable differences in flowering and fruiting from sea-level to 300 m (1000 ft) while the mean size of the plant is reduced from 9.7 cm (3.8 in) at 130 m (425 ft) to 5.5 cm (2.2 in) at 330 m (1080 ft) altitude. This reduction in size of plants has led to the selection of many dwarf forms and species characteristic of high altitudes and exposed coasts. Creeping willow (*Salix repens*) on the coast, dwarf willow (*Salix herbacea*), dwarf birch (*Betula nana*) in many bogs together with dwarf forms of heather (*Calluna vulgaris*) and sea plantain (*Plantago maritima*) all show such a response.

THE HISTORY OF VEGETATION IN SUTHERLAND

This apparently immutable landscape has cast its cover several times since the last great glaciers finally retreated from corries and straths 10,000 years ago. Compared with other parts of Britain, so very little is known about the history of vegetation in the far north. However, peat in its great abundance throughout Sutherland is the source of information. Firstly, large pieces of debris, roots of trees silver in the sun, or glistening seeds of bogbean (*Menyanthes trifoliata*) from the basal peat, give clues to the past. But these fragments are only part of the story. Throughout the peat, from the remains of yellow ochre reeds to jet black cotton grass and fibrous sphagnum near the surface, are microscopic remains, pollen grains. They have been stored each year, each season, to demonstrate a change in vegetation for the whole region. These changes from tundra to trees to blanket bog are generally agreed to have been triggered off by major climatic changes lasting thousands rather than hundreds of years.

There is evidence that trees, which have had such an influence on the floral diversity of the District, suffered further with the use of timber for building, for charcoal and for iron smelting in Strath Naver. More recently birch has been used for cotton bobbins in Spinningdale. Yet changes brought about by man are not just recent. The many prehistoric remains in Sutherland suggest that the removal of forests has been a continuing process over several thousand years. Charcoal and iron slag show that man used forests as fuel for smelting and later in his efforts at land improvement for lime-kilns, although coal from East Sutherland was used to fire the kilns at Heilam Ferry. Sinclair in the *First Statistical Account* (1793) suggests that iron was mined prior to the Scandinavian invasions. Fuel was also used in corn drying kilns.

Evidence of a number of extensive fires can be found in the charcoal remains especially near the north coast. Thus man locally, if not extensively, destroyed or managed vegetation. In spite of this there are plants still present as part of the flora which are considered to be relicts of the cold post-glacial period. Mountain aven, widespread in Britain as the ice retreated is now a common but localised plant in Sutherland, whereas the net-leaved willow, one of two willows quoted by Spence (1904) as occurring under peat on glacial drift, is much rarer, being confined to Durness.

MOUNTAINS

A combination of complex geological strata and extremes of climate make the mountains of Sutherland an interesting habitat for many rare plants. This habitat has as much in common with the mountains of Europe as it does with the rest of Britain. Plants found on these mountains are often grouped into those with arctic, alpine or arctic-alpine distribution. Some of the rare mountain plants from Sutherland have an arctic distribution outside Britain being absent from European mountains and having a generally circum-polar distribution. This group includes the russet sedge (*Carex saxatilis*), the two-flowered rush (*Juncus biglumis*) — a plant with only one locality — alpine hair grass (*Deschampsia alpina*) and the tiny white-flowered rock whitlow grass (*Draba norvegica*). In contrast, those species considered alpine, such as the cyphel (*Cheleria sediodes*) are rare, found only in the north of Britain and tend to be confined to the central massif of Europe. The cyphel is not uncommon throughout Sutherland as far east as Ben Griam Beg. Other plants considered to have a similar distribution but less common are the purple oxytropis (*Oxytropis halleri*) which is locally abundant at sea level in the parish of Farr and the rare mountain pansy (*Viola lutea*) with only one location. The largest group of mountain plants can be classified as arctic-alpine, occurring both in arctic regions and on some or all of the European mountain ranges. These plants include the well-known purple saxifrage (*Saxifraga oppositifolia*) and mountain avens (*Dryas octopetala*), both of which are found at sea level on the north coast. While most plants come into the category of arctic-alpines there are some which have a disjunct or separated distribution. A rare plant of Sutherland and of Britain is the Norwegian sandwort (*Arenaria norvegica*). It has been recorded on river shingle at Inchmnadamph, on Rhum and in Shetland yet otherwise it is only known from Iceland and western parts of Scandinavia. Scandinavia.

Cushion plants and dwarf shrubs are often characteristic of exposed climates. The moss campion (*Silene acaulis*) with its bright green moss-like cushion only a few centimetres high is a typical arctic-alpine plant found on mountain ledges and in the north and west on sea cliffs. This plant has deep rose petals and commonly flowers in August. Many plants grow with their stems creeping and leaves pressed against the ground. The dwarf willow (*Salix herbacea*) is common on the high hills of Sutherland, whereas the net-leaved willow (*Salix reticulata*) is recorded from only one site in Durness. Of the family Ericaceae, the alpine bear-berry (*Arctuous alpinus*) with its conspicuous orange-bright autumn leaves and the trailing azalea (*Loiseleuria procumbens*) are both adapted to the harsh, stony, dry conditions on high mountains, although the former plant is found on rather wetter ground on Whiten Head. In many places plant communities are dominated by grasses, sedges, rushes, mosses and lichens. A wide-spread type of montane grassland heath is that composed of matgrass (*Nardus stricta*) and the silver hair moss (*Rhacomitrium lanuginosum*) found especially where snow lies for any period of time. In some places the reindeer lichen (*Cetraria islandica*) forms a complete mat mixed with stiff sedge (*Carex biglowii*) and another lichen *Cladonia uncialis*. On stony windswept areas the three-leaved rush (*Juncus trifidus*) grows along with the viviparous form of sheep's fescue (*Festuca vivipara*). Low vegetation along the Ben Hope plateau contains dwarf willow (*Salixa herbacea*) and alpine lady's mantle (*Alchemilla alpina*).

The mountain habitat undoubtedly contains the greatest number of rare plants of any habitat in Sutherland. Of sites worth visiting, Ben More Assynt has, perhaps, the greatest number of rarities with Ben Hope, Klibreck, Ben Loyal, Foinaven and Meall Horn as slightly less interesting areas. The three-flowered rush (*Juncus triglumis*) and the rarer two-flowered rush (*Juncus biglumis*) both occur on Ben More Assynt together with the equally rare chestnut rush (*Juncus castaneus*). The alpine rush (*Juncus alpino-articulatus*) has been reported from Ben Loyal. Several of the very early records for mountain plants were rediscovered in the early 50's and 60's, an example being alpine meadow grass (*Poa alpina*), first recorded in 1826 and again in 1959. The rare eyebright (*Euphrasia frigida*) has been found on Ben Hope and Ben Loyal. Several of the mouse-eared hawkweeds (*Hieracium spp*) occur above 750 m (2,500 ft) on rocky ledges. In this extremely difficult taxonomic group the species *H.globisiflora, H.marginatum, H.pseudocurvatum* and *H.exmium* are all present at high altitudes but are very rare. There is no distinct pattern to the distribution of these mountain plants. The very rare alpine saxifrage (*Saxifraga nivalis*) is found on both Ben More Assynt and Meall Horn while alpine mouse-ear (*Cerastium alpinum*) is confined to Ben Griam Mor and Beg, Foinaven and Ben Hope. Similarly the northern rock rose (*Cardaminopsis patraea*) is a rare plant of Ben Griam Beg and Foinaven. Of the non-flowering plants, a rare variegated horsetail (*Equisetum variegatum*) is found in wet banks on Ben More Assynt. There are three interesting alpine ferns in Sutherland. One of the buckler ferns (*Dryopteris assimilis*) has been recorded from Ben More Assynt and more recently from Ben Stack, Ben Hope, Foinaven and Carnstackie. Alpine lady fern (*Athyrium alpestre*) is found on Ben More Assynt while parsley fern (*Cryptogramma crispa*) is a very rare plant from Klibreck. There is little doubt that there are still many discoveries to be made amongst the mountains of Sutherland. Don's couch (*Agropyron doniatnum*) is a good example as it was first discovered near Inchnadamph as late as 1951 and previously only known from the Ben Lawers range nearly 320 km (200 miles) farther south. A fascinating account of this plant is given by Raven and Walters (1956).

MOORLAND

Anyone who viewed Sutherland from the plain of A'Mhoine might well consider that moorland or blanket bog were synonymous with Sutherland and indeed Wittle's map (1950) produced as a guide for beekeepers shows 60-70% of the District dominated by heather (*Calluna vulgaris*). The remains of tree stumps buried in the peat would indicate that in many places this vegetation was produced by the destruction of an older forest by man and a changing climate. In fact, this apparently endless moor is a mosaic of different vegetation types composed of dwarf shrubs, grasses, sedges, rushes and *Sphagnum* moss. Towards the west coast where drainage is restricted, rainfall high or the water table permanently close to the surface a wet heath or blanket bog community develops. This wet vegetation is based upon three species, in varying combinations: heather (*Calluna vulgaris*), cotton grass (both *Eriophorum vaginatum*, with its single white head and *Eriophorum angustifolium* with three or four heads) and deer grass (*Trichophorum caespitosa*). On sloping ground in the west, deer grass and heather dominate the shallow soils. Lichens often have an important part to play in these communities. On low ground up to 450 m (1500 ft) deer grass is found with cotton grass especially on the flat 125 m (400 ft) contour which forms much of central Sutherland. A noticeable feature here is the "hummock and hollow" structure in which several species of *Sphagnum* moss cause the build up of plant debris on hummocks which invariably bear heather, cross-leaved heath (*Erica tetralix*) and bog myrtle (*Myrica gale*). In addition the insectivorous plants the sundews (*Drosera spp*) and butterworts (*Pinguicula spp*) are commonly found. At higher altitudes this bog gives rise to a mixture of heather and cotton grass which locally can contain dwarf birch (*Betula nana*) especially north and south of Ben Loyal and by Crask Inn. On the south side of Ben Loyal there are extensive patches of alpine bearberry (*Arctuous alpina*) while to the north cloudberry (*Rubus chamaemorus*) and dwarf cornel (*Chamaepericlymenun suecicum*) occur. Where bogs have been affected by fire, drying out may take place and lead to the spread of *Rhacomitrium* moss. McVean and Ratcliffe (1962) refer to an excellent example of this at the south-east end of Loch Meadie. Moorland and blanket bog are extensively grazed by sheep and deer, yet where these animals cannot gain acess, on islands in lochs or on steep cliffs there may be a refuge for many species. Thus in the middle of these areas are lochs with islands on which trees grow and sometimes plants like the royal fern (*Osmunda regalis*) which is particularly sensitive to grazing pressure.

LOCHS AND LOCHANS

Anglers become very quickly acquainted with the vegetation of lochs and lochans, but the casual observer may be attracted by the obvious white water lily (*Nymphea alba*), the yellow dash of colour from lesser spearwort (*Ranunculus flamula*) or a haze of delicate blue-flowered water lobelia (*Lobelia dortmarna*) breaking the surface of some dark lochan. But lochs are diverse in character and vegetation. Clearly the size range is considerable from the large deep lochs like Loch Loyal to shallow peaty hollows which may dry up one summer in every ten. There are acid brown, almost black stretches of water with a few sparsely-scattered stems breaking the surface to clearer water associated with limestone or shell sand which can support a richer vegetation and, incidentally, larger fish. The chemistry of each loch is different. Spence (1964) gives data for Loch Stack which is acid with a pH of 5.4 and an organic mud containing 70% carbon compared with Loch am Aigail which is alkaline, with a pH of 8.6 and the bottom of the loch composed of 85% coarse and fine sand. With such a range of conditions it is difficult to make generalisations about the vegetation of lochs, but like icebergs nine-tenths of their interest lies under water. A glass bottom bucket similar to that used by pearl fishermen can reveal a completely new world of plant life.

In some cases a stretch of water may have associated with it a peripheral zone of swampy land in which grow birch (*Betula pubescens*), bog myrtle (*Myrica gale*) and willows (*Salix spp*). In shallow, standing water the bottle sedge (*Carex rostrata*) and bog bean (*Menyanthes trifoliata*) dominate. In the deepest water grow bog pondweed (*Potomageton polygonifolium*) and broadleaved pondweed (*Potomageton natans*) along with the aquatic moss (*Fontinalis antipyretica*) at depths of 1 m(3 ft). The common reed (*Phragmites communis*) or flote-grass (*Glyceria fluitans*) form the margins to lochs where conditions are slightly less acid. At Loch Croispol, an alkaline loch on Durness limestone, the narrow band of common spike rush (*Eleocharis palustris*) and shoreweed (*Littorella uniflora*) mixed with Chara (*Chara aspera*) give way to broad stretches of fennel pondweed (*Poto mageton pectinatus*), which is rare outside Durness. Farther out where there is deeper water, the long stalked pondweed (*Potomage-*

ton praelongus) is found with the alternate water-milfoil (*Myrio-phyllum alterniflorum*) and other species of Chara.

While it is clear that water chemistry can determine to some extent the aquatic flora of a particular loch, substrate also has a considerable influence. The white water lily tends to grow on organic debris while the common spike rush is associated with stony substrates. The lack of reed swamp on stony or gravelly soils is worth mentioning together with an apparent lack of vegetation on sandy margins of lochs, although the awlwort (*Subularia aquatica*) is found occasionally in such shallow water. There is little evidence to suggest that the vegetation of the margins of these lochs is changing at any appreciable rate.

COASTAL CLIFFS AND BEACHES

In these days of increasing access to the coastline, it is worth considering one of the major sites of public pressure in Sutherland — the coastal beaches and their associated vegetation. On the east coast where wave action and exposure are less severe, sand has built up into relatively stable flat areas, the extensive links at Cuthill, Dornoch, Coul and Ferry Links being good examples. These are typical of east coast dune pasture and dune heath upon which the game of golf has been founded and camping sites are now sprouting. In these low-lying flat dunes are hollow, damp dune slacks containing the fragrant orchid (*Gymnodemia conopsea*), the frog orchid (*Coeloglossum viride*) and the common twayblade (*Listera cordata*) with its two large basal leaves. One rare plant which is relatively common in Sutherland and is found in these systems is the baltic rush (*Juncus balticus*), with its easily recognised stockade of dark green shoots running in straight lines across the slacks. On the west and north coasts, high winds drive sand up to 130 m (400 ft) at Invernaver where the dune systems are less stable and on flat areas, such as the terrace at the mouth of the River Naver, mobile wandering dunes form. Ritchie and Mather (1969) have reported on the areas around sixteen major tourist beaches in the north and west of the District. Many of these beaches have a high proportion of shell sand giving rise to a wide range of vegetation types some of which are associated with high calcium content in soils. In almost all cases beach sand gives way to dry machair and dune slack invariably passing through a pioneer or relatively unstable marram grass (*Ammophila arenaria*) dominated vegetation. Machair is a flat sand surface covered by peculiar stabilised groups of plants composed of short grasses and with an abundance of herbs. It is basically composed of common bent grass (*Agrostis tenuis*), sheep's fescue (*Festuca rubra*), sand sedge (*Carex arenaria*), a complement of legumes including hop trefoil (*Trifolium campestre*), white clover (*Trifolium repens*), red clover (*Trifolium pratense*), kidney vetch (*Anthyllis vulnaria*) and bird's foot trefoil (*Lotus corniculatus*). The narrow-leaved vetch (*Vicia angustifolia*) and wood vetch (*Vicia sylvatica*) both occur in these dunes but the latter is much rarer being confined to the north and west. There are usually a wide range of Composites, like golden rod (*Solidago virgaureae*), yarrow (*Achillea millefolia*) and many others, present in this rich pasture. Two plantains, the ribwort plantain (*Plantago lanceolata*) and sea plantain (*Plantago maritima*) form an important part of this vegetation.

There are other plants which through their growth form are able to stabilise sand, even on some of the steepest slopes. Crowberry (*Empetrum nigrum*), mountain aven (*Dryas octopetala*), and creeping willow (*Salix repens*) are all found binding sand on the Invernaver Nature Reserve. A net-work of buried stems is often exposed due to blow-outs or where sheep have been lying. Ring counts on these plants have shown that some of the creeping willow is at least 80 years old, the original stems having been buried over 60 cm (24 in) below the present soil surface and representing a build up of sand on these areas of 1.3 cm (0.5in) per year. Juniper (*Juniperus communis*) on the same site has been estimated to be of a similar age. Thus, while marram grass on the dunes has the ability to grow through large deposits of sand, the dwarf shrubs seem to be associated with much smaller deposition rates. Mosses also play an important part in the stabilisation of these dunes.

A feature of coastal plants is their relatively small size. In dune systems and on exposed cliff tops, many plants are reduced to almost unrecognisable forms. The weeds of open ground like groundsel (*Senecio vulgaris*), ragwort (*Senecio jacobea*) and dandelion (*Taraxacum officionale*), usually so large and lush when met with in gardens or agricultural land, are confined on dunes to small, often pale, rosettes of leaves, very important in the dune system, but easily overlooked. Three factors control their size, especially on the exposed dune pasture; they are grazed by sheep, the sand has little reserve of nutrients or water and they are found in a position which is exposed to high winds. Other plants are confined to coastal areas for different reasons. The plants of salt marsh, sea cliff and sea shore must be able to withstand periodic immersion in salt water. In addition, those plants growing on sandy or shingle shores have a highly unstable substrate to cope with. Thus the sea sandwort (*Honkenyia peploides*) and sand spurrey (*Spurgularia rubra*) are common while frosted orache (*Atriplex lacunata*) is much rarer. The sea sandwort often forms miniature dunes by means of its creeping stolons which last more than one year, whereas the sand spurrey is an annual depending upon prolific seeding and a widespread dispersion of seeds. Other halophytes, or salt-tolerant plants, such as annual seablite (*Suaeda maritima*) and prickly saltwort (*Salsoli kali*) occur in salt marshes, the former being confined to the eastern seaboard. A rare plant of sheltered estuaries of the north coast is the curved sedge (*Carex maritima*) found on sand-flats at the mouth of the River Naver. On the east coast at Little Ferry is a maritime plant which is found only at this one site in Sutherland. This plant is the beaked tasselweed (*Ruppia maritima*). As long ago as 1914 Magnus Spence writing in *Flora Orcadensis* noted that " Ruppia maritima, first discovered in the Oyce of Firth by Dr. Boswell, where it was new to Great Britain. Now it has been found along the sea border of Sutherland and Ross." The coastal areas, in contrast to those inland, rarely suffer more than occasional frosts or very high summer temperatures. In many cases the coastal vegetation of Sutherland contains a mixture of northern, alpine and indeed southern plants. While common scurvy grass (*Cochlearia officinalis*) used by the mariners of early sailing days in Arctic waters as a protection against scurvy is found throughout Northern Britain as both a coastal and mountain plant, Scottish scurvy grass (*Cochlearia scotica*) and Danish scurvy grass (*C. dancia*) are confined to coastal areas and usually where saltwater inundates their habitat. The bunches of star-white or softly pink flowers and lush green fleshy leaves are a feature of salt marsh and sea cliff. The sea milkwort (*Glaux maritima*) is often found in similar sites from the north-west coast to Golspie and Dornoch. Thrift or sea pink (*Armeria maritima*) is confined to sea shores, high mountains and, oddly, serpentine areas inland and on the coast, although such serpentine areas are limited in Sutherland. Sea campion (*Silene maritima*) is much more confined to sea cliffs although it does occur on high mountains of the west coast but not those in Sutherland. Scentless mayweed (*Tripleurospermum maritimum*) with its large nodding daisy heads is found among the clefts of sea cliffs, in dunes and on shingle beaches. This species is largely maritime in Sutherland whereas in the rest of Britain it is known from inland localities. There are two subspecies, a coastal form, subspecies *maritimum* and an inland form, subspecies *inodorum*. The parsley smelling leaves of Scots lovage (*Ligusticum scoticum*) are frequently found along the sea cliffs of Northern Sutherland. This is a true coastal plant confined to Scotland and a few sites in Northern Ireland. Of the ferns, sea spleenwort (*Asplenium murinum*) is a feature of the coastal areas of the north and west. There are also lichens, tarspot (*Verrucaria maura*) and *Rhamalina siliquosa* with its grey brittle covering on rocks which are characteristic of the spray zone. One moss, *Grimmia maritima* appears to inhabit areas affected by spray.

PLANTS OF DISTINCTION

With such widespread nutrient-poor, acid conditions in Sutherland, it is not surprising to find a number of plants which have apparently adapted to these conditions by obtaining their supply of nitrogen from sources other than those of rainwater and soil. Perhaps the best known of these plants which trap insects is the common butterwort (*Pinguicula vulgaris*) with its pale yellow-green slightly sticky leaves. Insects are trapped on the leaves and there digested. The beautiful violet flowers with a white patch on their lips are a common sight by wet boggy ground beside roads throughout the north and west of the District. Much rarer, but worth looking for, are the smaller paler, purple-tinged leaves of the pale butterwort (*Pinguicula lusitanica*) with its delicate pale lilac flower and yellow throat. This species has a distinctly western distribution, being absent from the east of the District.

Alongside the butterworts are often found sundews, hidden among the heather, along with bog myrtle, sphagnum and cotton grass. These bright-red glistening rosettes fringed with glandular hairs are found for much of the year with either the remains of a dry flower stalk or from June to August with delicate white, self-pollinated and half-closed flowers. Darwin was one of the first people to make extensive observations on the ability of sundew to trap insects. The insects are caught on red sticky glandular hairs and entangled in this state they die and are subsequently digested by excretions from the glands. All three British species are found in Sutherland and are separated upon leaf shape and flower stalk characteristics. The great sundew (*Drosera anglica*) and the long-leaved sundew (*Drosera intermedia*) have long leaves, while those of the sundew (*Drosera rotundifolia*) are almost round. The great sundew is separated from the long-leaved sundew by a much longer flowering stalk. A sterile hybrid between *D. rotundifolia* and *D. anglica* is found which is similar to *D. intermedia* but has a much longer flower stalk. Both *D. intermedia* and the hybrid occur only in the north and west.

Much less noticeable, because they float in lochans and ditches and flower very rarely in northern districts are the bladderworts. These aquatic plants can have stems up to 0.5 m (1.6 ft) in length forming a mat just under the water surface. Early botanists thought that the bladders were necessary as flotation chambers to keep the plants at the water surface. While this may be so, green bladders borne on the numerous stem leaves do trap small animals (mainly insects) by means of hairs and the animals are then digested. The great bladderwort (*Utricularia vulgaris*) has only one type of stem whereas the intermediate bladderwort (*Utricularia intermedia*) and the lesser bladderwort (*Utricularia minor*) have some stems with bladders on leaves and others without. The former has denticulate leaf segments.

SILVER AND DOWNY BIRCHES

From the records in the *Flora of Sutherland* it would appear that both tree birches have a widespread distribution in the District, being found in every parish, yet the silver birch is much more restricted in its distribution since it is a plant of lower ground. It is rare to see any silver birch at the limits of the present tree line and most birch woodlands are dominated by downy birch. The matter is further confused by the fact that these two species produce a hybrid with intermediate characteristics which is quite difficult to recognise. In addition, the downy birch of the north of Scotland is by no means the same downy birch as that in the south of England and is recognised as a distinct subspecies, *odorata*. It is a much more shrubby plant in which the buds are sticky, giving the plant a resinous odour as the young leaves open. Some individuals have an extremely strong smell even when the leaves are mature. These mature leaves are generally smaller in this subspecies and the life span of the tree may be somewhat greater in the northern climates. Trees of 156 years old have been recorded from Strath Naver whereas the southern variety is often quoted as being an old tree at 70-80 years of age.

DWARF BIRCH (*Betula nana*)

Pennington (1969) in her book on the *History of British Vegetion* notes the very striking "relict" distribution of the dwarf birch. This plant was widespread in Britain 10-20,000 years ago as the ice from the last glaciation retreated, but now it is found only on the high mountains of Northern Scotland. It is suggested that the plant has been able to exist undisturbed in several localities, since leaves and pollen have been found at all levels in some peat profiles. In Sutherland, where the plant is recorded from the wet moors and bogs of three parishes, it is relatively abundant in places. On the slope of Ben Loyal it occurs along with one of the tree birches, downy birch (*Betula pubescens* subspecies *odorata*) and hybrids between the two species are formed. Similar hybrids have been recorded from Scandinavia and Iceland. The hybrid is no more than 1.2 m (4 ft) high and looks like a miniature downy birch, which even when brought to Aberdeen and grown in the Botanic Gardens retains its characteristics. The true hybrid nature of the plant is expressed in the number of chromosomes found in the cells of this organism. In each cell of downy birch there are 56 chromosomes while in dwarf birch the number is 28. Hybrids from Ben Loyal have 42 chromosomes. This is an extremely interesting and rare plant recorded from only one other site in Britain, at the head of Glen Clova.

SOME USES OF PLANTS

A search of old floras and herbals tells us a little of the part that common plants played in the life of isolated communities. The importance of scurvy grass to fishermen and sailors in Arctic regions has been mentioned previously. Juices extracted from the leaves of the common butterwort have been used (according to Murray's *Northern Flora*) as a substitute for rennet in the manufacture of cheeses. "This property is well known among the poor people of Scotland." It also has the rather doubtful property of curing sore nipples. Another plant of acid pools, the bogbean, contains a bitter ingredient used as a laxative in jaundice. In Aberdeenshire the same plant was said to be used in brewing, while in a footnote Murray records "in the Outer Hebrides, where there is a deficiency of tobacco, islanders consoled themselves by chewing the root of bogbean". Lady's bedstraw (*Galium verum*) seems to have been a most useful plant since an extract was supposed to coagulate boiling milk. The roots of the plant, so we are told, produce a good brownish-red dye which is used in the Outer Hebrides where the plant is abundant in pastures. Lightfoot states that "roots of yellow flag (*Iris pseudocorus*) are used to dye black in Arran and some others of the Western Isles and that in Jura, they are boiled with copperas to make ink". Brooklime (it has the extraordinary latin name *Veronica beccabunga*) is frequent in streams. Flesh wounds yielded to the tender brooklime, it was used as an antiscorbatic in beer and finally as a poultice for piles. Even the common ivy did not escape attention. Hooker observed that "an ointment made of leaves of *Hedera* is much valued by the highlanders as a cure for burns." Several trees such as rowan and ash were supposed to possess magical properties although the latter can never have been important in Sutherland since it is a tree of warmer climates and better soils. Birches have several well-known domestic uses. One plant which, perhaps thankfully, is not found in Sutherland but occurs in Orkney and Inverness is henbane (*Hyoscyamus niger*). Murray says that in large doses it is a decided poison. He quotes the following observations by Mr Witner in a treatise on vegetable poisons. "Mr Witner has related the history of six persons in a family who were poisoned to eating Hyoscyamus by mistake instead of parsnips. Several were delirious and danced around the room like maniacs; one appeared as if he had got drunk". Murray quotes no plant as a useful antidote.

This section on plant life has been written firstly as a general introduction to plants in their habitats in Sutherland and secondly to complement the accounts in John Anthony's *Flora of Sutherland* which contains much more detailed information about individual species.

APPENDIX

Changes in the vegetation of Northern Scotland in the postglacial period.

Years before present	Period	Climate	Vegetation type
	Pre-boreal	Arctic sub-arctic	Dwarf, dwarf birch Juniper, Sedges, Crowberry
9,600			
	Boreal	Warmer and drier	Birch and hazel a little pine
7,500			
	Atlantic	Warm and wetter	Pine and birch Alder increases
5,000			
	Sub-boreal	Continuing warm but dry	Decline of pine Spread of birch and heaths
2,500			
	Sub-atlantic	Cold and wetter	Birch and heaths Blanket bog

Chapter six

BIRD LIFE

PAST HISTORY

There are few records of bird life in Sutherland before the 19th century. The earliest evidence comes from the lower deposits of the bone caves at Allt nan Uamh, Inchnadamph (see page 135) where the following were identified: teal, wigeon, tufted duck, long-tailed duck, eider, common scoter, grey plover, little auk, red grouse, ptarmigan and chaffinch. There is nothing extraordinary in this list, although there is a suggestion that in prehistoric times ptarmigan were relatively commoner than red grouse as there were "pinion bones of ptarmigan in lenticular layers containing the remains of hundreds of individuals".

The Embo chambered cairn (see page 138) produced a different assortment including unidentified ducks, several specimens of great auk, guillemot, razorbill, gannet, shag, fulmar, a grebe (? red-necked), lapwing, capercaillie, starling and a thrush (species unknown). The capercaillie became extinct in Scotland in the late 18th century; bones of the great auk have also been found in Caithness excavations and the bird survived as a breeding species in Orkney until the early 19th century.

Sir Robert Gordon's bird list of 1630 is short and some of the names are not clearly identifiable. He includes partridge, plover, black-cock, grouse, swan, "bewters" (bitterns), turtledoves, heron, starling and a woodpecker. Pennant in his 1769 tour makes brief mention of grouse, blackgame and ptarmigan and mentions in passing that "The grey water wagtail quits this country in winter, with us it resides." It is unfortunate that Pennant recorded so little on this occasion as he was a good naturalist and a careful observer.

The real foundations of bird-study in Sutherland were laid by Prideaux John Selby, a noted Northumbrian ornithologist who together with Sir William Jardine the great Scottish naturalist and other companions toured the west and north of Sutherland in 1834, almost as soon as the road from Kylesku to Durness was completed. They had with them " a light boat suspended upon a four-wheeled carriage and drawn by two horses . . . it could be shipped or unshipped at any time with perfect ease " as a means of exploring the lochs. It is not clear whether they actually travelled in the boat on its carriage as did Charles St. John fourteen years later. Selby was a careful and accurate observer who published an annotated list of 96 bird species which is in fact the basis of all Sutherland bird studies.

The rush started a dozen years after Selby's paper was published — Sir William Milner in 1847, Charles St. John the notorious osprey shooter in 1848 and John Wolley in 1849. All were collectors of skins and eggs: St. John published more data than the others but was really rather a poor observer. Among them they exterminated the ospreys and harried the eagles which were under great pressure from other quarters following the recent introduction of sheep farming and the rising fashion of game preservation for sport.

Mention must also be made of J. A. Harvie-Brown, one of the greatest Scottish naturalists of all time, who was passionately fond of Sutherland and published relevant papers and bird lists. Another naturalist, Thomas E. Buckley, lived in Sutherland for several years, first at Balnacoil and later at Glenrossal on the Cassley before moving to Inverness. Buckley wrote several papers on the birds of Sutherland and collaborated with Harvie-Brown on " A Vertebrate Fauna of Sutherland, Caithness and West Cromarty " and the corresponding volumes on " The Moray Basin". These two works together with Harvie-Brown and Macpherson's " North-West Highlands and Skye " cover in a unique manner the whole vertebrate natural history of Sutherland as it was at the close of the last century.

In a modern brief review of the District's birds it seems sensible and convenient to start with the area most profitable for the bird-watcher at all seasons — the coastline of the south-east.

ESTUARIES AND COASTLINE

At all seasons the coastline from Lothbeg Point south to the Dornoch Firth, which includes the Fleet Basin, can produce something of interest, with ducks and waders in profusion. Shelducks are common breeders, though surprsingly far inland as a rule — one may encounter, a shelduck leading her ducklings through woods and

over roads, fields and dykes to reach the sea — and flocks of over
100 or more may be seen in late autumn. Mallard and teal form
winter flocks of 100 to 500 with several thousand wigeon, smaller
numbers of pintail and occasional shoveller, pochard, scaup, tufted
duck and goldeneye all winter, but the greatest attraction lies in the
sea-ducks. The eider was uncommon before about 1940 but has
gradually increased and is now a common breeding bird with winter
flocks, particularly off the mouth of Loch Fleet, numbering up to
2,000, with occasional king eiders in recent years.

From November to April, with peak counts in December and
January, the sea in this area holds large flocks of scoters numbering
anything from 1,000 to 3,000 birds. In most years velvet scoters
predominate, identified by their white wing patches. About mid
October the beautiful long-tailed ducks arrive from the Arctic.
Noisy and restless, they winter in large numbers between Golspie
and Tarbat Ness, scattered at first but congregating in packs of 1,000
or more before they leave in early May.

Saltmarsh and sandbanks throng with waders in autumn and
winter: oystercatcher, knot, dunlin and bar-tailed godwit are
numbered by the thousand, but in the case of the waders the
autumn migration is early, beginning in July, and at this time one
may see some of the godwits still resplendent in their bright chestnut red summer plumage. Curlew, redshank, golden plover and
sanderling are in smaller flocks and while there is always the chance
of seeing less common species such as ruff, dusky redshank and
grey plover, several extreme rarities have been recorded in recent
years, for example buff-breasted, white-rumped and stilt sandpiper,
all casual American visitors. Experienced sea-watchers may find
divers, grebes, skuas and shearwaters.

Oystercatcher, ringed plover, common and arctic tern and rarely
and erratically the sandwich tern are among the species nesting along
the shores, with a few colonies of little tern which unfortunately
often choose spots where human disturbance on the beaches is
greatest. There are no cliff-nesting seabird colonies along the east
coast except where the large cormorant colony at the Ord of Caithness extends just south of the District boundary.

Similar situations pertain along the north coast as at Borgie,
the Kyle of Tongue and Balnakeil, but the sand and saltmarsh there
is much less extensive than in the south-east and the numbers of
birds much smaller; on the west coast suitable wintering places for
wildfowl and waders are also very restricted. The north and west

coasts come into their own with their sea-bird colonies, notably on Faraid Head, the Clo Mor and Handa. The first has a fine and accessible puffin colony and inaccessible auk colonies on the stacks; the Clo Mor has one of the largest puffin colonies in Britain, as well as guillemots, razorbills and kittiwakes, all of which are also found on Handa although there are fewer puffins there. In the past few years the great skua has begun to colonise the north and west: breeding has been established in several locations — Island Roan, Handa and possibly places on the mainland. The arctic skua, a long-established breeder in Caithness, has always been rare in Sutherland but has recently bred successfully on Handa under the watchful eye of the R.S.P.B. summer warden.

Of the other islands the only one with auk and puffin colonies of any consequence is Bulgach, offshore from Sandwood. The Island Roan group, Hoan Island and possibly some of the Badcall Islands have storm petrel colonies. Islands Roan and Hoan have wintering flocks of barnacle geese which frequently cross to the adjacent mainland. Ringing research has shown that these geese breed in East Greenland, whereas the Spitsbergen barnacles winter exclusively in Dumfries-shire and that there is no exchange between populations.

LOCHS AND RIVERS

Sutherland is a land of lochs, yet few are rich in bird life, many being barren, oligotrophic and often birdless, apart from a pair or two of common sandpipers or divers — redthroats on the small tarns and blackthroats on the larger sheets of water. Scattered throughout the District, however, one finds small, rich pools surrounded by sedges and reeds, often with floating bog and a black-headed gull colony, a species much scarcer in the west irrespective of availability of habitat. Some of these small lochs have gone so far in the process of eutrophication that there is more marsh than loch. Here one finds a wealth of birds: snipe, wigeon, teal, mallard, occasional gadwall, perhaps grey-lag goose or water rail, or grass-hopper warblers reeling in the evening. Here too one is certain to find greenshanks with young, screaming and dive-bombing, and for the fortunate few a pair of wood sandpipers, miniature replicas of greenshanks.

On one of these marshy lochs several pairs of slavonian grebes bred regularly for several years then disappeared for no apparent reason. Little grebes are surprisingly uncommon, as are waterhens except in the south-east, and the few pairs of coots (one of Sutherland's really rare birds!) are all on these small eutrophic pools. The limestone lochs of Durness are in a special class and support among other species a thriving colony of tufted ducks which first appeared in 1935. Scaup have been recorded in the breeding season.

The characteristic bird of all streams (from rivers to hill burns) is the dipper, less commonly the grey wagtail, and of the rivers the goosander, a bird not well tolerated by keepers. Not so long ago dippers (known as "kingfishers" in the old records) were on the vermin lists with a price on their heads! Ospreys always arouse interest and excitement. These beautiful birds were never common in Sutherland but nested on rocky islets in a few lochs in the west and on the well-known site on Ardvreck Castle. Being regarded as harmless and attractive they were never destroyed by keepers but were utterly exterminated by skin and egg collectors in the 1840's. Ospreys began to appear on passage on the rivers, notably the Naver, Helmsdale and Laxford in the 1940's, gradually becoming more frequent and it seems only a matter of time before a re-colonisation will take place. The new race of ospreys breeding elsewhere in Scotland are all tree-nesters and so far have shown no interest in the old castle and rock sites.

The two birds intrinsic to the moorland scene are, of course, the meadow pipit and skylark, the former ubiquitous and the latter often the only other bird encountered on hours of tramping on some lower moorlands. On the other hand the merlin, natural predator of both, is surprisingly scarce. Kestrels, whose prey is largely short-tailed voles, are still plentiful and well distributed. The magnificent peregrine survives on several inland sites though unfortunately many of these are too well-known and subject to persistent harrying by collectors of various types who have done so much to deprive the people of Sutherland of their rightful heritage of wild-life.

The golden eagle is now worth money — alive and free — as this is the one bird the tourist wants to see. There are about 250 pairs of eagles in Scotland and Sutherland has no more than its share of these, though a diminishing one as eagles are still poisoned and shot on several estates and are otherwise sensitive to human disturbance. The buzzard on the other hand thrives: its main prey is rabbits, though some sporting proprietors regard it as inevitable that buzzards must perish from the poison which is laid illegally and irresponsibly for "vermin" (unspecified).

The red grouse belongs to heather moorland and nowhere else, for its existence is completely dependent on the presence and quality of heather which must be managed artificially for good grouse production. The days of the 6,000 bird bag in Sutherland (as in Akroyd's time) have gone. The decline of the red grouse finds a parallel in that of the blue hare, with no justification for attributing this to either disease or vermin. Ptarmigan are still widespread though subject to great natural fluctuations and may be found on every mountain from the Griams and Ben Armine westward and down to 305 m (1000 ft) or less on the Capeside of Durness.

Golden plovers seem to favour the higher-lying level moorland areas, higher probably than curlews. One does not have to search long in Sutherland for a sight of a greenshank, but whimbrel, so much sought after, has only one confirmed breeding record in recent years. This leaves us with two " blue riband " mountain birds — dotterel and snow bunting. The first snow bunting's nest ever found in Scotland was on Ben More Assynt in 1886, but not even half-a-dozen have been discovered since on the Sutherland hills. Dotterel is even more uncertain: St. John says " breeds on Clibreck " but gives no source for his information. However, there is a specimen in the Dunrobin museum labelled " Clibreck 18th June, 1846 " — i.e. two years before St. John. There was no confirmed breeding record in Sutherland from that year until 1967 when a nest was found in a place remote from any of the high mountains and a pair was seen in another suitable habitat in 1974.

CULTIVATED LAND AND GARDENS

In this miscellaneous category it is possible to comment on a few species only. The spread of the collared dove is one of the ornithological phenomena of the century, and who would believe that Buckley could say of the great tit in 1882 — " I have never seen this species myself " — as indeed by then it had not yet reached Sutherland, and a dozen years before that the starling was reckoned a rarity!

Magpies bred in South-East Sutherland until the 1920's when they were finally exterminated by gamekeepers — 56 were shot at Dunrobin between 1873 and 1880 — and only in the last two years have stragglers started to re-colonise their old haunts. Their near relatives, the crows, show an interesting change in the distribution of carrion crows to the south-east and hoodies to the north-west with a hybrid zone between. This zone is gradually moving in a north-westerly direction with black carrion crows replacing the hoodies, and hybrids are now found as far west as Achfary. "Rarity" is only relative and a visitor may be astonished to find that in the west a greenfinch is a rarity indeed and that very few locals have ever seen a jackdaw, of which there is only one colony in West Sutherland, at Knockan, almost on the Ross-shire boundary.

Corn buntings have virtually disappeared in recent years and one may soon listen in vain for the once familiar cornrake which in the last score of years has gone from everywhere except the extreme north-west corner. Rooks and wood-pigeons too are uncommon in the west; the latter is a summer migrant and the former a casual visitor only. Almost the only known rookery in West Sutherland was blasted out many years ago by a gamekeeper in a misguided burst of enthusiasm.

WOODLANDS

A limited area of native pine forest remains in Sutherland (Fig. 23) and the birds of the relict birch and oak woods will be chaffinch, wren, tree-creeper, tits, redstart, robin, perhaps great-spotted wood-pecker, tree-pipits and wood warblers, though it needs a fine sunny day for the last two species to be in full song. A new and changing habitat has appeared in the great areas of coniferous forest planted by the Forestry Commission and private landowners throughout the District. Unfortunately, no systematic study has been made in this area of the succession of bird colonists in coniferous forest at different stages and one can only refer to these in general terms.

The most spectacular of the early colonists are short-eared owl and hen harrier, which are attracted by the improved nesting habitat of long heather and food supply of voles which become scarcer as the trees mature. A less obvious colonist is the grasshopper warbler, recorded in recent years, and soon robins, wrens and song thrushes move in. At a later stage chaffiniches, coal tits and goldcrests become plentiful and it seemed only a matter of time before crested tits would appear, as in fact they did in 1956, and breeding was confirmed in the Shin Forest in 1977. Likewise, crossbills are now breeding in both South-East and North Sutherland.

Blackgame are birds of scrub and forest edge. Formerly plentiful but perhaps over-shot (e.g. 127 in Altnaharra in 1871), they virtu-ally disappeared by the 1930's, but are now becoming plentiful again in the Shin and Borgie Forests. The magnificent capercaillie had not been known since Sir Robert Gordon's time until an attempted re-introduction at Skibo in 1870, which failed, but immigrants appeared in 1910 and soon colonised all suitable woods in the south-east. Wood-pigeons require arable land as feeding territory and colonise forests wherever this is available: consequently they are less common in the north and west.

Just as harriers and short-eared owls appear with the creation of suitable feeding and nesting conditions, sparrow-hawks re-appear in the new forests as natural predators on small woodland passerines, but for some reason tawny and long-eared owls are still not widespread except in the south-east.

In general, much information is lacking on forest birds but it is not too late for a research project to be undertaken on the distribution and succession of bird species in the new forests of Sutherland,

MIGRATION

It is customary to classify birds as residents and summer or winter migrants, but these classes are, in fact, unreal and misleading. There is a general movement south or to the coast of many birds in winter. Some birds which are usually regarded as residents may in truth be migrant or partly so: meadow pipits leave the moors in autumn, chaffinches leave the woods and form flocks on open ground near farms or other human habitations, and in the west even wood-pigeons appear to be summer visitors only.

The passage south of bird flocks in autumn is much more noticeable than the arrival or passage of summer migrants in spring but although both take place on a broad front, possibly affected by wind direction, it seems that autumn migrants are more likely to be channelled into clear-cut routes. Examples of this may be seen in the flocks of pink-footed geese from Iceland using Strath Halladale as a flight-line, and, on the west the Greenland geese following the line of Laxford — Lochmore — Loch Shin.

There seems to be a tendency for the autumn flocks of fieldfares, redwings and blackbirds to follow the river valleys, but not invariably, and of course the speed of migration may depend on weather and food supply. Who has not, for instance, seen on a fine autumn day large flocks of redwings and fieldfares delay to clear the valleys of rowan berries?

In the north, especially on the higher ground, it is not so much a question of listing migrants as there may remain few other than ptarmigan, grouse, eagles and ravens, or, at lower altitudes, buzzards and hoodies. Astonishingly, the stonechat remains faithfully in its territory even in the hardest of weather when the dipper has moved down to the coast to avoid the extremes of cold.

On the coast the auks: guillemots, razorbills and puffins have left their nesting cliffs in August; only the black guillemots, now white, remain in their breeding area. The divers move down to the sea, but in the west and north a diver on the sea in winter is more likely to be a great northern rather than a native black or red-throat.

RECENT CHANGES IN STATUS

A few of these are listed briefly:

FULMAR — First recorded at the Clo Mor in 1897. In 1902 a pair was seen on Handa, and even in 1912 only these two sites were known. The fulmar is now common almost everyhere on the coast and on many inland sites.

TUFTED DUCK — Was unknown until 1935 when it first nested on Loch Caladail, Durness. It is now a regular breeder on all the limestone lochs.

EIDER — In 1848 was known only on the Rabbit Islands, Kyle of Tongue; it spread to Loch Eriboll in 1881 and Lochinver in 1904 but was not known on the east until 1915 when a nest was discovered at Navidale. In the 1950's it was found near Golspie. The large flocks off Loch Fleet are a recent feature.

BRENT GOOSE — Common in winter on Loch Fleet until about 70 years ago but is now quite unknown.

HEN HARRIER — Common until the 1880's but completely extermi-nated soon after. Re-appeared near Lairg in 1945 and is now fairly common in suitable habitats.

OYSTERCATCHER — In 1871 " Never comes inland to breed "; in 1882 seen once or twice up the Brora river but only stayed a day or two. Now breeds inland in many parts of the District.

WOODCOCK — None seen in 1834. In 1848 it had recently commenced breeding and was plentiful in the south-east by 1853. Common in all suitable habitats by 1887.

NIGHTJAR — Plentiful in many parts of Sutherland in the last century; decreasing by 1920 and now only one or two pairs remain.

GREAT SPOTTED WOODPECKER — First recorded in 1910 and the first nest found in 1925; now thinly distributed throughout the D strict wherever there are old trees.

HOUSE MARTIN — Formerly a cliff-nester, e.g. Stronchrubie Cliffs, and common on Durness cliffs especially Smoo Cave. It is now very scarce in the north and west and seldom seen on cliffs except possibly near the Ord of Caithness.

GREAT TIT — Unknown anywhere in Sutherland before 1900 and is now one of the most common birds.

BLUE TIT — Unknown in the west even in the 1920's and is now extremely common everywhere.

STARLING — Before 1870 it was rare and only found on the coast; few inland records were made before the end of the century.

COLLARED DOVE — The most dramatic spread of any bird species in recent years: not known west of Turkey before 1930, it reached Eastern England in 1955. It was first recorded in Sutherland in 1963 (Lochinver), in 1964 at Dornoch, Durness and Skerray; it is now found throughout the District wherever there are human habitations.

A CHECK LIST OF THE BIRDS OF SUTHERLAND
(Old County Boundary)

Including records published in "British Birds" and "Scottish Birds" to December, 1977.
Status recorded for Faunal Areas (Vice-counties) — boundaries shown on outline map.
Nomenclature:- Voous, 1977. "List of Recent Holarctic Bird Species" British Ornithologists' Union.

Symbols:
1. Faunal Areas (See Fig. 8):
     - e   South-East Sutherland.
     - w   West Sutherland.
     - n   North Sutherland.

2. Status:
     - R   Resident.
     - S   Summer.
     - W   Winter.
     - P   Passage.
     - O   Occasional.
     - B   Breeding.
     - *   No record later than 1900.

Red-throated Diver (Gavia stellata) e **SB&W** wn **SB**
Black-throated Diver (Gavia arctica) e **SB&W** wn **SB**
Great Northern Diver (Gavia immer) en **W** w **W&OS**
White-billed Diver (Gavia adamsii) e **OW**
Little Grebe (Tachybaptus ruficollis) ewn **SB (very local)** &W
Great Crested Grebe (Podiceps cristatus) e **OW** n **OP**
Slavonian Grebe (Podiceps auritus) ewn **W&P (formerly** e **SB)**
Black-necked Grebe (Podiceps nigricollis) e **OW** w **OP**
Black-necked Grebe (Podiceps nigricollis) e **OW** w **OP**
Fulmar (Fulmarus glacialis) ewn **SB**
Cory's Shearwater (Calonectris diomedea) e **OP**
Great Shearwater (Puffinus gravis) en **OP**

Sooty Shearwater (Puffinus griseus) **ewn P**
Manx Shearwater (Puffinus puffinus) **ewn P**
Storm Petrel (Hydrobates pelagicus) e **OP** w **P&?SB**
Leach's Storm Petrel (Oceanodroma leucorhoa) ew **OP**
Gannet (Sula bassana) **ewn P**
Cormorant (Phalacrocorax carbo) **ewn RB**
Shag (Phalacrocorax aristotelis) **ewn RB**
Bittern (Botaurus stellaris) **en O**
Little Egret (Egretta garzetta) e **O**
Grey Heron (Ardea cinerea) **ewn RB**
White Stork (Ciconia ciconia) **en O**
Glossy Ibis (Plegadis falcinellus) e **O**
Spoonbill (Platalea leucorodia) e **O**
Mute Swan (Cygnus olor) e **RB**
Bewick's Swan (Cygnus columbianus) e **O** n **O***
Whooper Swan (Cygnus cygnus) e **O**
Bean Goose (Anser fabalis) e **O**
Pink-footed Goose (Anser brachyrhynchus) e **P&W** wn **P**
White-fronted Goose (Anser albifrons) **ewn OP**
Grey Lag Goose (Anser anser) **ewn RB L&P**
Snow Goose (Anser caerulescens) **en O**
Canada Goose (Branta canadensis) w **O**
Barnacle Goose (Branta leucopsis) e **OW** wn **W**
Brent Goose (Branta bernicla) e **OW**
Ruddy Sheld-duck (Tadorna ferruginea) n **O*** **(1 rec.-1892)**
Sheld-duck (Tadorna tadorna) **en RB&W,w OB**
Wigeon (Anas penelope) **ewn RB&W**
Gadwall (Anas strepera) **en OB,OW**
Teal (Anas crecca) e **RB&W,wn SB (rare and local in west)**
Mallard (Anas platyrhynchos) **ewn RB**
Pintail (Anas acuta) e **W&OB,n OB**
Garganey (Anas querquedula) w **O**
Shoveler (Anas clypeata) e **OP&W,w OB*,n O**
Pochard (Aythya ferina) e **W,w OB,n O**
Ring-necked Duck (Aythya collaris) n **O**
Tufted Duck (Aythya fuligula) e **W,w OB,n SB**
Scaup (Aythya marila) e **W,w OB,n OB***
Eider (Somateria mollissima) **ewn RB**
King Eider (Somateria spectabilis) e **OW&S**
Steller's Eider (Polysticta stelleri) e **O**
Long-tailed Duck (Clangula hyemalis) **ewn W**
Common Scoter (Melanitta nigra) e **W&S,w O,n B**
Surf Scoter (Melanitta perspicillata) e **OW**
Velvet Scoter (Melanitta fusca) e **W,w P,n O**
Goldeneye (Buchephala clangula) e **W&OS,wn W**
Smew (Mergus albellus) n **O**
Red-breasted Merganser (Mergus serrator) **ewn RB**
Goosander (Mergus merganser) e **O,wn B**
Honey Buzzard (Pernis apivorus) e **O***
Red Kite (Milvus milvus) e **B*,w O**
White-tailed Eagle (Haliaeetus albicilla) **ewn B* (last known 1901)**
Hen Harrier (Circus cyaneus) **en RB,w O**
Sparrow Hawk (Accipiter nisus) **ewn RB**
Buzzard (Buteo buteo) **ewn RB**
Rough-legged Buzzard (Buteo lagopus) **en O**
Golden Eagle (Aquila chrysaetos) **ewn RB**
Osprey (Pandion haliaetus) **en P,w B*&P**
Kestrel (Falco tinnunculus) **ewn RB**
Red-footed Falcon (Falco vespertinus)**en O**
Merlin (Falco columbarius) e **P,wn RB**
Hobby (Falco subbuteo) **ewn O**
Gyrfalcon (Falco rusticolus) **en O**

Peregrine (Falco peregrinus) ewn **RB**
Red Grouse (Lagopus lagopus) ewn **RB**
Ptarmigan (Lagopus mutus) ewn **RB**
Black Grouse (Tetrao tetrix) ewn **RB**
Capercaillie (Tetrao urogallus) e **RB,n O**
Red-legged Partridge (Alectoris rufa) e **RB** (introd. 1970)
Partridge (Perdix perdix) en **RB,w B***
Quail (Coturnix coturnix) ewn **O**
Common Pheasant (Phasianus colchicus) en **RB** (introd. to n)
Water Rail (Rallus aquaticus) en **W, w W&?B**
Spotted Crake (Porzana porzana) w **OS**
Baillon's Crake (Porzana pusilla) e **O***
Corn Crake (Crex crex) ewn **SB**
Moorhen [Waterhen] (Gallinula chloropus) ewn **RB** (very local in w)
Coot (Fulica atra) ewn **RB (very local)**
Common Crane (Grus grus) en **O**
Oystercatcher (Haematopus ostralegus) ewn **RB**
Black-winged Stilt (Himantopus himantopus) e **O**
Dotterel (Charadrius morinellus) n **OB**
Ringed Plover (Charadrius hiaticula) ewn **RB**
Golden Plover (Pluvialis apricaria) ewn **SB**
Grey Plover (Pluvialis squatarola) e **W&P,wn P**
Lapwing (Vanellus vanellus) ewn **SB&P**
Knot (Calidris canutus) en **P&W,w P**
Sanderling (Calidris alba) e **P&W,wn P**
Little Stint (Calidris minuta) e **P wn O**
White-rumped Sandpiper (Calidris fuscicollis) e **O**
Pectoral Sandpiper (Calidris melanotos) w **O**
Curlew Sandpiper (Calidris ferruginea) e **P,n O**
Purple Sandpiper (Cildris maritima) e **W,wn P&W**
Dunlin (Calidris alpina) e **W&B,wn P&B**
Stilt Sandpiper (Micropalma himantopus) e **O**
Buff-breasted Sandpiper (Tryngites subruficollis) e **O**
Ruff Philomachus pugnax) e **P,w O**
Jack Snipe (Lymnocryptes minimus) e **W,wn O**
Common Snipe (Gallinago gallinago) ewn **RB**
Woodcock (Scolopax rusticola) ewn **RB&W**
Black-tailed Godwit (Limosa limosa) ew **P,n P&OB**
Bar-tailed Godwit (Limosa Lapponica) en **P&W, w P**
Whimbrel (Numenius phaeopus) ewn **P (has bred e&n)**
Curlew (Numenius arquata) ewn **RB**
Spotted Redshank (Tringa erythropus) en **OP**
Redshank (Tringa totanus) ewn **RB**
Greenshank (Tringa nebularia) e **SBP&W,wn SB&P**
Green Sandpiper (Tringa ochropus) ewn **O**
Wood Sandpiper (Tringa glareola) e **O,n SB**
Common Sandpiper (Tringa hypoleucos) ewn **SB**
Turnstone (Arenaria interpres) ewn **P&W**
Red-necked Phalarope (Phalaropus lobatus) w **OP,n OS**
Grey Phalarope (Phalaropus fulicarius) e **O*,w O**
Pomarine Skua (Stercorarius pomarinus) e **P,n O**
Arctic Skua (Stercorarius parasiticus) e **P,wn SB**
Long-tailed Skua (Stercorarius longicaudus) en **O**
Great Skua (Stercorarius skua) e **P,wn SB**
Little Gull (Larus Minutus) w **O**
Bonaparte's Gull (Larus philadelphia) w **O**
Black-headed Gull (Larus ridibundus) ewn **RB (very local in w)**
Common Gull (Larus canus) ewn **RB**
Lesser Black-backed Gull (Larus fuscus) ewn **SB**
Herring Gull (Larus argentatus) ewn **RB**
Iceland Gull (Larus glaucoides) ewn **OW**

Glaucous Gull (Larus Hyperboreus) **ewn OW**
Great Black-backed Gull (Larus marinus) **ewn RB**
Ross's Gull (Rhodostethia rosea) **n O**
Kittiwake (Rissa tridactyla) **e P.wn SB**
Sandwich Tern (Sterna sandwicensis) **en P&OB,w P**
Common Tern (Sterna hirundo) **ewn SB**
Arctic Tern (Sterna paradisea) **ewn SB**
Little Tern (Sterna altifrons) **e SB,n OS?B**
Guillemot (Uria Aalge) **e W,wn SB**
Razorbill (Alca torda) **e W,w SB&W,nSB**
Black Guillemot (Cepphus grylle) **e OW,wn RB**
Little Auk (Alle alle) **ewn O**
Puffin (Fratercula arctica) **e OW,wn SB**
Pallas's Sand Grouse (Syrrhaptes paradoxus) **en O***
Rock Dove (Columba livia) **wn RB**
Stock Dove (Columba oenas) **e RB,n O**
Wood Pigeon (Columba palumbus) **en RB,w SB**
Collared Dove (Streptopelia decaocto) **ewn RB**
Turtle Dove (Streptopelia turtur) **ewn OP**
Cuckoo (Cuculus canorous) **ewn SB**
Barn Owl (Tyto alba) **e RB**
Scops Owl (Otus scops) **e O***
Snowy Owl (Nyctea scandiaca) **n O**
Long-eared Owl (Asio otus) **ewn RB**
Short-eared Owl (Asio flammeus) **en RB,w O**
Tawny Owl (Strix aluco) **ewn RB [rare and local in w]**
Tengmalm's Owl (Aegolius funereus) **e O***
Nightjar (Caprimulgus europaeus) **e S?B,w O*,nO**
Swift (Apus apus) **en SB w OS**
Kingfisher (Alcedo atthis) **ewn O**
Bee-eater (Merops apiaster) **en O**
Roller (Coracias garrulus) **e O**
Hoopoe (Upupa epops) **e o*,wn O**
Wryneck (Jynx torquilla) **en O**
Green Woodpecker (Picus viridis) **e O***
Great Spotted Woodpecker (Dendrocopos major) **ewn RB**
Skylark (Alauda arvensis) **en RB w SB**
Shore Lark (Eremophila alpestris) **e O**
Swallow (Hirundo rustica) **ewn SB**
House Martin (Delichon urbica) **ewn SB**
Sand Martin (Riparia riparia) **ewn SB**
Tree Pipit (Anthus trivialis) **ewn SB**
Meadow Pipit (Anthus pratensis) **e RB wn SB**
Rock Pipit (Anthus spinoletta) **ewn RB**
Yellow Wagtail (Motacilla flava) **n O**
Grey Wagtail (Motacilla cinerea) **e SB&W,wn SB**
Pied/White Wagtail (Motacilla alba) **e SBP&W,wn SB**
Waxwing (Bombycilla garrulus) **ewn P**
Dipper (Cinclus cinclus) **ewn RB**
Wren (Troglodytes troglodytes) **ewn RB**
Dunnock [Hedge Sparrow] (Prunella modularis) **ewn RB**
Robin (Erithacus Rubecula) **ewn RB**
Redstart (Phoenicurus phoenicurus) **ewn SB**
Whinchat (Saxicola rubetra) **ewn SB**
Stonechat (Saxicola torquata) **ewn RB**
Wheatear (Oenanthe oenanthe) **ewn SB**
Ring Ousel (Turdus torquatus) **ewn SB**
Blackbird (Turdus merula) **ewn RB**
Fieldfare (Turdus pilaris) **ewn P**
Song Thrush (Turdus philomelos) **e RB wn SB&W**
Redwing (Turdus iliacus) **ewn P&SB**

Mistle Thrush (Turdus viscovorus) **ewn SB**
Grasshopper Warbler (Locustella naevia) **en S?B, w SB**
Sedge Warbler (Acrocephalus schoenobaenus) **ewn SB**
Barred Warbler (Sylvia nysoria) **n O**
Lesser Whitethroat (Sylvia curruca) **en OS**
Common Whitethroat (Sylvia communis) **ewn SB**
Garden Warbler (Sylvia borin) **ewn OS**
Blackcap (Sylvia atricapilla) **ewn OS&W**
Wood Warbler (Phylloscopus sibilatrix) **en SB,w S**
Chiffchaff (Phylloscopus collybita) **e SB,wn S**
Willow Warbler (Phylloscopus trochilus) **ewn SB**
Goldcrest (Regulus regulus) **ewn RB**
Firecrest (Regulus ignicapillus) **e O**
Spotted Flycatcher (Muscicapa striata) **ewn SB**
Pied Flycatcher (Ficedula hypoleuca) **ew O,n OSB**
Long-tailed Tit (Aegithalos caudatus) **ewn SB**
Willow Tit (Parus montanus) **e OB,w O**
Crested Tit (Parus cristatus) **e RB**
Coal Tit (Parus ater) **ewn RB**
Blue Tit (Parus caeruleus) **ewn RB**
Great Tit (Parus major) **ewn RB**
Tree Creeper (Certhia familiaris) **ewn RB**
Golden Oriole (Oriolus oriolus) **n O**
Red-backed Shrike (Lanius collurio) **en O**
Lesser Grey Shrike (Lanius minor) **n O**
Great Grey Shrike (Lanius excubitor) **ewn W**
Jay (Garrulus glandarius) **en O**
Magpie (Pica pica) **ewn O [formerly bred e]**
Chough (Pyrrhocorax pyrrhocorax) **wn RB* [last rec 1848]**
Crow [Carrion and Hooded] (Corvus corone) **ewn RB**
Jackdaw (Corvus monedula **ewn RB [very local w]**
Rook (Corvus frugilegus) **en RB,w O [formerly bred w]**
Raven (Corvus corax) **ewn RB [very local e]**
Starling (Sturnus vulgaris) **ewn RB**
Rose-coloured Starling (Sturnus roseus) **ewn O**
House Sparrow (Passer domesticus) **ewn RB**
Tree Sparrow (Passer montanus) **e RB,wn O**
Chaffinch (Fringilla coelebs) **ewn RB**
Brambling (Fringilla montifringilla) **ew W,n w&OB [one breed rec.1920]**
Greenfinch (Carduelis chloris) **en RB,w O**
Siskin (Carduelis spinus) **ewn RB**
Goldfinch (Carduelis carduelis) **ewn OW&P**
Linnet (Acanthis cannabina) **en RB ,w SB**
Twite (Acanthis flavirostris) **ewn RB**
Common Redpoll (Acanthis flammea) **ewn RB**
Crossbill (Loxia agg.) **en RB,w P**
Trumpeter Finch (Bucanetes githaginea) **w O**
Bullfinch (Pyrrhula pyrrhula) **ewn RB [B not confirmed in n]**
Hawfinch (Coccothraustes coccothraustes) **ewn O**
Lapland Bunting (Calcarius lapponicus) **ewn O**
Snow Bunting (Plectrophenax nivalis) **en W&OB,w W**
Pine Bunting (Emberiza leucocephalus) **e O**
Yellowhammer (Emberiza citrinella) **ewn RB**
Rustic Bunting (Emberiza rustica) **n O**
Reed Bunting (Emberiza schoeniclus) **ewn RB**
Red-headed Bunting (Emberiza bruniceps) **w O**
Corn Bunting (Miliaria calandra) **ewn RB [local and decreasing]**
Lazuli Bunting (Passerina amoena) **w O [probable escape]**

Chapter seven

OTHER WILD LIFE

INTRODUCTION

Describing the Natural History of Sutherland presents considerable difficulties and not the least of these is the impossibility of fixing an arbitrary point or base-line on the time scale at which it can be said "This is how Sutherland formerly appeared". There has been perpetual change, natural and man-induced ever since the ice disappeared ten thousand years ago; even comparatively recently there is clear evidence of a succession of cold winters and wet summers between 1760 and 1810 which affected woods, crops and domestic animals to an extent which contributed towards a major change in the whole human history of the District.

Palaeobotanical and historical evidence all point to a land formerly clad largely with birch, rowan, hazel and juniper, with pine and oak in the drier valleys — an admirable habitat for the "red deer of massive size" (Millias 1904). Early man had little effect on this, but for about two thousand years a highly organised man with his animals has by felling, grazing and burning gradually removed most of this cover. The people of Strath Naver were described in 1250 as being a pastoral race, the *Caerini* (probably a Latinised name from the Celtic *caora,* a name applied up to recent times to the native *Kerry* or *Keerie* sheep).

In addition to sheep and cattle the 18th century farmers and small tenants kept large numbers of goats, and furthermore, practised a system of transhumance to the shielings. No animal in this world will eradicate woodland more rapidly than the goat and in the parishes of Assynt and Eddrachilles alone there were reckoned to be 2,300 goats at the close of the 18th century. Modern sheep farming and crofting with their increased grazing pressure and uncontrolled burning have contributed to produce a depauperate and declining ecosystem. Extensive burning on rocky ground increases the amount of rock and soil exposed; succeeding rains can cause rapid leaching and this continued extraction eliminates the re-cycling of minerals. Every bird or animal carcase removed from the hill depletes the reserves of calcium and phosphorus and so few salmon are ever allowed to return to the rivers that there are few kelts to die to leave their bones to nourish their descendants.

The climatic and physical condition, the regeneration of arable land and replanting of woodland are all described elsewhere in this book, so it is with all the foregoing in mind that one makes a brief survey of the wild-life of our District.

PAST HISTORY

The earliest mammalian records come from the Bone Caves at Allt nan Uamh, Inchnadamph and from the chambered cairn at Embo. Bones were found also in the brochs at Dunrobin, Strath Brora and Kintradwell. In the Bone Caves were found bones of several species still surviving in Scotland — otter, badger, fox, many limb bones of frog and toad and red deer antlers "of massive size". There were also representatives of an arctic fauna, brown bear, northern lynx, arctic fox and immense quantities of reindeer antlers totalling approximately four hundred individuals.

The mammalian remains from Embo were mainly those of domesticated animals, amphibia, red squirrel and otter; these, together with fish and sea-bird remains perhaps indicate a different mode of life of the people rather than a different fauna. The brochs held rather more — reindeer, red deer, roe, fox, wild cat, wolf (or large dog), cetaceans, marine molluscs and fish besides domesticated animals.

No osteological data however can give any idea of how long the reindeer and wolf survived: one must rely on historical evidence, which is sadly lacking. Of the reindeer there appears to be no historical record in Sutherland and there is even some doubt among scholars as to whether it was red-deer or reindeer which Jarls Rögnvald and Harald hunted in Caithness in 1159.

Wolves certainly survived in Sutherland well into historic times, but even so, the occurrence is not well documented. Sir Robert Gordon's references to wolves in the early 17th century are well enough known, as is the killing of the Glen Loth wolves by hunter Polson, although this story stems from oral tradition only. At all events it appears that the wolf was exterminated from Sutherland between 1690 and 1700 and that the last known were in Achmore (Assynt), Strath Halladale and Glen Loth. Likewise, the story of the use of the grave-yard on Handa as security from wolves comes from oral tradition apparently not recorded before 1841 and popularised in Mrs Ogilvy's poem which is quoted in full by Millais. If there is any factual basis for the legend it is curious that it is not mentioned by Alexander Falconer, Parish Minister of Eddrachilles, in his very full and carefully compiled account of the parish in 1793, the more so because he records that there were eight burial grounds in the parish (some disused) and that the brochs had been used as cemeteries "down to the present times, which practice had its arise probably from their being a security from the ravages of wolves".

Regrettably the polecat must be added to past history. Where man failed with the marten he succeeded with the polecat — common in Selby's time and completely exterminated by the end of the century, the last definite records being about 1903 from Lairg and Inchnadamph.

Existing Mammals

HEDGEHOG. In 1789 Pennant recorded that hedgehogs were found as far north as the Forth and Tay and no farther. In Sutherland there is no positive record for hedgehog earlier than 1872 at Tressady, Rogart, but this may well have been from an introduction as in 1895 Harvie-Brown stated that the hedgehog was not yet found in the wild state in Sutherland, although introduced on several occasions. For instance, in 1888 Mr Houston brought two of each sex from Ross-shire to Kintradwell and turned them loose in his garden, whence they escaped.

The late Mr. John Scobie, Achfary, recalled the astonishment of a trapper at finding the first hedgehog ever known in the west caught in a fox trap at Lochmore. This would probably have been in the 1920's, but it was much later than that before it colonised the north coast. It is now well distributed throughout the District wherever there are woods or gardens, but it is essentially a creature of the forest edge and consequently rarely found actually in coniferous forest. The hedgehog often becomes a road casualty, largely due to its liking for carrion, emerging at night to eat corpses of animals killed by road traffic.

MOLE. Although some writers have recorded the mole as rare or unknown in the North and West Highlands in the mid 19th century, Selby reckoned it "plentiful" in 1834. Evidently then, as now, the mole's distribution in Sutherland was limited only by suitable habitat and availability of food supply, which consists of terrestrial invertebrates, mainly earthworms. It is found therefore wherever the soil is neither too acid nor too stony, especially in permanent grassland and open deciduous woodland anywhere in the District. It is astonishing how molehills may be found on isolated patches of suitable soil even at considerable elevation, such as on the greens showing the sites of old small-holdings or shielings.

SHREWS. All three species certainly occur in Sutherland although their detailed distribution is not fully known. Common and pigmy shews appear to be pretty well ubiquitous wherever there is low ground cover, the former more restricted to woodlands and the latter to open land, shores and sand-dunes, e.g. the island of Handa, where it has been recorded. Feeding habits are similar, mainly small invertebrates, although smaller items are selected by pigmy shrews.

The water shrew, whose usual habitat is clear, unpolluted streams is also found on boulder and rocky beaches in north-west Scotland. It has been recorded from Handa, but in general the distribution seems to be more localised and commoner in the west and north than the south-east. The food as described by Harvie-Brown consists of small aquatic creatures, including salmon fry.

BATS. Only two species of bat have so far been recorded in Sutherland, the pipistrelle and the long-eared bat. The former is the small bat so familiar on fine summer evenings almost anywhere in the District, even in the extreme north-west where it is more thinly distributed. The long-eared bat is a species more of sheltered, thinly wooded areas than of villages and human habitations. It certainly occurs in Rogart and in all probability elsewhere in South-East Sutherland. A third species, Daubenton's bat, also a woodland inhabitant, has been recorded as far north as the Beauly Firth and may well turn up in our area.

RABBIT. The rabbit is a native of North-West Africa and the Iberian peninsula introduced to Britain as a food species in the 12th century. At what date rabbits were introduced to Sutherland is not known. Sir Robert Gordon does not mention them but they were established on the Rabbit Islands, Tongue, by 1793. In 1812 rabbits were kept in warrens at Dunrobin, the Little Ferry and Dornoch Links, and were present in Durness. To these places they had presumably been introduced as the Sutherland family still employed a warrender at that time. Selby saw none in 1834 and they were not introduced to Handa until about 1870.

Now, in spite of setbacks by myxomatosis from the 1950's onwards, the rabbit thrives everywhere it can burrow and bite. It is especially plentiful and prolific in coastal dune areas and is scarcest on the Lewisian gneiss of the west where there are large areas with no rabbits, in which apparently they cannot live, — e.g. Scourie and Badcall, although plentiful on the neighbouring Torridonian sandstone of Handa and the dunes and machair of Oldshoremore.

BROWN HARE. The brown hare is restricted to the grasslands of the south-east and is an associate of arable farming. Never normally plentiful in Sutherland it quite suddenly increased in a spectacular manner in the 1950's following the severe reduction in number of rabbits by myxomatosis, presumably by removal of inter-specific competition. This lasted only a few years however and hares are now thinly distributed in suitable habitats. At one time in the last century they were observed in the limestone area of Assynt and recently have been reported from Strath Oykel, lower Strath Naver, Tongue and upper Halladale.

MOUNTAIN HARE. The mountain hare is an inhabitant of heather moorland and alpine grassland, though seen also on dry rocky hill-tops especially where there are associated grassy patches. Over 50% of the food of mountain hares throughout the year is heather on which it is almost as dependent as is the red grouse, with a marked preference for short, young heather. Moor management and conditions favourable to grouse are also suitable for hares, and it has been shown that not only is quantity of heather important but that grouse. have marked preference for, and better performance on, moorlands on base-rich soils. This presumably applies also to hares.

Eradication of woodland and encouragement of heather moorland would therefore provide a new and suitable habitat for both hares and grouse in Sutherland, with a preference for the drier and less acid soils of the east. A decline in hare population began early in the west, however, as even in 1875 it was noted hares were becoming scarce in Assynt, whereas "several thousands" were said to have been shot on the Griams about 1860-1870 and there are actual bag records from Badanloch (Akroyd) viz:—

1887	grouse 4386	hares 509
1888	grouse 835	hares 430
1889	grouse 1489	hares 976
1890	grouse 2817	hares 926

It has been shown that burning and grazing are much more liable to produce deterioration of habitat and elimination of heather in the west than in the drier east, as is well seen in the Cumberland fells, where little heather now remains. Hares, however, remained relatively common in the west until the 1930's since when they have virtually disappeared. More remained in the north where there was a temporary increase in the 1950's, but in general they are now exceedingly scarce in the west but less so in the east.

RED SQUIRREL. It was included in Sir Robert Gordon's list but subsequently became extinct following the destruction of the old forests. About the middle of the 19th century it was becoming plentiful again in Ross-shire and in 1869 had re-colonised South-East Sutherland. The increase of new coniferous plantations of course provided an excellent habitat and by the late 1940's squirrels were so common in the south-east that many could be seen any day in the older plantations, even on fine days in winter, and large numbers were shot by the foresters. None was recorded in the north or west. About 1954 every squirrel suddenly disappeared and it is a fact observed by many that this coincided exactly with the initial explosive outbreak of myxomatosis in rabbits. From that time squirrels have been virtually non-existent in the Golspie-Uppat woods and very scarce in Skibo but recorded as present in Oykel and Rose-hall.*

VOLES AND MICE. The field vole is almost certainly the commonest small mammal we have, and the most widespread. Wherever there is rough ungrazed grass the field vole is found. A specially-favoured habitat is the lush tangle of grass in young forestry plantations, where it swarms. It is preyed upon by many birds and mammals: in the young forest situation it attracts short-eared owls and hen harriers, and in general is eaten by domestic and wild cats, weasels, foxes, kestrels, buzzards and many others. Sometimes it increases to plague proportions; then, predators increase in number and rear larger families.

The bank vole, distinguished by its longer tail and ears and reddish fur is possibly less common than the field vole. In habitat it prefers thicker cover — deciduous woodland and scrub, and to a lesser extent coniferous woodland: in these situations it is more likely to be preyed on by tawny owls and weasels than by the diurnal birds of prey. In Sutherland it may be found anywhere the habitat is suitable, but has been recorded on Handa in much more open conditions.

---

* Since the text was written there have been several sightings in the Golspie-Uppat woods.

The water vole is a larger and very attractive beast (often known as the water rat) which inhabits the banks of lowland rivers, streams and ditches. There are two colour varieties, brown and black, the latter being the form found in the north of Scotland. Although its distribution is not fully known it is probably the least common of the voles in Sutherland. There are records from Naver, Loyal and Assynt, but it is likely to be found anywhere in the lowland parts of the District where the habitat is suitable.

The two species of mouse are the house mouse and the wood mouse, otherwise known as the long-tailed field mouse. The former is more closely associated with man, buildings and domestic animals, the latter with gardens, scrub and woodlands: both are found throughout the District within limitations of habitat.

FOX. The fox is a versatile, adaptable opportunist which two hundred years of intensive persecution have failed to eradicate; indeed it has been said that regular shooting merely perpetuates a population of well-dispersed, healthy foxes! Foxes are essentially nocturnal animals and some idea of their presence and peregrinations may be seen by following their tracks in snow. They are widespread throughout the District, not only in the higher, thinly-populated areas but are said to be common and increasing even on the outskirts of Dornoch. The urbanisation of foxes is of course now prevalent throughout the country.

Foxes are almost omnivorous, killing and eating large numbers of small mammals, especially field voles, wood-mice and rabbits. They will take lambs, alive or dead and, occasionally, poultry. They are also shore-line scavengers and on the Clo Mor, perhaps elsewhere too, foxes subsist almost entirely on seabirds. The fox has no enemies except man and the golden eagle, which in some areas takes considerable numbers of fox cubs. In the early 1930's an epidemic of mange, the precise diagnosis of which was not confirmed, decimated the foxes on the north mainland, and in recent years foxes suffering from some form of mange have been repeatedly observed in west Sutherland.

PINE MARTEN. The pine marten is a woodland animal which in Selby's time was said to be "abundant in mountainous districts", particularly in woods. There was a price on its head, however (two shillings and sixpence (12½p) plus the value of the skin) in Sutherland from the early years of the 19th century onwards with the result that by 1900 it was virtually exterminated in the north of Scotland except for a few places on the west coast, notably Assynt and the Reay Forest where it continued to exist mainly as a refugee among rocks and cairns. In the 1920's a gradual recovery began, partly due to absence of keepering during the First World War and partly due to the restoration of the old habitat by the Forestry Commission. This increase continued until the mid 1940's when there was again a marked diminution on numbers, this time for no apparent reason. This attractive animal is still scarce in Sutherland and very difficult to observe. Its main stronghold is still in the remote glens of the west though recently it was reported from the afforested parts of East Sutherland.

STOAT AND WEASEL. These are often confused: the stoat is larger, turns white in winter and has a distinct black tip to a longer tail. The stoat preys largely on rabbits and the weasel on small rodents; the distribution of these predators depends largely on availability of food supply and varies greatly in different parts of Sutherland. Both are scarce in the west, and on the Lewisian gneiss where there are few rabbits, stoats are seldom seen. Both are tolerably common however in the north and east.

MINK. This is a North American species which has been bred in fur farms in Britain since 1929. Feral mink populations are now established in many parts of the country and mink have been reported recently in South-East Sutherland, presumably escapees from a former mink farm at Creich.

BADGER. The status of the badger is difficult to assess as it is a nocturnal animal whose presence may be completely overlooked. Common in the 18th century it was much persecuted and exterminated in some areas, though not completely throughout the District. It is now plentiful in the north and west and occasional in the south-east. In the north its presence is popularly attributed to a pair which escaped from captivity at the Tongue Hotel in the 1920's and are said to have re-populated the district. Simultaneously, they have recovered in the west and were probably never exterminated in the Reay Forest.

Badgers are omnivorous opportunists and will eat small mammals, especially young rabbits and, even worms and grubs; their presence may sometimes be detected by finding the remains of bumble-bees' nests which the badgers have dug up to eat the larvae. They also eat a great deal of vegetable matter, even bulbs planted in gardens and have a bad reputation for raiding hen-houses in some places and litter-bins in others.

OTTER. The otter is another attractive animal which has been mercilessly persecuted for the past two hundred years on very dubious grounds, as its damage to fishing interests has never been properly assessed and is probably grossly over-estimated. Otters feed almost entirely on fish, but this includes crustaceans, flounders and eels. The otter is still fairly widely but thinly spread in Sutherland, commoner in the west and, in the winter months especially, very much an inhabitant of the shore and sea lochs. Its presence may often be detected by tracks and marks when the animal itself is not in evidence.

WILD CAT. The wild cat was virtually exterminated along with martens and pole-cats but made a temporary recovery in the 1920's, roughly contemporaneously with the martens' come-back. When grouse and hares declined in the 1930's so did the cats. In recent years there has been an increase again in the afforested areas of Sutherland but an assessment of status is made difficult by three factors: the wild cat is a nocturnal, woodland creature exceedingly difficult to observe: feral cats revert to wild-type in colour and these will hybridise with true wild cats.

SEALS. The two types which concern us are the grey seal and the common seal. Seals are a familiar sight around our coasts but differentiation of the two species is not always easy. Generally speaking, the seal of the south-east coast is the common seal, which has a breeding area on the sandbanks of the Dornoch Firth, whereas both species are found on the north and west coasts, though breeding areas there of the common seal are not well defined. The grey seal is the Atlantic seal: two breeding places are known in Sutherland, the caves of Eilean nan Ron (Island Roan), and the caves around Freisgill on Whiten Head. Small numbers may breed on the islands off the west coast — a pup was seen ashore on Handa two years ago. Suleskerry was an important breeding station before the lighthouse was built, whither the men of Sutherland went annually to procure seals for skins and oil. A harp seal, a Greenland species, was killed in Loch Nedd in 1905.

RED DEER. The diminution in size of Scottish red deer following the destruction of the forests and impoverishment of the habitat has been known to scientists and studied by them for many years. The non-genetic nature of this change was pointed out by Professor Julian Huxley in light of experience with animals which were introduced to New Zealand forests and grew to vast size. Reference has already been made to Sutherland relics of very large red deer but one of the most massive pairs of antlers ever found came from Strath Halladale where it was dug up in a semi-fossilised state, and is described by J. G. Millais. It carried 26 points and had an average beam circumference of 21.6 cm (8.5 in).

A great deal of modern red deer research has been undertaken on the Reay Forest, and while this may not be typical of the whole of Sutherland, it covers the west in general. Deer numbers were found to be low compared with the rest of the Highlands, approximately one per 13 hectares (33 acres) compared with one per 9 hectares (22 acres) in Ross-shire forests, a reflection of the low carrying capacity of the Sutherland habitat — peat covered gneiss and sterile quartzite tops — but where richer outcrops such as limestone occur then deer use increases markedly and such areas are seldom free of deer.

As with most places weights have tended to decline, a fact not related to culling the best heads but to adaptation of the animal to a declining habitat. Therein lies the success of the Sutherland red deer, the production of a small, hardy, slow-growing race as a reaction to a mean environment. There is evidence that maturity is delayed compared with other highland areas, shown in the later antler growth; it is usual for young males to develop antler knobs in their second year, but in Sutherland " knobbers " may be three years old, this delay being partly due to shortage of calcium and phosphorus. Also, many young deer die on the hill in the cold, wet winters but this is a natural mortality. The Sutherland red deer is a product of its environment and attempts to improve them by introduction of " fresh blood " or English park stags are quite unrealistic.

In numbers, red deer may have increased slightly following the destruction and opening up of the forests, but decreased after the Clearances and introduction of large-scale sheep farming, only to increase again with the protection afforded by the creation of deer forests and the clearance of sheep from the poorer grazing with further extension of the deer forests in the latter half of the 19th century. As to actual numbers, one early estimate is of 1500 deer in Sutherland about 1830, but whether or not this is accurate, the number is probably nearer 20,000 now.

SIKA DEER. This is a Japanese species which has been imported to various parts of the British Isles. In Sutherland a small population is established in the afforested parts of the Oykell valley.

FALLOW DEER. These were introduced to Rosehall in the 19th century to a "deer park" where a herd of 270 existed in 1877, and about the same time fallow deer were reported from the woods near Dornoch, presumably escapees from Rosehall: none now survives. In the early 1930's a herd of white fallow deer was introduced to the Uppat woods on the Sutherland estate. In the 1950's these were still quite often seen, but gradually died out and the last survivor is believed to have been killed by a windblown tree about 1970.

ROE DEER. Roe have increased greatly in numbers and range in direct proportion to the increase in afforestation. Wherever new forests are established roe inevitably appear and it has long been recognised that they will cross wide tracts of tree-less moorland to colonise new habitats. As an example of this, the first conifers were planted in Strathy Glen in 1950 and eleven years later a pair of roe had already appeared. The numbers of roe which can be tolerated in a forest depend on the age of the trees. In young, vulnerable plantations vigorous control measures have to be undertaken, but once the trees are well grown the controls may be reduced to allow for a healthy population in balance with the habitat.

WILD GOAT. In the west, original highland goats were part of the crofters' stock until recent times and were kept by the Ardmore crofters up to about 50 years ago. Some survived in a completely wild state in the Ceathramh Garbh (The "Rough Quarter" between Loch Inchard and Loch Laxford) until only a few years ago, and indeed there may still be a few survivors. There are "wild" goats on the Morvich Rock in Rogart, but these were probably of more recent origin, settled there to graze the face of the rock to keep the sheep from difficult places.

REPTILES AND AMPHIBIANS

The common lizard is found almost everywhere although it is often seen merely as "something" moving rapidly in grass or heather, but the slow-worm is poorly recorded and probably much less common or widespread. The adder is found throughout the lowland parts of the District but is patchy in distribution, probably commoner in woodland margins in the south-east. It is said to be much rarer in the west than formerly, but would be much more in evidence in hot, dry summers and therefore more numerous in the 1920's.

The three species of newt have all been recorded, although their distribution is not well documented. The rough or crested newt is

10. Smoo Cave, Durness   *(J. Campbell)*
11. Shin Falls, near Lairg   *(J. Campbell)*

12. The Dornoch Firth   *(J. Campbell)*
13. Loch Fleet   *(J. Campbell)*

14. Sango Bay, Durness   *(J. Campbell)*
15. Dornoch and Eastern Lowlands   *(A. Smith)*

16. Stone Stripes on Ben Armine   *(D. Balfour)*
17. (left) Eider Duck's nest, Kyle of Tongue   *(J. Selby)*
18. (right) Primula Scotica   *(J. Selby)*

the most aquatic, an inhabitant of deep water such as quarry holes, and is the least common. The smooth newt is very common on damp ground, peat cuttings, etc., and seems to be more widespread than the palmate newt. Frogs and toads are both well distributed and it is surprising how often one will come across frogs in damp heather even quite high in the mountains.

FRESHWATER FISH

In common with everywhere else north of the Highland boundary fault the present native freshwater fish of Sutherland date from the disappearance of the last glaciers some ten thousand years ago. These fish colonised the rivers and lochs by following the coastline northwards as it became progressively ice-free. It follows, therefore, that only species able to live in both fresh and salt water were involved, so the number is comparatively small, viz., Atlantic salmon, sea and brown trout, char, common eel, the three-spined stickleback and possibly the smaller ten-spined stickleback. One might also include the flounder which may penerate miles upstream, as on the Naver and the Dionard, and possibly the thick-lipped grey mullet which enters the lower reaches of some streams and rivers in late summer. Lampreys are also present: certainly the brook lamprey is found north of the Great Glen, and lampreys of unrecorded species have been found in the Helmsdale River.

From the original sea-going trout and char the present " landlocked " non-migratory populations have evolved. There are no seagoing char in the British Isles now but these are common in the Arctic. In contrast to this there are now thirty-one species of fresh-water fish recorded in Scotland, but most have been imported at some time. Some brackish water dwellers might be included, such as saithe, small lythe and the common goby, all of which occur within the impoundment of The Mound. These fish can tolerate almost pure fresh water for short periods.

Fortunately for the angler the waters of Sutherland are almost free from pike and perch, common in East Ross, where they were imported centuries ago from the Midlands of England. There are no pike in Sutherland and although small-scale introductions of perch have been attempted there is probably only one surviving population. Another alien fish which is making its way northward is the minnow, a member of the carp family, now well established in the lochs of the Kirkaig system and possibly others. This species has been introduced by trout anglers tipping out unused live bait.

The life histories of salmon and trout are well known but less so is that of their close relative, the beautiful pink and gold char. There is probably a higher density of char waters in Sutherland than in any other part of Britain. In all these waters char compete with the more aggressive trout and are forced to live mostly in mid-water where they feed on animal plankton. However, the char population of Loch Borralie, Durness, a rich limestone loch, is noteworthy. Here char grow exceptionally large as they feed also on bottom-living animals and sticklebacks. Specimens of 9.5 kg (2 lb) and over have been caught; elsewhere they do not usually exceed 0.17 kg to 0.22 kg (6 oz to 8 oz). Incidentally, char, contrary to general opinion, can thrive in shallow lochs which become relatively warm during the summer. Some brown trout may learn to feed largely on char shoals and as a result grow into " ferox " or " great lake trout ". These very large trout are features of many Sutherland lochs, for example Loch Shin, Loch Naver and Loch Assynt.

The best known of all the fresh water fish is, of course, the Atlantic salmon, a migratory species which ascends every river round the Sutherland coasts, even quite small streams like the Carnaig, near The Mound, where about the year 1864 one of the first salmon ladders was constructed to allow the fish to bypass a series of waterfalls. Salmon rivers are, needless to say, a valuable sporting asset but the salmon has been subjected to so many other methods of capture, both in rivers and in the sea, legal and illegal, that it is almost becoming a threatened species. A new development in West Sutherland is salmon farming, the hatching and rearing of the fish to marketable size in floating sea cages, a fascinating, and it is hoped, successful enterprise though scarcely one to describe in detail in a section on " wild-life ".

A few lochs have populations of rainbow trout, which originate from the Pacific coast of North America. These are maintained by stocking as the species has not so far established itself as a breeding species in Scotland. Though not a fish, the fresh-water mussel deserves a mention as an inhabitant of some Sutherland rivers, the Laxford, Naver, Helmsdale and perhaps others. " Pearl fishing " is a very old established practice and some fine specimens of pearls have been found in mussels taken from these rivers. The status of several species of freshwater fish in Sutherland is not well known and a systematic survey might bring to light some hitherto unrecorded native species or introductions.

INVERTEBRATES

The study of invertebrates is largely one of specialisation, but in a general survey it is not out of place to mention one or two interesting species. For example, Sutherland has an isolated and little-known population of the Artaxerxes butterfly, which is the northern form of the brown argus and in some years at least the beautiful small copper is plentiful in a mixed woodland habitat. On fine sunny days in summer a pleasant occupation is watching the colourful dragonflies mating and egg-laying. Eleven species have been recorded from Sutherland including the largest British species, the magnificent black and yellow *Cordulegaster boltonii*. In the west, the four-spotted dragonfly *Libellula quadrimaculata,* a large species with a broad hairy body, is commonly seen in fine weather but the commonest of all is the brilliant silver-blue damsel-fly *Enallagma cyathigerum*. A Sutherland special is *Sympetrum nigrescens,* a recently described species, the first known specimens of which were collected in Scourie, Tongue and Skelbo.

Part two

HISTORICAL

Chapter eight

THE DISTANT PAST

The first inhabitants of Sutherland of whom we have any knowledge were neolithic (New Stone Age) farmers. Their way of life was based on a primitive agriculture and husbandry, supplemented by hunting. They did not, however, have any metal, so flint, chert and stone were used for the essential cutting tools such as knives, scrapers and axe-heads. Good quality pottery would have been made, mainly open bowls up to 23 cm (9 in) or more in diameter. A variety of organic materials, which generally decay in the course of time, must have been used for many purposes — wood for building, wood or bone for hafts of axes and other tools, wood or leather for containers, leather and wool for clothes, to mention a few.

The phase during which the first neolithic peoples moved north to establish themselves in Sutherland is totally obscure. They must have come in small groups into a land unaffected by human activity, a land which, in the more favourable climatic conditions of the period, would have been extensively forested, the infertile parts largely peat-free scrubland, and only the highest land would have been bare. Sea level would have been higher, and there would have been extensive salt marshes in the estuaries. The first settlers probably arrived about 3700 B.C. (or 3000 b.c. on radio-carbon dating, which it is now known must be calibrated to give much earlier real dates).

There are only the slightest indications of the presence of any people before the neolithic immigrants' arrival. At one time it was thought that evidence of palaeolithic occupation had been found in the caves at Allt nan Uamh near Inchnadamph, but this claim is now discounted. The caves undoubtedly contained bones of an arctic fauna including extinct species, but the human burial and sparse indications of human activity were not associated with them. A few flints of mesolithic type have been found on the links along the east coast. There are tiny blades, points, scrapers and cores of microlithic type, mainly of ginger-brown flint, now in the museum at Dunrobin Castle and the National Museum of Antiquities. Their numbers are so few that only occasional groups of nomadic hunter-fishers seem to be indicated. However, there are a number of mounds on the links to the west of Dornoch, between Dornoch and Golspie, and particularly at Little Ferry, which contain layers of midden largely composed of shell debris, oyster, mussel, cockle, limpet and periwinkle, but also including pieces of bone and worked flint, quartz and chert. The mounds are 6 m to 30 m (20 ft to 100 ft) in diameter, and sited 3 m to 9 m (10 ft to 30 ft) above high water. Until these mounds have been scientifically investigated it is uncertain whether some, or all, are the result of mesolithic or neo-lithic occupation (Tait 1869, 1870; Davidson 1948, 31 - 3).

The probability that there was occupation on the links through the long neolithic period is supported by the very large numbers of typically neolithic artifacts collected there, and now in the two museums already mentioned. There are hundreds of leaf-shaped arrowheads, and as many scrapers of all sizes, as well as waste material from working sites. Some of the flint is ginger-brown or red, from the flint beds in Buchan (not far away by sea), and some is grey in colour, but the great majority of finds are of grey chert, of inferior quality to flint but which none-the-less was made into presentable arrowheads and scrapers. There is a single rim sherd of neolithic pottery from Little Ferry.

Apart from these indications of coastal settlement, nothing is known of neolithic occupation sites in Sutherland, and the sites of neolithic houses are indeed notoriously difficult to locate, except for aberrant stone examples of the later neolithic known from Orkney. Stone axe-heads, the essential tool of neolithic farmers, have been found by chance in various parts of the District. These axes were made in great numbers throughout the neolithic period, and the best axe-heads came from certain centres or " factory sites " where the most suitable stone was exploited and traded over surprisingly long distances. At least one of the Sutherland axe-heads came from Tievebulliagh in northern Ireland, and at least two probably from the Langdale valley in the English Lake District. Arrowheads, too, have been found here and there in the District, besides on the links.

It may be safely inferred that all the habitable land was occupied in the course of the millennium after the first farmers arrived, for many of their stone tombs have survived and it is unlikely that the occupation sites were far away. As will be seen

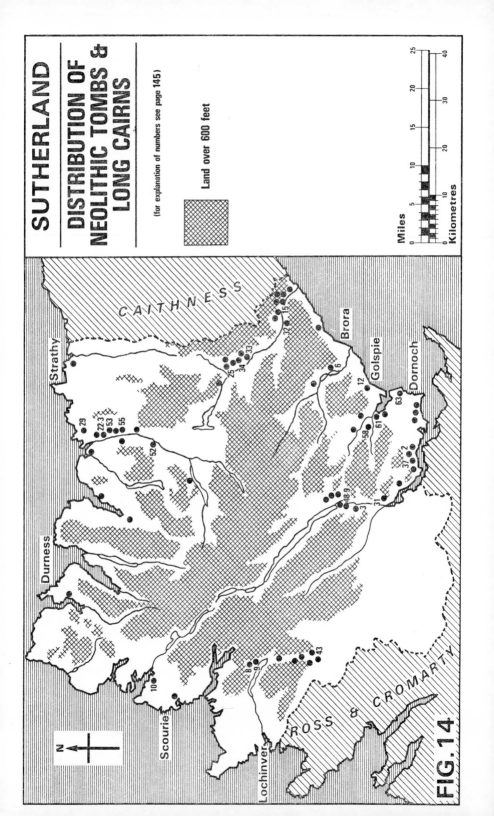

SUTHERLAND

DISTRIBUTION OF NEOLITHIC TOMBS & LONG CAIRNS

(for explanation of numbers see page 145)

▨ Land over 600 feet

FIG. 14

from the map (Fig. 14) the distribution of the tombs is on the hill-sides of the straths and smaller glens, near the coast though seldom on the links, and on the limestone near Durness and Inchnadamph. The siting of the tombs, and presumably of the settlements, is on naturally well-drained land, often on a hillside with a southern aspect. There is a notable concentration of tombs between Inchna-damph and the head of Strath Oykel, half of them just in Ross-shire, and more have been found in a recent survey: the enriched pasture provided by the limestone was certainly the reason, and a more vivid contrast with the whole of the west mainland north of Oban, which is notably bare of tombs, could hardly be imagined.

About fifty-seven tombs of passage-grave type are known in Sutherland, of which twenty-one have been totally destroyed or very severely damaged, about thirty survive with substantial remains, and about six are still so complete that little or nothing of the interior structure is visible. The most interesting sites have been listed on page 145, and the numbers quoted are those in the catalogue of sites published by the writer (1963, 304 - 32; 1972, 572 - 86).

Essentially these structures consist of small stone-built chambers covered by round cairns, with access from the outside provided by a low-roofed passage. They vary considerably in size and detail of plan and construction (Fig.15). Their study is further complicated, in some cases, by later additions, either to extend the chamber, add a second chamber, to enlarge the cairn, or elaborate its external appearance. Passage-graves were built in various parts of Western Britain and in Ireland, and also in parts of west Europe, to a variety of designs. All those in Sutherland, as far as can be seen, belong to one group which evolved in the Western Isles and north main-land of Scotland. Detailed information from the Sutherland tombs is lacking, as only three have been excavated, and the report on the most important of these has not yet been published. Needless to say, there is no direct dating evidence, but comparisons with other sites allow a rough estimate that the earliest may have been built about 3700 B.C., and the last ones perhaps about 3000 B.C. Some, at least, were used for burials for another 500 years or more, before being finally ritually sealed. Indeed, some were of cult interest right into the middle bronze age; at Embo (63), for instance, burials of this period were inserted into the mound.

The first passage-graves were small and simple, as is to be expected in the earlier pioneer phase of neolithic settlement. The chambers were built of large slabs, often split boulders, set in a rough circle or square, the gaps between them filled with dry masonry. All the visible chambers are now roofless, but judging by similar sites in adjacent areas and what is known of The Ord North (48) a large capstone was used, either resting directly on the upright slabs, or on a few courses of massive horizontal slabs set to overhang slightly the wall below and so reduce the span. The roof of the Achu (2) chamber was recorded when complete, and it seems to have been unique among Scottish tombs in having the ends of long radial slabs jammed against a small central keystone (Curle 1910). The diameters of the chambers may be as little as 1.5 m or 2 m (5 ft or 6 ft) and the height even less. The cairns were small and the passages consequently short, though a surrounding cairn was necessary both to support the walling and provide a ramp for the placing of the cap-stone. The tombs of Allt Sgiathaig (8), and Embo (63) before additions were made, are likely to be early examples. Rather larger chambers with the walls heightened for a taller vault but of the same simple plan are known at Achu (2) and Invershin (31). Kyleoag (37) and Loch Borralan (43) are similar except that there is a small carefully built recess in one corner.

Development of the chamber plan involved building an outer compartment or antechamber, normally smaller in area and roofed by slabs at a lower level than the chamber. Also, there was a liking for narrowed entries formed by a pair of transversely-set portal stones, at the outer end of the passage, between passage and antechamber, and between antechamber and chamber. Examples of bipartite chambers can be seen at Achany (3), Badnabay (10), Rhives (12), The Ord South (49), Skail (52), and Torboll (58), some being rounded in plan and some rectangular. An interesting variant of the bipartite plan exists at Skelpick Long (53) and The Ord North (48) where both parts of the chamber are round in plan, of the same size, and both roofed under relatively high false-vaults, the outer part of the latter chamber still complete and over 2.5 m (8 ft) high. These must have been amongst the largest chambers in the District.

A more elaborate chamber plan evolved from combining the bipartite chamber with that which had a side cell, placing the low-roofed cell on the axis, followed by the chamber with high false-vault, and the low-roofed antechamber. An almost perfect structure of this type was to be seen at Kinbrace Burn (33) until it was vandalised, and other examples, where the roofing arrangements are not certain, at Allt nam Ban (6) and Fiscary (29). Another version of the tripartite plan is at Coille na Borgie South (23), where the first

FIG. 15 — PLANS OF NEOLITHIC TOMBS

0 2 4 6 8 10 METRES
0   10   20   30 FEET

1. LOCH BORRALAN EAST (43)

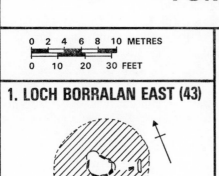

2. KYLEOAG (37)

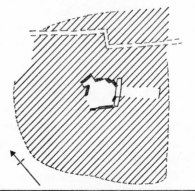

3. ACHN (2)

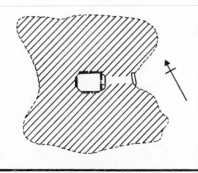

4. EMBOL (63)

Cists

5. TORBOLL (58)

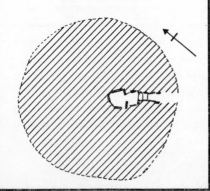

6. FISCARY (29)

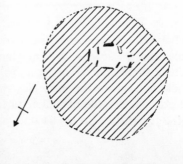

and central compartments are roofed by slabs, and the innermost part was at a higher level.

It is known that passage-graves were used in a variety of ways, sometimes for a great number of bodies, sometimes for few, and sometimes to receive cremated bones. Sometimes there were parts of many pots, and other artifacts, and sometimes none. It is certain that chambers were used over long periods, and must have been cleaned out at intervals. When Achu (2) was excavated in 1909 an adult skeleton was found, and a few fragments of bone (Curle 1910). The excavations at Embo (63) in 1960 produced a few scattered bones and skulls belonging to three adults, one child and one infant. Over these was a layer of soil and stones, and on this incomplete remains of three adults, an adolescent, four children and two infants, all disturbed by later burials (Henshall and Wallace 1965). No neolithic pottery was found in either tomb, but fragments of several pots were found at The Ord North. When chambers ceased to be used for burials they were often deliberately sealed, by a layer of earth or rubble placed over the chamber floor, or by blocking or walling up the passage, or both. At Achu there was 0.9 m (3 ft) of rubble on the floor, which must have been deliberately placed there as the excavator had found the roof intact. At Embo laid stones blocked the passage, and a shallow layer of earth overlay the lower burials, but later burials above had not been sealed.

Although round cairns are the normal covering of passage-graves, a proportion of the cairns in Sutherland are, in fact, of some other shape, oval, heel-shaped, square with four projecting " horns", or elongated. A few also have façades of upright stones on either side of the entrance. These features are due to later additions, probably reflecting the importance of the structures to the community as cult centres, with a consequent desire to make the external appearance more impressive. The round cairns might be made into larger round or oval cairns. Excavations elsewhere have shown that heel-shaped and square cairns were added to pre-existing round cairns, sometimes as only a stony platform from which the original cairn would project like a rough dome. The last two shapes seem to be a peculiarity of the north of Scotland and their origin is obscure, except that their shape emphasised the tomb entrance and provided a forecourt for any ceremonies which might be performed there. The best example of the rare heel-shaped cairn is Kyleoag (37), and cairns with four horns may be seen at Achu (2) and Skelpick South (55).

Long cairns (Fig. 16) have quite a different origin from passage-graves, deriving from the long mounds (made either of earth, or turves, or stones, the first two being technically " barrows ", the last " cairns ") known in Southern and Eastern England, and in small numbers in Southern and Eastern Scotland. These monuments are impressive, averaging 30 m to 60 m (100 ft to 200 ft) long, up to 3m (10 ft) high at the wider east end, and diminishing in height and width towards the west end. They generally contained some kind of rectangular wooden or turf-built mortuary structure in which were burials, or incomplete skeletons, or cremated bones. Unlike the stone chambers, they were not intended for continued access over a period, and they occupied only a small part of the large mound. In various parts of Britain the long mounds spread westwards and northwards into areas where stone burial chambers were the established funerary monument, and the long mounds were either superimposed on the tombs or were adopted and adapted by the tomb-builders.

There are twelve long cairns in Sutherland, eleven of them in the Strath of Kildonan or Strath Naver, the twelfth near Golspie. Some of them can be seen to cover passage-graves, and of these some at least, and possibly all, were later additions to the tomb, as indicated by the differing axes of the chamber and cairn at Skelpick Long (53), and at Coille na Borgie South (23) where the entry into the passage is not even in the centre of the façade. Sometimes the long cairn was not physically linked to the earlier cairn, as at the adjacent Coille na Borgie North (22). At this site the passage-grave with façade faces north, the long cairn on almost the same axis faces south, with only 1.8 m (6 ft) between them. There is no sign of a chamber in the long cairn. At other sites, where the long cairn appears to have been built in isolation, there is no sign of a chamber, though admittedly at Kilearnan (32) and Creag an Amalaidh (61) it may be because the cairn is too intact. One outstanding question, which cannot be answered without careful excavation, is whether any of the last group of cairns contains a mortuary structure of the type known from the long mounds to the south, in which case the mound could date nearly as early as the first passage-graves in Sutherland.

One isolated example of a tomb not of passage-grave type must be mentioned. By Ardvreck Castle is a small rectangular chamber (9) divided into three compartments by low transverse slabs stretching right across the chamber, and surrounded by an oval cairn. The chamber is of Clyde type, known mainly from Argyll, the Clyde

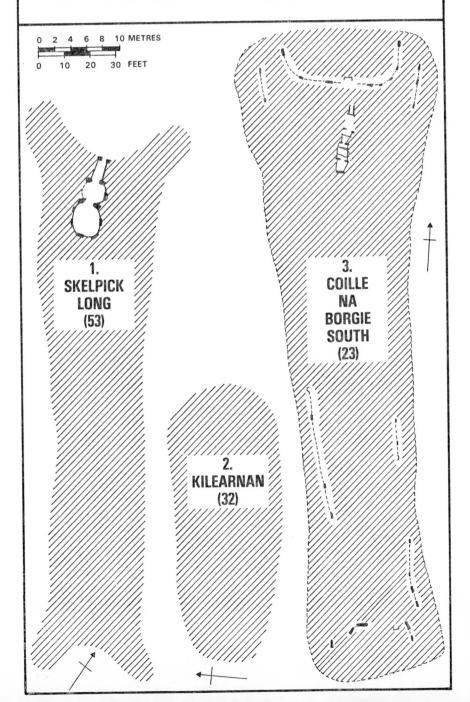

FIG.16 — PLANS OF SUTHERLAND LONG CAIRNS

0 2 4 6 8 10 METRES

0 10 20 30 FEET

1.
SKELPICK
LONG
(53)

2.
KILEARNAN
(32)

3.
COILLE
NA
BORGIE
SOUTH
(23)

estuary and South-West Scotland. Except for a single chamber in Ardnamurchan and three in North Uist, it is the only example north of the Great Glen.

The later neolithic, the time in the northern mainland when tomb-building had largely or entirely ceased though some of the tombs were probably still in use, and which in its later stages saw the arrival of the Beaker people, is poorly represented in Sutherland. Except for a few sherds from The Ord North (48), there is a total dearth of the coarse but highly decorated pottery of the period, though, as with the dearth of early neolithic pottery, this must be due to a mixture of chance and lack of sustained research by pre-historians. Among the flint collections from the east coast links there are a few artifacts which belong to this period, such as lop-sided and hollow-based arrowheads, flaked knives with ground edges, small so-called fabricators, and occasional flints with fine ripple flaking.

In view of this it is perhaps surprising that there are a number of rarer non-utilitarian high quality objects from the District. Mainly they are from the coastal areas of the Dornoch Firth and up to Golspie, reflecting both the relative fertility of these regions, and the collecting interests of the Sutherland Estates during the 19th century. There is a beautiful axe of jade, the green stone polished to a high gloss, and certainly an object of great value in a non-metal-using community, both because of the exotic material imported from Europe, probably from the Alps, and because of the immense amount of time its manufacture has entailed. There are also two fine flint axes, and part of a third, which must have been valuable prestige objects for the same reasons, the flint coming from England either as a roughout or more likely as a finished article. Several of the mysterious stone balls with either four or six knobs, purely Scottish artifacts and almost certainly of ritual use, have been found; they are formed with remarkable regularity and skill. The ovoid stone macehead from Assynt is another prestige object, though not of out-standing quality. Technically and aesthetically the most remarkable object is the rare faceted macehead of white flint found at Airdens, near Bonar Bridge. The beautiful but laborious faceting of the surface, a stylisation of the uneven surface of a macehead cut from an antler burr, gives a special quality to an object already deeply satisfying in form and material.

APPENDIX

List of sites with worthwhile visible remains.

NOTE: Mention of a site does not imply right of access, and permission to visit should be sought. The sites are listed alphabetically (Henshall 1963 or 1972) with catalogue number in brackets, followed by a map reference. Almost all these sites are Scheduled Ancient Monuments and it is an offence to interfere with them in any way.

ACHANY (3) NC 571019. — Bipartite rectangular chamber, oval cairn, façade.

ACHU (2) NH 674910. — Single-compartment chamber, cairn with horns to front and rear.

ALLT NAM BAN (6) NC 857077. — Tripartite chamber, unusually long passage, oval cairn.

BADNABAY (10) NC 218467. — Constructional stones only of bipartite chamber, traces of round cairn.

CAEN BURN SOUTH (15) ND 013177. — Long cairn, boulder kerb across E end, two slabs showing on axis probably part of a chamber.

COILLE NA BORGIE NORTH (22) NC 715590. — At the N end, a rectangular cairn with part of a chamber, and remains of a façade; to the S, a long cairn; both cairns edged by spaced upright stones.

COILLE NA BORGIE SOUTH (23) NC 715590. — Long cairn edged by spaced upright stones, façades at N and S ends; in N end a tripartite chamber and passage askew to the cairn axis.

CREAG AN AMALAIDH (61) NH 756973. — Small long cairn.

CREAG NAN CAORACH WEST (25) NC 869310. — Square cairn with horns, the probably tripartite chamber partly exposed.

EMBO (63) NH 817926. — Two single-compartment chambers in an oval cairn; also a Bronze Age cist between them.

KILEARNAN (32) NC 923184. — Fairly intact long cairn.

KINBRACE HILL LONG (34) NC 871291. — Two relatively untouched adjacent cairns with a common axis, the upper square, the lower long.

KYLEOAG (37) NH 663911. — Single-compartment chamber with side cell, heel-shaped cairn.

LOCH BORRALAN EAST (43) NC 262112. — Chamber similar to Kyleoag, round cairn.

SKAIL (52) NC 712469. — The constructional slabs of a bipartite chamber, round cairn.

SKELPICK LONG (53) NC 722567. — Bipartite chamber and passage, long cairn.

SKELPICK SOUTH (55) NC 723561. — Intact horned cairn.

TORBOLL (58) NH 741994. — Bipartite chamber, round cairn.

Chapter nine

BRONZE AGE TO BROCHS

THE BRONZE AGE IN SUTHERLAND

A student of prehistoric archaeology once commented, no doubt in exasperation, that " The Bronze Age people never lived and the Iron Age people never died ". Like most aphorisms, the statement approximates more to a state of knowledge than to reality. It is certainly the case that the kinds of evidence available for the Bronze Age are qualitatively different from the evidence afforded by the large numbers of living sites available to researchers interested in the Iron Age. Very few domestic sites have been definitely assigned to the Bronze Age in Scotland and none has been recognised in Sutherland. The material falls into four main categories with the emphasis on funerary and ritual sites. Funerary structures, cairns and cists, are by far the most numerous monuments of the Bronze Age in Sutherland. " Megalithic " sites — standing stones, stone circles and stone rows — are among the most impressive structures surviving from the prehistoric past. Metalwork, the third main source of information, is restricted in quantity and type compared with the southern and eastern parts of Scotland. Even more restricted are the examples of Bronze Age art.

The apparent absence of Bronze Age domestic sites is a perennial problem but that does not mean it should be ignored. Examples of Bronze Age houses, although few in number, do occur elsewhere in Scotland. Excavation of the site at West Plean, Stirlingshire, provided evidence of a round house with timber walls and lacking stone foundations (Steer 1955-56). Insufficient is known about farmsteads of this kind to conclude whether cultural differences are involved or whether the ring-like enclosures delimited by a bank of earth and boulders are normal in upland areas where timber was less available than stone. Although the evidence is not conclusive, a recently excavated hut-circle near Burg, Isle of Mull, with low walls of earth and stone and a hitherto unrecorded form of entrance may be of Bronze Age date.* Hut circles were widely used in the Iron Age, the dwellings of the common people many of whom must have been descended from earlier Bronze Age populations. As a result of their excavations of Iron Age hut-circles at Kilphedir in the Strath of Kildonan, Fairhurst and Taylor (1970-71) postulated, "a cultural continuum from the Late Bronze Age."

A variety of reasons has been suggested for the absence of Bronze Age houses on the north-west mainland. One such proposition is that Bronze Age people were essentially nomadic. The available evidence does not entirely support this view. Beaker pottery from the earliest phase of the Bronze Age in Britain contains impressions of wheat and barley. The evidence from West Plean suggests an economy based on peasant agriculture, a form of mixed farming familiar in Scotland from the Neolithic up to and including the 18th century. It is, of course, possible that over extensive areas of the Highland Zone the emphasis was on stock-rearing rather than agriculture during the Bronze Age. Even so, seasonal vertical migration of animals — transhumance — would fit this economic pattern. The problem of identification of living sites remains.

It is unfortunate that hut-circles have tended to be treated as a group, although some workers have commented on the variety of forms identifiable in the field (Reid 1966-67). Surprisingly, little excavation has taken place in Sutherland and little is known of precise distributions, of differences in form, of the period of use and of the economy. Whether or not the different forms imply differences in function or date it is clear that hut circles were used over a long period. It is within this group of structures that Bronze Age, as well as Iron Age, domestic sites must occur. The apparent scarcity of Bronze Age living sites is probably a result of the failure to recognise them (see pages 157 to 162).

Knowledge of simple copper and gold metallurgy was brought to Scotland by the makers of Beakers who reached South-West Scotland while the chambered tombs were still in use and penetrated at least as far as Ardnamurchan. Few Beakers have been found in Sutherland. The examples from Cambusmore, Dornoch and from Dunrobin may be seen in collections held in Dunrobin Castle Museum. Another, found in a cist in a gravel pit (Strath Naver: NC 702457) was gifted to the National Museum of Antiquities. The present whereabouts of a fourth, apparently found in a cist at Betty-

* Awaiting publication.

hill, is unknown. The Sutherland finds are markedly peripheral to a large concentration of Beakers in Aberdeenshire, evidence of immigration from the Rhineland and the Low Countries in the two centuries after 2000 B.C. Penetration inland from the coastal plain was effected by way of the principal river valleys, especially the Dee and Don. Beyond the Moray Firth, the sporadic finds of Beaker pottery probably indicate a spirit of exploration rather than systematic colonisation and settlement.

The Beaker from Dunrobin (Mitchell 1933-34) was found in a cist with 18 quartz pebbles, 118 shale discs, 6 of which were perforated, and the skeleton of an eighteen-year-old female. Beaker colonists appear to have formed a distinctive physical type; round-headed and stockily built in contrast with the long-headed, more slender contemporary populations of West Europe. The skeletal material from a cist found in Strath Naver (NC 719482) broadly conforms. The cist, covered by a capstone some 1.42 m (4ft 8 in) long by 0.76 m (2 ft 6 in) broad, appears to have been incorporated within a small cairn of rounded boulders. The unburnt skeleton was unaccompanied by grave-goods. Organic material does not normally survive well in the acid soils of Highland Scotland. In this case, the exceptionally well-preserved skeleton has made reconstruction of the main physical characteristics possible. Cranial capacity was large, at 1610 c.c. considerably greater than the mean for the modern Scottish male population. The man was some thirty years old, robust and 1.75 m (5 ft 9 in) tall. He was a little taller than the average man from the cists of Aberdeenshire and his face is a little longer although the round head is typical. Perhaps this skeleton provides very tentative evidence for the mixing of Beaker immigrants with the idigenous Neolithic population.

Publication of the Royal Commission's volume on Sutherland drew attention to the large numbers of cairns which exist in the District. The Inventory distinguishes between chambered cairns, round cairns which may have contained burials, and "clearance heaps". Little excavation of cairns of ostensible Bronze Age date has taken place and field-workers come up against many of the same problems faced by their predecessors over seventy years ago. External examination of a cairn often adds little to existing knowledge. In its simplest form a cairn is a heap of stones without a kerb. Sometimes cairns of this kind cover a burial in a cist or grave (Strath Naver: NC 719482). Many cairns are encircled by a kerb or peristalith (Loch Loyal: NC 620482) made up of upright slabs or boulders. Kerb stones were essentially functional, serving as a retaining device, although many seem unnecessarily large for their task. Boulders forming the cairn material are normally of such a size that one or two men could conveniently carry them. Many cairns are small, often little more than a few metres in diameter. There is, however, considerable variation in diameter, some very large cairns being recorded. The cairn at Arnaboll (NC 468580) on the west side of Loch Hope measures some 27.0 m (88 ft) in diameter.

Most round cairns of the kind described have been dated to the second millenium B.C. They normally contain a single burial, a change in custom from the multiple interments associated with the chambered tombs of the preceding Neolithic period. Burials may be accompanied by grave furniture including tools and weapons, personal ornaments, ritual objects and ceramics. In some instances no enduring objects were placed with the dead.

No definitive distribution map of cairns in Sutherland is available. Much work remains to be done in assessing the distribution of cairns in relation to the solid geology, the superficial deposits and soils. In the absence of domestic sites for study the question arises as to how far the cairns are an indication of a settlement pattern of which little is known. In general, it must be recognised that the premium placed on good cultivable land in Sutherland ensured succession of settlement within what are often small, well-defined areas. At the head of Loch Eriboll, a cairn (NC 400543), an Iron Age souterrain, long houses "cleared" in the early 19th century and a modern shepherd's cottage all lie within a few hundred metres of each other. A particularly interesting example of a group of cairns apparently associated with other classes of ancient monument occurs at Baile Mhargait (centred NC 700612) on the west bank of the Naver opposite Bettyhill. There is a settlement of at least eight huts, evidence of a field-system and numerous stone mounds. Within the field system there are at least three, perhaps six, burial cairns and three cists. In the present state of knowledge it is not possible to assess the temporal relationship of the various monuments. There must be other instances in which earlier settlement was destroyed by the succession of later communities. Cairns tend to remain because they are difficult to obliterate unless there is a conscious effort to destroy them. Their sites may give clues to the location of past settlement. Many cairns seem to have been sited so that they could be seen from the arable area (Keoldale:

NC 388664), often on false crests or ridges (NC 730623) beyond which the land would have been used for grazing rather than cultivation. Others are located at high elevations in harsh, inhospitable environments. Above the 300 m (1000 ft) contour on the Durness Peninsula cairns (NC 387586) are to be found in an area of exposed quartzite pavement where there is little evidence of soil formation ever having taken place. These cairns were not necessarily directly associated with any form of settlement, not even temporary summer shelters such as might have been used by pastoralists tending transhumant animals. This group of cairns may form a cairn cemetery which was added to over several generations (Fig. 17). Use of sites for ritual and burial purposes over many centuries is well attested in prehistoric Europe (Piggot 1947-48) with certain localities, whatever the initial reason for their use, coming to be regarded as " sacred ". Another cairn cemetery (NC 426561) on the margins of the better land around Eriboll, almost certainly settled in Bronze Age times, is visible from the group on the Durness Peninsula. It may be significant that the cairns at NC 387586 lie between Bealach Loch na Seilg and Bealach Mor, the two main passes across the Durness Peninusula. The most direct route between the two main settled areas, around Eriboll and on the western margins of the Peninsula, would be across the loch by boat and over the passes. It is known that in the more recent past routes of this kind were in common use.

Cairns occur singly (Loch Loyal: NC 620609), in pairs (Farr: NC 720548) and in groups or cemeteries. Barrow cemeteries figure prominently in the literature on the Bronze Age in England. Stonehenge barrow cemeteries are often composed of distinctive barrow forms making it possible to construct some kind of sequence. In Sutherland, distinctive forms attributable to a specific phase of the Bronze Age have not been recognised. Excavation would be required to establish temporal sequences. Fieldworkers in the south have recorded three types of cairn cemetery, two of which have been recognised in Sutherland. Stretching in an arc from the large cairn at NC 387586 is a series of much smaller cairns composed of large boulders and slabs of quartzite. These may form a linear cemetery although without excavation it is difficult to be certain of the exact status of some of the cairns. A dispersed cairn cemetery, not planned round a central point or in a line, occurs along Allt Eriboll between grid references NC 426561 and 430447. There are some forty cairns in this group, although some are almost certainly clearance cairns,

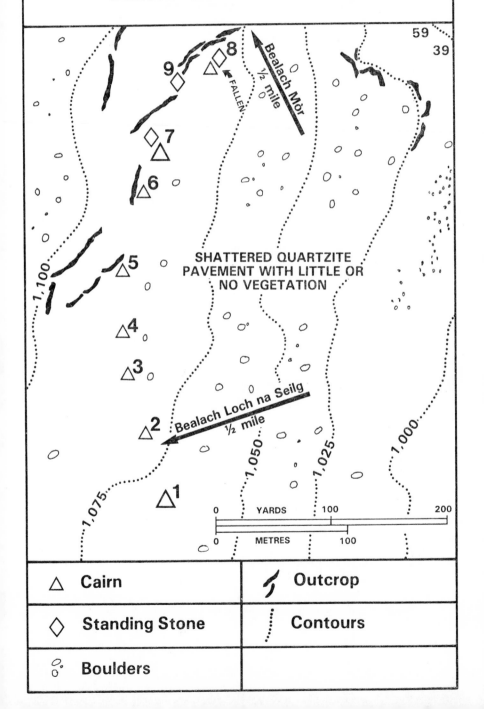

FIG.17 — BRONZE AGE CEMETERY — 35 NE

△	**Cairn**	⌇	**Outcrop**
◇	**Standing Stone**	⋮	**Contours**
⦵	**Boulders**		

with perhaps twelve hut circles and several large circular enclosures in close proximity. Nuclear cemeteries, based round an earliest cairn or barrow, have not been recognised in Sutherland.

There has been no modern systematic excavation of the Bronze Age cairns of Sutherland. Sporadic finds have been made under circumstances which often makes it difficult to comment constructively on them. The most interesting single find was discovered during road making activities in 1938. The cairn (NC 717551) contained a cist in which a jet button and parts of a jet necklace were found. Jet necklaces are generally considered to be of Middle Bronze Age date (c. 1500 - 900 B.C.). Many, perhaps all, graves with jet necklaces were those of women and evidently women of some importance.

Bronze Age art is often associated with cairns, as at Dornoch (R.C.A.H.M.) where the capstone of a cist was decorated with a cup-mark. The ornamentation of rock faces (Kinloch: NC 562527), standing stones and cist slabs with motifs known as cup marks or cup-and-ring marks is widespread in Britain and Ireland. The majority are simple cup-like depressions, Learable (NC 894240) and Dunrobin Museum, although a number of such depressions are surrounded by one or more continuous or broken grooves (Lochan Hakel: NC 569526). There is a similarity between the cup-and-ring markings and decorations on some Irish chambered tombs. Eoin MacWhite (1946) has suggested that the Irish art derives from North-West Spain and Northern Portugal. He notes that the rock carvings have a distribution in Ireland which coincides with the areas richest in copper and gold. A connection between ornamentation on rock faces and early metal prospecting is not impossible although in Southern Scotland it has been shown that only about 53% of rock carvings are within 10 km (6 miles) of copper or gold workings or known deposits. If only non-portable examples with more complex carvings are considered then in Southern Scotland 84% of sites are within 10 km (6 miles) of copper or gold (Morris 1967-68). The cup-marked stone at Learable is within 5 km (3 miles) of Kinbrace Burn, along the banks of which gold digging was carried out in 1869. Piggot has suggested that the carvings may be a form of sympathetic magic, placed there to induce the desired characteristics, perhaps metal-bearing properties, within the stone.

Perhaps because they are so impressive, perhaps because they catch hold of the imagination — for whatever the reason single standing stones, stone circles and stone rows are probably more familiar to the general public than any other class of ancient monument. These antiquities, along with henges and Neolithic chambered tombs, are often collectively referred to as megaliths (Greek megas, great; lithos, stone). Megalith is a convenient descriptive term, no more than that, and it must be emphasised that large stones were used in various very different kinds of structure attributable to very different cultural contexts. Some of the stones erected during the Bronze Age in Sutherland were very large indeed. Th standing stone at Ospisdale (NH 716895) attains a height of over 3.35 m (11 ft) and one of the uprights in the circle at Dalharrold (Clach an Righ: NC 679391) is 2.44 m (8 ft) high and 1.06 m (3 ft 6 in) broad at the base, although admittedly these cannot match the menhir (Welsh: maen, stone: hir, long) at Locmariaquer in Brittany which was nearly 20 m (over 65 ft) in height when intact. Compared with these examples the stones used in some of the stone circles (Shin River: NC 582049) and in the stone rows (Learable Hill: NC 893 234) may seem small, often projecting only some 45 cm (1 ft 6 in) to a little more than 60 cm (2 ft) above the ground. Stone circles and stone rows display wide variation in their overall dimensions and in the sizes and shapes of stones used. "Megalithic" is not a wholly accurate description for some of these sites and there is certainly no evidence that a classification based exclusively on the size of stone used in connection is either helpful or valid.

In *Megalithic Sites in Britain* (1967) Alexander Thom has established that the erectors of standing stones had developed a geometry and were capable of making accurate astronomical observations. Sophisticated skills of this kind suggest the existence of specialists possessed of a range and depth of knowledge which can only have been accumulated over a lengthy period. Stone circles and alignments were laid out accurately using complicated geometry, including Pythagorean triangles and the construction of rings with flattened portions involving the use of at least two radii, each of which had to be integral. Statistical analysis of British sites led Thom to conclude that stone rings were laid out in integral numbers of a unit. He has called the unit the megalithic yard: MY equals 2.720 ft (0.90 m), a length which may be the human pace. He has also convincingly demonstrated that stone rings and stone rows are aligned on the extreme rising and setting positions of the sun at the solstices, the corresponding points for the moon, and on first magnitude stars. Groups of standing stones may have been set up to record careful

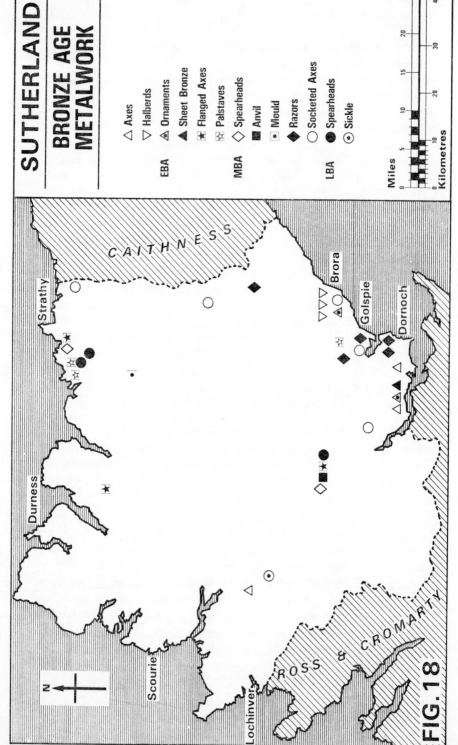

SUTHERLAND
BRONZE AGE METALWORK

△	Axes
▽	Halberds
◬	Ornaments
▲	Sheet Bronze
✦	Flanged Axes
✧	Palstaves
◇	Spearheads
■	Anvil
⊡	Mould
◆	Razors
○	Socketed Axes
●	Spearheads
⊙	Sickle

EBA

MBA

LBA

Miles

Kilometres

FIG. 18

astronomical observations, a visible record of man's activity demonstrating a fact about the universe.

The intellectual activities of man and his religious ideas during the prehistoric period must largely remain matters for conjecture. It does, however, seem likely that alignments and circles formed centres for ritual activity related to the rhythm of the seasons and to the longer term movements of the sun and moon.

The stone rows on Learable Hill have been shown to be aligned on the sun with three definite azimuths each giving a calendar declination (Thom 1967). This site consists of four stone rows each two megalithic yards apart with a menhir and cairns in close association. Immediately to the north lie two other clear stone alignments. They are very similar to the Communion Stones (Dumfriesshire) where four rows of boulders are also spaced two megalithic yards apart. Perhaps the outstanding European example is in southern Brittany where the alignments at Le Ménec, Kermanio and Kerlescan contain 2750 stones varying in height from 0.60 m (2 ft) to 3.7 m (12 ft). It would apear that almost four thousand years ago, throughout a wide distribution area, very similar sites were being used for precisely the same purposes. Stone rings also demonstrate remarkably similar characteristics. A flattened circle of Thom's type A at Le Ménec is closely paralleled by similar structures in Britain, all of which are geometrically similar. It would appear that whatever cultural differences may have existed, the inhabitants of Bronze Age Britain, and beyond to Brittany, had a defined and widely accepted religious and ceremonial life. Viewed in this way, the standing stones of Sutherland (e.g. Plate 19) are more than a visible record of man's activity. They are decipherable symbols of the remarkable achievements of our prehistoric ancestors and suggest a sophisticated social organisation that is only beginning to be understood.

Detailed analysis of Bronze Age metalwork is not possible in a short contribution of this kind. Moreover, the evidence from Sutherland is fragmentary (Fig. 18). Many types of artifact found elsewhere in Scotland do not occur in the District, adding to the problems inherent in any study of Scottish Bronze Age metalwork.

Evidence available for the Early Bronze Age is, in many respects, more complete than for the Middle and Late Bronze Age. Typology and distribution are common sources of evidence for all three phases. Grave groups, often with pottery associations, and correlations with stone moulds provide additional material for the earliest phase. In contrast, discussion of Middle Bronze Age metalwork (c. 1500 - 900 B.C.) including flanged axes, palstaves, looped spearheads and rapiers depends almost entirely on typology. The absence of associated finds, whether in graves or hoards, places strictures on lines of enquiry. Graves with metalwork are practically unknown for the Scottish Late Bronze Age although hoards are available for study.

In Sutherland, the outstanding find of Early Bronze Age metalwork occurred early in this century during rock blasting operations at the west end of Loch Migdale. The Migdale hoard contained a flat axe, eight armlets, forty-three tubular beads of sheet bronze, two bronze sheet fragments, five sheet cones, an ear-ring, and six V-shaped buttons of jet. Flat axes, typical of the Early Bronze Age, have also been found at Golspie, Inchnadamph and Skibo. The tubular beads of sheet bronze have parallels in England, Ireland and on Continental Europe in the Danube Valley from Bavaria eastwards (J. Coles 1968-69). Beads of this kind and sheet cones similar to the Migdale examples have been found in Unetician contexts, a Bronze Age culture centred on Czechoslovakia. Halberds, typical artifacts from Early Bronze Age sites over wide areas of Europe, probably had a similar Central European origin. The hoard from Baile-nan-Coille in Strath Brora contained three halberds.

The Middle Bronze Age is remarkable for an apparently abrupt change in the style of metalwork. Flanged axes (Kirtomy, Farr), looped spearheads (Craggan Soiller, Farr) and razors (Balblair, Creich) have been found in Sutherland. Other typical Middle Bronze Age types — dirks and rapiers — are absent. One of the two anvils found in Scotland, either of Middle or Late Bronze Age date, comes from the Kyle of Oykel. It consists of a flattened conical block with fine grooves for the shaping of bronze wire or for gold-working (J. Coles 1963-64). It is the kind of artifact which may have belonged to an itinerant bronze-smith.

In the Late Bronze Age new types of weapons and implements appear. These include the leaf-shaped sword and socketed axes. No examples of swords have been found in Sutherland but various forms of socketed axes occur, for example at Bonar Bridge, Golspie and Kildonan. Distribution of Late Bronze Age artifacts is markedly south and east in Scotland with few finds appearing in the north and west. The total number of finds attributable to the Late Bronze Age in Sutherland is very small: five socketed axes, three spearheads and a sickle.

The brief survey of metal artifacts emphasises the difficulty of constructing a coherent account of the Bronze Age in Sutherland. Evidence is often fragmentary and incomplete. Sometimes this is because there has been a lack of systematic fieldwork and excavation. In other instances the evidence does not, or is not known, to exist. Yet the Bronze Age past is stamped on the landscape. There are large numbers of antiquities of Bronze Age date, many of them relatively well preserved, and potentially valuable sources of information. Future work in Sutherland may well provide the clues necessary to solve some of the very many outstanding problems faced by students of the Scottish Bronze Age.

DOMESTIC PRE-HISTORIC ANTIQUITIES IN EAST SUTHERLAND

Study any Ordnance Survey (6 in) map of Sutherland, in particular East Sutherland, and one is likely to notice immediately the high numbers of "enclosures" or "hut circles" or perhaps "field systems" annotated in "antiquity" type. These are the farmhouses and fields of our ancestors of 2000 or perhaps 3000 years ago and are the subject of this section of the chapter, together with their associated structures. It must be stated at the outset that any discussion on domestic pre-Christian antiquities will pose more questions than provide answers, for despite the quantity of huts surviving in North Scotland and specifically in East and North-East Sutherland, much research needs to be done, primarily to establish the time span of their occupation.

In its simplest form, a hut circle is circular or oval, ranging in internal size from 4 m to 5 m (c. 13 ft to 16 ft) across to more than 14 m (46 ft), though the average is about 10 m (33 ft) in diameter. This would indicate a floor area of about 78 m^2 (840 ft^2) or the equivalent of a small three-bedroomed house. The method of wall construction is usually difficult to assess due to the inevitable heather covering and peat growth, though in most cases some boulders of an inner or outer retaining wall can be seen protruding through the peat. The thickness of the walls of these simple huts has never been measured at less than 1.1 m (3.5 ft) and rarely exceeds 2 m (6.5 ft). The outer and inner leaves retain a core composed of earth or rubble or perhaps vegetative material, or a combination of these materials; this core would probably have little or no stabilising effect, but was probably more in the nature of insulation (Fig. 19.1 (NC 770052)). It must be stressed that some huts have no stones visible in their construction, and many cases occur where two huts lie within a few metres of each other, yet one may be free of visible stone, and the other demonstrate a well-built wall face or faces and a rubble core.

It is conceivable that the dry-stone walling amply demonstrated by Dr H. Fairhurst in his excavations at a settlement of five huts at Kilphedir (NC 990194) may not be universal; some huts may be wholly or partly built of turf or similar perishable material. In at least three examples, two within a few hundred metres of the Kilphedir settlement (NC 992194 and NC 988200) and another in Strath Brora (NC 764072), a well-constructed stone-walled hut has been built within a larger and earlier " turf " hut.

Dr Fairhurst's Kilphedir excavations revealed that one of the huts (Kilphedir hut V) had been modified and re-occupied. The wall had been extended outwards at the entrance to form an elongated passage 4.6 m (15 ft) long. This type of hut occurs throughout East and North-East Sutherland and is characterised by a thickening of the wall at the entrance, and a more massive wall, 2 m to 3 m (6.5 ft to 10 ft) thick and surviving up to 1.4 m (4.8 ft) in height. The example at Kilphedir is worthy of a visit as the excavation is still open but other good examples occur at Caen Burn (ND 010185), Kilearnan (NC 913182) and Kinbrace (NC 868296). In the few cases where a souterrain or earth-house survives with a hut, it is probably without exception with this Kilphedir hut V [see also Caen Burn (ND 010185) and Kilphedir (NC 991190).]

So, tentatively, three basic hut types seem to exist in Sutherland; these are the relatively stone-free possible turf built (Type A), the boulder-faced example (Type B), and the more massive but again boulder-faced examples with a long entrance passage (Type C). Hut types A and B constitute about 90- 95% of all examples, but to confuse the issue, type A and B huts occur with an extended (C) entrance. (See Figs. 19.1 to 19.3 for typical examples.)

Other variations occur in prehistoric dwelling types too numerous to describe in detail. The collection of at least four Caithness wags in Glen Loth is worth noting (see Fig. 19.4). A wag is a roughly rectangular stone-built dwelling with orthostatic roof supports. These are probably the only examples of wags outside Caithness, though a curious rectangular dwelling can be seen in Uppat Wood (see Fig. 19.5 (NC 872018)) which is wag-like, though lacking the characteristic upright slabs forming stalls.

At Kilearnan (NC 914184) and in Strath Brora (NC 857049) (see Fig. 19.6) are five examples of huts with a rectangular " annexe " with no dividing wall between the two. These " key-hole " dwellings at Kilearnan are in close proximity to huts of A, B and C type, all within a large field system.

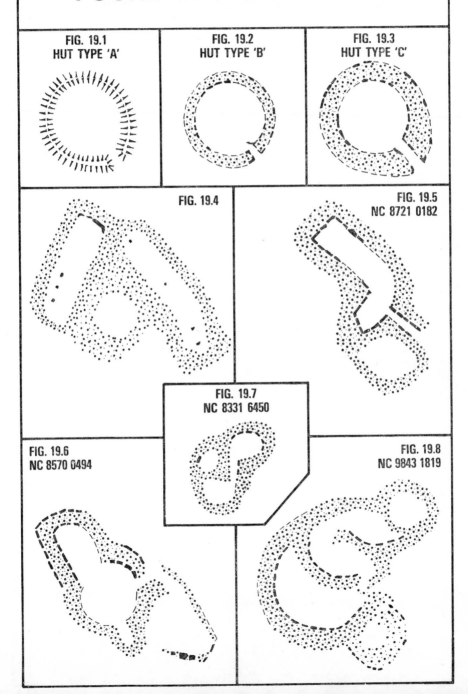

FIG.19 — HUT CIRCLE TYPES FOUND IN SUTHERLAND

**FIG. 19.1
HUT TYPE 'A'**

**FIG. 19.2
HUT TYPE 'B'**

**FIG. 19.3
HUT TYPE 'C'**

FIG. 19.4

**FIG. 19.5
NC 8721 0182**

**FIG. 19.7
NC 8331 6450**

**FIG. 19.6
NC 8570 0494**

**FIG. 19.8
NC 9843 1819**

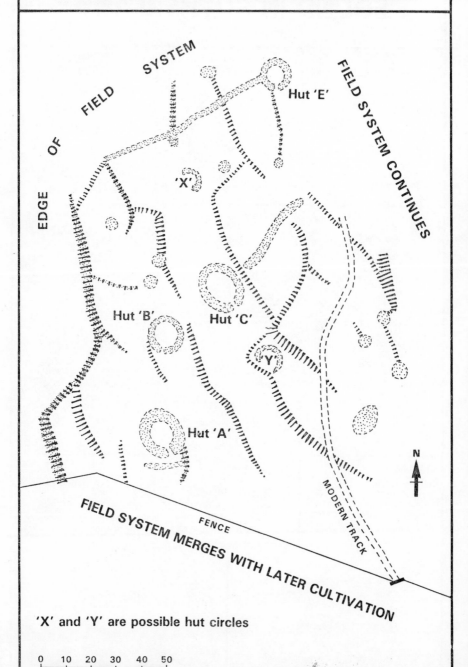

FIG.20 — FIELD SYSTEM
CAEN BURN — ND 014 183

EDGE OF FIELD SYSTEM

FIELD SYSTEM CONTINUES

Hut 'E'

'X'

Hut 'B'

Hut 'C'

'Y'

Hut 'A'

N

MODERN TRACK

FENCE

FIELD SYSTEM MERGES WITH LATER CULTIVATION

'X' and 'Y' are possible hut circles

0 10 20 30 40 50
METRES

Several examples of dwellings have recently been discovered in the north coast valleys [see Fig. 19.7, Strathy (NC 833646), and Armadale (NC 790632)] which comprise a series of small circular or sub-circular chambers conjoined within a common wall. The wall exhibits the usual facing of large stones on edge and a rubble core, suggesting contemporaneity with the hut circles.

Several nucleated homesteads have been found in the Strath of Kildonan (NC 984181) and on the east coast (ND 04871). An enlargement of the former is shown (Fig. 19.8) but they are all different and defy analysis, and again the construction technique of boulders on edge retaining an earth rubble core with a wall 2 m to 3 m (6.5 ft to 10ft) thick is evident.

With the exception of the wags, almost all the huts and variants described above are situated within areas of cultivation. The sites chosen for occupation and cultivation are usually on well-drained, gently sloping ground with a southerly aspect, invariably away from the valley floors and coastal plains which would tend to be poorly drained and were probably afforested. (The classic exception is the magnificent settlement on the raised beach at the mouth of the Naver (NC 700611 (Plate 20)). Perhaps 90 - 95% of settlements are between 46 m and 49 m (150 ft and 160 ft) O.D. An area to be cultivated was cleared of land stones, which were either heaped or spread along the edge of the plot. Thus it is possible in some cases to determine the extent of the plots by the stone clearance bounding them; they are small, varying from 15 m (49 ft) by 10 m (33 ft) up to about 50 m (164 ft) by 25 m (82 ft). One of the best examples of a field system is alongside the Caen Burn (ND 014183, Fig. 20). Here one can see quite clearly contiguous field plots separated by stony lynchets, linear clearance or ruinous walls, and stone clearance heaps. The formation of lynchets suggests cultivation over a fairly long period, but the soil then as now was thin, and presumably when worked out further ground was prepared for cultivation.

The huts are usually found scattered throughout the field system on dry sites, perhaps on a knoll or set into a slope, though there are a number of examples of two or three huts being joined (Kilearnan NC 912182). There is no evidence of huts being deliberately sited near streams. Recent field work has revealed that burnt mounds or boiling mounds occur in association with the hut settlements. A burnt mound is the result of communal cooking over a period of time on a grand scale. Into a trough filled with water, stones heated on an adjacent fire were dropped until the water boiled. The food suitably wrapped was placed in the trough, and the temperature was maintained by the addition of more stones. The effect of dropping hot stones into cold water eventually would be to crack the stones, which were then discarded. The burnt mounds are piles of small " pot-boilers " and charcoal around the trough and fire forming usually a crescentic, kidney or horse-shoe shaped mound. They can be more than 12 m (39 ft) across and up to 2 m (6.5 ft) high, so clearly they were in use over a long period of time, probably by the whole community, for it is rare to find more than one to a single settlement (NC 874277). In all cases they occur near running water with the concavity towards the stream. To date about 70 burnt mounds have been discovered; all but one was on the edge of a hut settlement and field system. Similar mounds in Orkney have been dated from 1300 B.C. to 120 B.C.

Souterrains have already been mentioned; they remain enigmatic. It seems improbable that they were hiding places, as has been suggested; if the occupants wished to go to ground in the event of attack, it would surely be more logical to have had the hiding place some distance from the huts. Or better still, take to the hills! Certainly souterrains do survive with no hut visible, but so often it appears that huts had formerly existed at the site. On balance these underground constructions were more likely store houses, but it is uncertain why it was necessary to have the passage 10 m or 20 m (33 ft or 66 ft) long and why one at Golspie (NC 795987) should have a door check and bar-hole. The best examples in the east of the District are at Caen (ND 010185), Golspie (NC 795987), Kilphedir (ND 991190) and Suisgill (NC 903232).

Sutherland is unique in the high percentage of ancient monuments surviving above ground due to limited land use since their construction, and it is possible to establish a useful distribution pattern by scrutiny of the ground and air photographs. Already some 2000 to 3000 hut circles are known and surveyed in Sutherland and undoubtedly many more are yet to be found. It is hoped that a co-ordinated scheme of excavation, following on from Dr. Fairhurst's invaluable work at Kilphedir, will be undertaken to establish the hut types, their age and development, and their relationship to the burnt mounds and field systems. Two dates c. 500 B.C. and c. 130 B.C. were obtained at Kilphedir, but the association of huts and field systems to burnt mounds and the proximity to cairns, both chambered (NC 754148) and unchambered (NC 935098) suggests a much more extended time span. And were the straths deserted between the occupation of the huts and brochs and the pre-Clearance townships?

PREHISTORIC DEFENSIVE STRUCTURES

The prehistoric defensive structures of Sutherland can be divided into four main categories: hill forts, promontory forts, duns and brochs.

HILL FORTS

The first of the stone-walled hill forts in Scotland were probably built in the 8th century B.C. (i.e. in the late Bronze Age) and they may reflect major social upheavals. The earliest of the forts have timber frameworks in rubble cores, a building method that came from the Continent. This fact may lend weight to the argument that these forts were built by intrusive chieftains who held, or attempted to hold, sway over the local population. Timber-laced forts were obviously very vulnerable to fire as the many vitrified examples in Scotland illustrate. (Stone becomes vitrified when it is heated to temperatures so high that some of the mineral constituents melt.)

The most northerly example of a vitrified fort in Scotland occurs at Dun Creich (NH 651882), some 5.6 km (3½ miles) south-east of Bonar Bridge. Its location, crowning a magnificent peninsular site, is enclosed by an inner and outer rampart, the latter defining an area of 79 m by 67 m (260 ft by 220 ft).

The highest hill fort in Scotland, and the third highest in Britain, is located on the summit of Ben Griam Beg (NC 831412), 580 m (1903 ft) above sea level. Its position is a strategic one, commanding the approaches from the north and east coasts. The principal remains consist of a stone wall about 1.8 m (6 ft) thick encircling an area of c. 152 m by 60 m (500 ft by 200 ft).

Duchary Rock fort (NC 850050) occupies a readily defended site on a steep-walled rocky outcrop by Strath Brora. From the fort are spectacular views overlooking Loch Brora and eastwards out to sea. The enclosing walls are up to 3.7 m (12 ft) thick and are pierced by two entrance passageways, the main one in the north-west and a secondary one in the east.

The R.C.A.M.S. Inventory mentions two additional sites which might fall within the hill fort category. These are: East Kinnauld, in the parish of Rogart, located 1.6 km (1 mile) east of the station and Dalnamain, sited on a hillock on the south side of the road up

Strath Carnaig in Dornoch parish. Portions of a single wall up to
2.1 m (7 ft) thick were found at East Kinnauld, while parts of two
walls enclosing an oval-shaped area were identified at Dalnamain.

PROMONTORY FORTS

An Tornaidh Bhuidhe (NC 866661), located on a plateau near
Portskerra, is one of several suspected promontory forts situated
along the north coast of Caithness and Sutherland. Its natural
defences are so impressive that access to the site can only be gained
by walking along a narrow ridge whose flanks are extremely precipi-
tous.

Seanachaisteal fort (NC 405694), near Durness, had its defences
formed by cutting a ditch across the neck of the promontory and
raising an earth rampart to the seaward side of it. Small huts could
then have been constructed within the safety of the defences.

The Inventory also reported the existence of a construction
similar to Seanachaisteal not far from the ferry on the west side of
the Kyle of Durness.

At An Dunain, Culkein (NC 041340) 13 km (8 miles) north-
west of Lochinver, the remains of a substantial fortification may
still be seen. A 12 m (40 ft) wall, in places 2.1 m (7 ft) thick, provides the defence for the promontory which is divided into two by a
chasm bridged by a natural arch of rock.

Dun Mhairtein (NC 853663) is sited to the north-east of Baligill
village where, on a steep-walled promontory, are the remains of a
fortification. Seaward of the rampart wall are the indefinite foundations of a structure.

DUNS

A reduction in fort size in the highland zone, " probably led,
mainly after 100 B.C., to the widespread adoption of duns and
brochs " (Mackie, 1975). The word dun (prounced " doon ") is used
by archaeologists to define the smaller forts or fortified dwelling
places. Duns, constructed of dry stone walls that sometimes contain
passages and galleries, may be up to 6 m (20 ft) thick and 3 m
(10 ft) high, and enclosed oval or circular areas with diameters as
great as 21 m (70 ft). Evidence of timber houses and hut circles
within the enclosed area has been recorded in the Highlands and
occupation finds suggest that this fort building tradition had evolved
by the 1st century B.C.

Examples of duns in Sutherland may be seen at the following sites:

Loch Ardvair (NC 168332), north of Inchnadamph, where the dun remains lie on a tidal rock. Good sections of wall still exist.

Clachnessie Dun (NC 055315), north-west of Lochinver, is sited on a prominent rock that rises steeply from the shore.

Durness Dun (NC 384653) is close by the roadside and now in a very ruinous condition.

Durness Dun (NC 383677) is located on a promontory overlooking Loch Borralie.

Borgie Dun (NC 671588), set on a small bluff by the road, has its circular wall defined.

This tradition of fort building in the Highlands and Islands saw its highest expression in the bold sophisticated architecture of the brochs.

According to Euan Mackie (e.g. 1971 and 1977) archeological evidence shows that peoples from the south of England had moved in to the Atlantic Highland zone of Scotland by the 1st century B.C. and he believes that these incomers could have, in the Hebrides, stimulated the architectural development from stone fortlet to tall tower or broch (Old Norse " borg ", a place of defence) which, if Mousa in Shetland is a typical example, may have been up to or over 12 m (40 ft) in height. For the following two or three centuries these fortified towers were the prominent architectural feature of Atlantic Scotland.

Although it may be argued that brochs belong to a European tradition of fort building, they are found only in Scotland, more particularly in the Highlands and Islands where, north of the Great Glen, all but a dozen of the 510 or so identified brochs are located. Of this total, well over 60 have been recorded in Sutherland, 48 with measurable features (R C A M S 1911). Brochs, although often called " Picts' hooses " appear to have been built by the ancestors of the Picts.

Brochs can be described as massive circular towers, built of roughly-hewn stones set together without mortar or cementing material of any kind. The broch wall was generally solid and extremely thick anything between 3.7 and 5.5 m (12 and 18 ft) at its base and it surrounded an interior courtyard with a diameter which could vary from as little as 6.4 m (21 ft) at Castle Cole (NC 795133) on the Black Water, to double that figure at the ruined broch of Achaneas on the River Cassely.

The only entrance to the broch courtyard was through a narrow ground-level passage about 1 m (3 ft) wide, up to 1.5 m (5 ft) in height, and roofed by flat stone lintels. The entrance passage usually had checks for a massive door or doors as well as a corbelled guard chamber on the right with, occasionally, another chamber on the opposite side. Within the wall thickness, adjoining the courtyard, small bee-hive shaped chambers were sometimes constructed.

Above its base, usually solid for the first 3 m (10 ft) or so, the broch wall divided into two concentric walls. The inner of these had a vertical face while the outer presented a gentle batter which gave the structure a distinctive and attractive profile. At intervals of 1.5 or 1.8 m (5 or 6 ft) the inner and outer walls were bonded together by flat slabs of stone, thereby creating a succession of galleries running around the entire circumference of the broch. (The transverse stones might have served a second purpose, that of scaffolding, while the tower was being erected.) Each gallery was interrupted by a stair set between the inner and outer walls. This staircase ascended clockwise from the left of the courtyard to emerge at the top of the broch, having wound round half of the tower's circumference. From the galleries a series of openings or " windows " overlooked the courtyard and permitted light to enter the void between the two walls. These " windows " would also have served to lessen the load on the foundations.

The inner walls of brochs are believed to have contained a ledge (scarcement) or ledges on which a timber floor or floors sup-ported on posts set into the courtyard, would have rested. Thus, the broch can be envisaged as a community fortified dwelling where people lived, perhaps in temporary refuge, on at least two floor levels.

There is no conclusive evidence to say that brochs had roofs but it does seem possible that they had a light wooden roof, with a hole in the centre to permit smoke to escape.

Central wells or water tanks are sometimes found in brochs and later in their history (perhaps in Pictish times), additional stone furnishings such as slab partition walls and stone fireplaces were added. This secondary occupation of brochs can be complemented at other sites by the post-broch construction of extra-mural huts. However, it is generally accepted that the ditches and ramparts which gave additional defences are contemporaneous with the brochs.

The architecture of brochs is so strikingly similar that they may well have been built by a specialist class of architects to the order of a community or even a central authority. Further evidence supporting this idea was obtained when measurements of over 30 broch courtyards revealed that most of them were precisely circular and that all of them, whatever their shape, were laid out in exact multiples of "broch yards", (0.83 m, 2.14 ft), a unit of measurement only marginally greater than the "megalithic yard" used to lay out stone circles and alignments nearly 2000 years earlier (Mackie 1977).

Brochs, which tend to be located on or adjacent to arable land, predominate in the eastern half of Sutherland, by its coast, by lochsides and along the straths and glens. Sometimes they occur in distinct groupings as in Kildonan Strath, lower Loch Shin and in northern Strath Naver.

The broch people, incorporating a variety of local cultures, appear to have been peaceful agriculturalists, growing cereal crops (quern stones are a common find) and rearing cattle, sheep and pigs. Occasionally they hunted deer and at coastal sites shell-fish formed an important part of the diet with seals and wildfowl an additional prey. Finds associated with textile working are typical at broch sites, e.g. spindle whorls, bobbins and weaving combs, from which it would seem that the broch dwellers made clothes woven on primitive hand looms. These archaeological finds, then, do not suggest a war-like community and the general attitude has been to regard brochs as the defensive structures of a people who felt the need to protect themselves from aggressors.

The principal features of some of the more outstanding Sutherland brochs may be summarised as follows:

ALLT AN DUIN SKELPICK (NC 723575), now ruinous, occupies a rocky summit overlooking Strath Naver. The remains of a scarcement are still visible.

ARMADALE BURN BROCH (NC 799627), in an area of inhospitable moor, has well-defined external wall faces and passage.

CARN LIATH OR DUNROBIN BROCH (NC 870013), has a partly lintelled 5.5m (18ft) long passage with door checks, bar hole and guard chamber. Remains of the mural stair can still be seen. Within the courtyard two stone-lined pits were discovered, one of which may be a well. The brochs outworks show interference from more recent structures.

CARROL BROCH (NC 846065), above Loch Brora, has two sets of door checks (a feature not common outside Caithness and Sutherland) and a corbelled guard chamber opening to the right. From an unusually long cell leads the stairway.

CASTLE COLE BROCH (NC 795133), 5.6km (9 miles) north-west of Brora, has a picturesque site guarded by abrupt slopes and a double row of stone fortifications. There are two door checks in the passage and a guard chamber. The 6.4m (21ft) diameter courtyard is the smallest of any of the Sutherland brochs. Two chambers and several recesses are set back from the inner wall. Archaeological finds from the broch include: querns, stone lamps, pins and bone buttons.

DUN DORNADILLA (NC 458450; Plate 21), 5.6km (9 miles) north-west of Altnaharra, is the most substantial broch in Sutherland with part of the graceful batter of its outer wall standing to a height of 6.7m (22ft). A huge triangular lintel (this shape may be an engineering device to help spread the load on the foundations) is in place over the passageway.

GRUMMORE BROCH (NC 610367), on the north shore of Loch Naver has good sections of walling with evidence of chambers and a scarcement.

KILPHEDIR BROCH (NC 995188), stands within an enclosure formed by an impressive 2.7m (9ft) deep ditch with a rampart on its inner side. Door checks and a mural gallery are still visible.

KINTRADWELL BROCH (NC 929082), displays two door checks, a guard chamber, mural staircase and scarcement. Excavations uncovered a well and the site yielded 50 querns, stone mortars and pounders, a stone cup, spindle whorls, an iron spearhead and a dagger blade (RCAMS 1911).

STOER BROCH (NC 036278), a handsome ruin, has interesting features including a triangular lintel, the remains of an intra-mural stair, evidence of chambers and a defensive rampart of huge stones.

Chapter ten

THE PICTS AND
THE EARLY CHURCH

THE PICTS

Nowadays, most archaeologists refer to the peoples living in Northern Scotland during the few centuries prior to 300AD as the proto-Picts. Their various tribal locations have been given by the Roman geographer Ptolemy who, using sources compiled in the 1st century AD., listed ten tribes in the Highland area, including the Lugi in South-East Sutherland, the Smertae to their north, beyond them the Cornovii and to their west the Caereni.

The earliest known reference to the Picts is given by a classical poet who, in 297AD, referred to the "Picti", a name that may simply mean "the painted people". Shortly after, a Roman writer spoke of "the Caledones and other Picts", which suggests that a single tribe the Caledones, was part of a larger confederacy called the Picts.

Although no written documents (if they ever had any) of the Picts survive, a medieval manuscript, listing their kings, known as the Pictish Chronicle, does exist. Unfortunately, it throws very little light on our knowledge of the Picts and is regarded by scholars as being unreliable for events before the mid 6th century AD. For illumination of the Pictish period we have to refer to the Roman writer Marcellinus, to Adomnan the biographer of St. Columba, to the Venerable Bede and to various Irish Annals.

Sufficient information can be gleaned from these sources to reveal that the Picts, controlling an area north of the Forth-Clyde line, Dalriada excepted, comprised one of the most powerful nations in Dark Age Britain. There is the suggestion by Bede that Pictland, at least in its earlier period, may have divided into a Northern and Southern kingdom, as he speaks of the Northern Picts being converted by St. Columba and the Southern Picts receiving Christianity through St. Ninian. Adomnan makes no mention of such a subdivision of Pictland but from his writing it would appear that the well-ordered court of King Brude had a sphere of influence extending at least as far as Orkney, as Brude was able to offer Columba's missionaries safe conduct to these islands.

The work of archaeologists and philologists indicates that the Picts were an agglomeration of several different peoples of varying origins, cultures and languages. They seem to have used at least two languages: a non-Indo-European one that is still not understood and another which can be termed Pictish Celtic and is akin to Old Welsh. This Pictish Celtic has left strong traces in certain place names; this is particularly true of the element PIT, which referred to a share or portion of land in forest clearings. More than 280 of these PIT place names have been plotted between the Firth of Forth and South-East Sutherland (Whittington 1974-75). Their distribution is mainly away from the coast, with a preference for well-sheltered and well-drained positions below the 183m (600ft) contour. The known Sutherland PIT names include Pittentrail, Pitfour, Pitgrudy, Pitmean and Pitarxie. A striking point about the PIT placenames is that the suffix is not normally in Pictish Celtic but in that branch of the Celtic language introduced by the Scotti from Ireland, namely Gaelic.

The principal survivals of Pictish culture are the symbol stones (Table 9), those elegant works of a society whose craftsmen working in stone and metal exhibited a draughtsmanship and artistic skill that matched the highest achievements of Western Europe. Around 200 of these inscribed stones have been discovered north of the Forth-Clyde line and as their inscriptions are repeated in almost identical stereotyped form throughout Pictland, it has been generally agreed that they must be symbolic. The most common inscriptions are the V rod with crescent (normally the only elaborately decorated symbol), the double disc with rod, the Pictish beast and the mirror and comb — regarded by some as a feminine symbol. In all, a total of 50 stylised forms can be recognised. The animal designs are characterised by their sure draughtsmanship, economy of line and impression of speed and strength of the typical creatures portrayed, e.g. bull, wolf, deer and salmon (see stone No. 6 at Dunrobin Museum). On most stones the abstract symbols and animals are placed close together, or even touching each other, in a great variety of combinations.

Pictish symbol stones have been grouped into three classes (Allen and Anderson 1903). Of these, Class I stones, perhaps dating from as early as the 6th or 7th centuries AD, comprise single roughly-

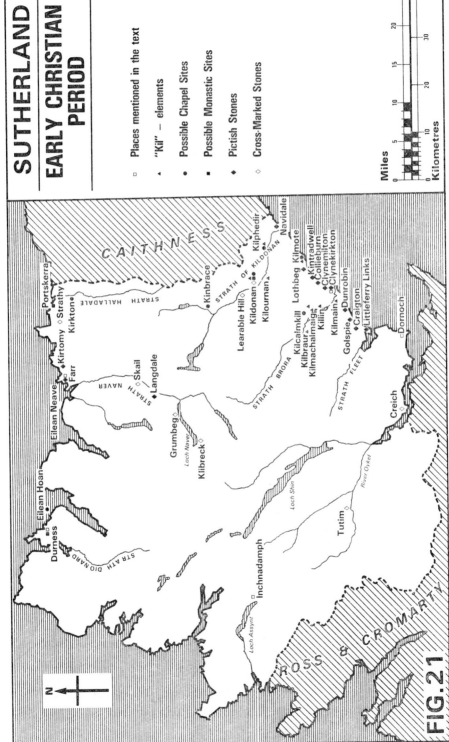

SUTHERLAND
EARLY CHRISTIAN PERIOD

□ Places mentioned in the text

▲ "Kil" – elements

● Possible Chapel Sites

■ Possible Monastic Sites

◆ Pictish Stones

◇ Cross-Marked Stones

Miles

Kilometres

CAITHNESS

ROSS & CROMARTY

Portskerra
Strathy
Kirtomy
Kirkton
Farr
Eilean Neave
Eilean Hoan
Durness

STRATH HALLADALE
Kinbrace
STRATH OF KILDONAN
Kilphedir
Navidale
Kilmote
Lothbeg
Kilbraur
Kilcalmkill
Killin
Kilmachalmaig
Kilmain
Kintradwell
Collieburn
Clynemilton
Clynekirkton
Dunrobin
Craigton
Golspie
Littleferry Links
STRATH FLEET
Dornoch
Creich

Learable Hill
Kildonan
Kilournan
STRATH BRORA
Skail
Langdale
STRATH NAVER
Grumbeg
Loch Naver
Kilbreck

Tutim
Loch Shin
River Oxkel
Loch Assynt
Inchnadamph
STRATH DIONARD

N

FIG. 21

dressed boulders with the characteristic symbols incised upon them. A remarkable concentration of these Class I stones occurs in East Sutherland, fifteen having been found within an 11km (7 mile) radius of Golspie, including the delicately carved specimen known as the Golspie Stone now housed with an outstanding collection of other inscribed monuments (mostly discovered during work on the Sutherland railway) in Dunrobin Museum. The fine incisions on the Golspie Stone portray a crescent with V rod, a Pictish beast and the mirror and comb placed, as always on a Class I stone, at the base of the monument. The Golspie Stone, formed of thinly-bedded sandstone was found in a field behind the village where it formed the slab on a small burial cist. Another Class I stone depicting a double crescent, snake and Z rod, mirror and comb (Plate 23), was discovered in 1977 near the shore to the east of Dunrobin Castle. Excavations at the site revealed a pitched stone kerb edging a sand and cobbled mound which overlay a cist grave 2.2m (7.2ft) long containing a female skeleton (J. Close-Brooks, pers. comm.). The find (Plate 22) is of interest for two reasons: few burials under symbol stones have been authenticated and the fact that the burial was of a female may support the view of those who envisaged the mirror and comb symbol as female. Such is the profusion and quality of workmanship on these Class I stones from around Golspie that it has prompted Dr. I. Henderson (1967) to speculate that the fertile lowlands of the Moray and Dornoch Firths may have been the area of origin for the earliest school of Pictish sculptors. Throughout Pictland the distribution of Class I stones and PIT place names are broadly the same but not quite identical as the PIT elements lie in between symbol stone locations which, however, correspond quite well with the siting of hill forts.

The Class II stones, perhaps 8th or 9th century in date, consist of carefully dressed slabs on which the sculpture in the early phase is brought out in shallow relief; at a later period the relief becomes increasingly pronounced until the effect is virtually three dimensional. Class II monuments, which are much more closely associated with ecclesiastical sites than the Class I stones, get away from the simpler symbolism of the Class I type and incorporate scenes that include interlace work, with one side of the slab dominated by a cross infilled with iconographic detail. Only one Class II stone of uncertain provenance is known from Sutherland. This 1.8m (6ft) stone has a relief cross on one side and on the other a number of incised symbols along with the portrayal of a man holding a knife and uplifted axe as if to slay the adjacent creature. Along a moulding on the right hand side of the stone is an ogam inscription. Ogam, believed to have originated in Ireland around the 4th century AD., is a formalised method of writing in which short incised lines are cut along a stone edge or against an incised base line.

Class III stones may post-date the mergence of the Picts and Scots and are thought to be of 9th or 10th century date. On these monuments only the majestic Celtic crosses, as on the Farr Stone are found; the enigmatic symbols of the Picts have now vanished from the face of history.

We can only speculate on the precise purpose of these symbol stones. Do they depict clan badges or indicate rank? Do they commemorate burials, conflicts or battles? Do they define a person's or a group's territorial influence? Are they portrayals of marriage bonds? Perhaps we shall never know.

To the astonishing number of finds of symbol stones in East Sutherland can be added the hoard of eleven Pictish brooches (of which few now survive) found at Rogart. More recently a bronze pin decorated with a man's head and interlace pattern was discovered in a garden in Golspie. The working technique and decorative details it convincingly to Pictish work of the 8th and 9th centuries AD. (J. Close-Brooks, 1974-5).

From what source or sources can we seek the origins of Pictish art? From the earlier Iron Age? From Anglo-Saxon, Northumbrian, Irish or Viking influences? Although certain correlations have plausibility, a convincing path for the evolution of this brilliant art has not yet been established.

Despite the abundant evidence of Pictish work in stone and metal no dwellings of undoubted Pictish age have yet come to light in Sutherland, but archaeologists have uncovered elsewhere in the Highlands and Islands domestic buildings and fortifications belonging to this, our earliest historic period.

THE EARLY CHURCH

It is interesting to note that in Professor Thomas's survey *The Early Christian Archaeology of North Britain* (1971) no mention is made of Sutherland. This is an area for which no documentation exists for ecclesiastical sites and organisation in the early Christian period. In a recently published historical atlas of Scotland (McNeill

& Nicholson, 1975) it proved impossible to locate, with certainty, even one early ecclesiastical site in Sutherland; for no structural remains can be attributed, without reserve, to a period before the 13th century. Christianity is unlikely to have reached this area before the time of the Columban mission, which was established in Iona from 563, but no early sources speak specifically of work of evangelisation in these northern parts.

In the 12th century Sutherland was within the diocese of Caithness. In all probability the cathedral at that time was at Halkirk for it was here that the bishops had an episcopal manor (Anderson, 1873). Towards the middle of the 13th century the diocesan centre was established at Dornoch where there was already a group of monks, with some connection with Dunfermline, settled in the period c.1139-1151 when this place may well have been under the bishops of Orkney (Crawford, 1976-7, Watt, 1969). Before the 12th century revolution in church administration in Scotland (as elsewhere in the Celtic world), with the creation of dioceses and parishes and the introduction of the reformed monastic orders, monasteries played a central role in the organisation of ecclesiastical affairs throughout the Celtic west and north.

It has not been possible, to date, to point to any site that can, with certainty, be declared as monastic and neither has it been possible to isolate chapel sites of the period which would have served the scattered population and would have, in the main, been visited by an itinerant clergy. The coast of Sutherland appears to be ideally suited to the establishment of small isolated ascetic communities of monks in the Irish tradition. In a recent study of the 'papar' place-name element (it suggests Irish-style hermitages), however, the author (Macdonald, 1977) was unable to quote an example in Sutherland but a number do occur in Orkney, Shetland, Caithness and the Hebrides. A few sites, nevertheless, do suggest to the archaeologist that there may be evidence on the ground for the existence of small monastic communities (Table 5) but only excavation is likely to reveal the true state of affairs.

Only the place-name expert and the archaeologist can fill in the gaps in our knowledge of the early church in Sutherland and one line of research, in which both can participate, is the examination of places where the prefix kil — ('cill') is present. This is a Gaelic element which means cell or church and would have been used in our area at a time when Gaelic speakers moved into the north-east of Scotland in the 9th and 10th centuries (Nicolaisen,

1975). The Sutherland examples, so far noted, are presented in Table 6 and in the case of Kilcalmkill the name of St. Columba in in its correct form — Colum-cille — is preserved. It is not possible, however, to associate the place directly with him for dedications were frequently made to saints long dead. Table 8 indicates that four of the five chapel (possible) sites listed have a kil- prefix.

The archaeological approach to the identification of monastic and chapel sites involves a study of such aspects as the shape of an existing churchyard enclosure which, from its circular or oval form, may show it to be early (Thomas, 1971); the occurrence of a single stone or a group of stones with a Christian connotation; enclosures or locations with buildings which do not seem to conform to the normal run of defence or settlement sites of a particular region. At Durness (Table 7) a curious site on a promontory may be an ascetic monastery or hermitage and there are parallels for it in Shetland (Lamb, 1973). An area 33m 108ft) by 9m (30ft), difficult of access and for settlement, has upon it terracing with the suggestion of 'house' platforms $1m^2$ ($10ft^2$) and with one 3m by 6m (10ft by 20ft). Another promontory site at Portskerra could also be monastic. It does not appear to have possessed strong defensive features (the siting itself is a strong one) and inside there are two or three amorphous platforms. Cross-marked stones, if not definitely associated with a known chapel or monastery, may lead to the identification of an early ecclesiastical site. It must be borne in mind, however, that the present location of such a stone, or stones, may not be the original one.

Pictish stones cannot all be used to suggest the location of ecclesiastical sites for, as Isabel Henderson has pointed out (Henderson, 1971), only about a quarter of the Class I (Symbol Stones) examples are associated with such sites. Although they have no obvious Christian symbols one has to agree with her that they are indeed influenced by such illustrated works as the Book of Lindisfarne and were initially set up in the earlier part of the 7th century when our area would have received, undoubtedly, its first missionaries. A concentration of stones in the Golspie vicinity may indicate an early centre of Christianity and the grandeur of such a cross-slab as that at Farr may well attest a Christian place of some importance. The cross depicted on the Farr stone is of some interest in that the curving terminal of the base of the shaft is reminiscent of 8th century Irish examples (especially at Clonmacnoise — Macalister,

1909) and to cross treatment in the Book of Lindisfarne. Other features on the stone, however, point to a 9th or 10th century date for its execution.

Oral traditions and place-names, which suggest the sites of early places of worship, must not be ignored. The Farr stone has long had legends attached to it and not far away is Eilean Neave — an island whose English name (Holy Island) and position suggests an early ascetic monastery or hermitage (Temperley, 1977). Water, for this waterless island, was obtained from a well near Skerray Pier (Temperley) and which is dedicated, interestingly enough, to " Chaluim Cille ". Holy wells abound in great numbers in the Celtic world and many, undoubtedly, were pagan centres of worship which were sanctified by the early missionaries. Columba, on a journey up the Great Glen, conducted such a ceremony (Anderson and Anderson, 1961). The presence of such wells may, again, be a clue to the existence of an ecclesiastical site nearby. Tradition also associates a hermitage with the pillar stone, in Strath Naver, bearing an incised cross (see Table 10) and known as " A Maol Ruadh " (Temperley).

It has been indicated that little, in detail, can be said about the early Church in Sutherland and that a number of disciplines need to be brought to bear upon the problem. It is to be hoped that further research and fieldwork will fill out our meagre picture of Sutherland in early Christian times (Fig. 21). Most of the existing evidence is found, as one would expect, in the south-east and more work, evidently, needs to be done elsewhere so that an assessment of settlement patterns can be made. Even in the south-eastern part of Sutherland much research needs to be undertaken on chapel sites and the locations of memorial stones. An intriguing site, here, is the broch of Carn Liath (see page 167) where superficial examination (pers. comm. by the late Dr. J. X. W. P. Corcoran) of extra-mural areas suggests the presence of small gravestones and thus opens up another line of inquiry — the possibilities of continuity of use of prehistoric sites or their re-use for different purposes.

TABLE 5 – ECCLESIASTICAL SITES referred to in the *Inventory of the Ancient Monuments of Sutherland*, 1911	
Inv. No.	**Description**
1.	**Inchnadamph.** Burial vault. Said to have formed part of the ancient parish church.
22.	**Clynekirkton.** Belfry tower.
102.	**Dornoch Cathedral.**
153.	**Durness Church.**

TABLE 6 – KIL- ('CILL') PLACE NAME ELEMENT	
Place	**Ordnance Survey Grid Reference**
Kildonan	Church at – ND/909207
Kilournan	NC/929189
Kilphedir	NC/9818
Kilmote	NC/9711
Kilbraur	NC/823100
Kilcalmkill	NC/850090 (House on North side of Loch Brora)
Killin	NC/856071
Kilmain	NC/874040
Kilmachalmaig	NH/503983

TABLE 7 – POSSIBLE EARLY MONASTIC SITES	
Site	**Ordnance Survey Grid Reference**
Durness (Aodann Mhor)	NC/407693 (Short note in *Discovery and Excavation* 1971, 44)
Portskerra	NC/867661
Kildonan	NC/910210 (vague scarp in the graveyard surrounding the present church – *ex inf. Keith Blood, OS Arch. Div.)* The name Tigh-an-Ab occurs nearby.

TABLE 8 – SUPPOSED CHAPEL SITES
(ex inf. Keith Blood, OS Arch. Div.)

Site	Ordnance Survey Grid Reference
Allt na h'Eaglaise	NC/889621
Kilcalmkill	
Kildonan	
Kilmote	NC/973114
Kilphedir	NC/989185
Kinbrace	
Kirkton	NC/889621 – Just south of this is **Allt na h'Eaglaise**.
Neave Island	NC/663642 – Chapel site is shown on OS map.

TABLE 9 – PICTISH STONES
Page references are to *J Romilly Allen's*
The Early Christian Monuments of Scotland.

Romilly Allen p:	Site	Notes
38-39	**Clynekirkton**	NC/885059. 3 stones. No. 2 said to be from Clynemilton Farm (Inv. No. 293).
39-41	**Clynemilton Farm**	NC/913069. 2 stones. (Inv. No. 294).
41	**Craigton**	No. 1 from Culmallie Kirkton. No. 2 from either Culmallie Kirkton or St. Andrew s, Golspie *(ex inf. Dr J Close-Brooks).* (Inv. No. 295)
51-53	**Collieburn**	(Inv. No. 299)
42	**Dunrobin**	NC/851006. SW of Castle and not E as recorded. *(ex inf. Dr J Close-Brooks).* (Inv. No. 292)
53-54	**Farr**	Class III. (Inv. No. 258)
48-50	**Golspie**	NC/8300. Cist with symbol stone found in 1942, *Proc. Soc. Antiq. Scot. 1942-3, 26* (Inv. No. 296)
43-45	**Kintradwell**	NC/919078. 4 stones. (Inv. No. 297)
45	**? Kirtomy**	
	? Little Ferry Links	4 fragments. (Inv. No. 298)
	Lothbeg	NC/9409. (Inv. No. 300)

TABLE 10 – CROSS MARKED STONES	
Inv. No.	
93	**Tutim**, Strath Oykell NC/436015
94	**Creich**, churchyard NH/634891
95	**Creich**, SE of church (also discussed in *Romilly Allen, see Table 5, pps. 54-55)* NH/634891
248	**Klibreck**, Loch Naver NC/595340
250	**Grumbeg** NC/633385
251	**Grumbeg.** These, and another new discovery, are now in Farr Museum. NC/633385
256	**"Red Priest's Grave"**, Skail. NC/714472
260	**Strathy** NC/831649
377	**Kildonan** NC/913208
380	**Learable Hill** NC/892235

Chapter eleven

VIKING SUTHERLAND

Although the name Sutherland clearly means the southern territory of the Norse earldom in Northern Scotland and there are strong local traditions of Viking and "Danish" raids and settlements, there is very little hard evidence for the Viking period in the District's history. Documentary references are few, either in Scottish or Scandinavian sources and the *Orkneyinga Saga* (Taylor, 1938) only mentions Sutherland on a mere handful of occasions.

The Northern Isles of Scotland were subjected first to raiding and then to intensive settlement by Vikings, mainly from Norway, from about AD. 800 onwards. Orkney, where a stable earldom was ultimately established, became the focus of their political power and from that base settlement and other activities spread across to Caithness and southwards along the east coast of Scotland. Although raiding took place all along the east coast there is no evidence that permanent agricultural settlement extended to the southern shores of the Moray Firth. The attraction of Ireland and the search for new land to settle took the Vikings along the north coast of Scotland and on to the Western Isles, where Lewis in particular was intensively settled. Viking activities in Sutherland must therefore be seen as an expansion from their main centre in Orkney and viewed in the light of the political situation of the time.

In the early part of the 9th century Sutherland was an integral part of Pictland as is confirmed by the several symbol stones recorded from the District (Table 9). After the union of the Picts and the Scots, political control appears to have oscillated between the Norse and the Scots on several occasions, and this marginal situation may account for the remarkable contrast between the very high density of Norse settlement names in Caithness and their relative scarcity in Sutherland. Settlement names are those which include elements meaning farm, homestead or similar terms as opposed to being merely descriptive of landscape features. Thorsteinn Olafsson claimed Sutherland as part of his kingdom in the early 9th century but there seems to have been a continual struggle, occasionally breaking out into active conflict between the Norse and Scottish chiefs from the 9th century onwards. It is important to recall also that the boundaries of Sutherland, as described in the documentary sources appear to have varied from time to time. For example the *Orkneyinga Saga* describes Ousdale (Eysteinnsdalr) as being the border between Sutherland and Caithness whereas today this valley is well within the parish of Latheron. Political control, however, must not be equated with extensive Norse settlement. After the battles for power large numbers of native Picts and Scots would simply have returned to their homes and continued their simple farming activities. The only change for these people would be their acknowledgement of a new overlord with whom they probably had little contact. Thus in large parts of Sutherland there is no reason to expect extensive evidence of Viking farmsteads, other archaeological remains or even Norse farm names. These should be expected only at places where actual Viking farming settlers established themselves whereas the names of landscape features are likely to reflect the political power to a greater extent. This accounts for many of the valley names of Sutherland ending in dale (O.N. dalr - a valley) — Langdale, Armadale, and Rimsdale.

Settlement names indicate that the process of Norse agricultural colonisation was very much as one would expect. The better, flatter open lands along the northern shores of the Dornoch Firth, which at least for part of the period was the frontier line of Norse territory, and Strath Fleet attracted early settlement as is witnessed by names like Embo, Skibo and Skelbo. Areas of similar landscape with easy access to the sea such as the Brora region are also likely to have attracted settlement. The gradual process of expansion from the plains of Caithness into the neighbouring valleys of Sutherland is witnessed by the line of Norse settlements along Strath Kildonan and Strath Halladale, e.g. Eilderabol (Eldrable), Gilaboll, Dviaboll, Leirabol, Borrobol. It is surely indicative that Old Norse was the spoken language of both these valleys for a time when the names Strath Halladale and Strath Helmsdale include both the Gaelic and Norse words for a valley! An interesting group of settlements appear to have been established around Lairg (Torroboll, Colaboll) which may represent settlers moving up from the Kyles of Sutherland or penetrating through Rogart. The names, however, are late and Viking raiding took place in this area much earlier as is indicated by the fact that the Rogart hoard of Pictish brooches must have been buried in the face of a Scandinavian raid (Wilson, 1973).

Westwards from Strath Halladale, along the north coast, place names suggest that the extent of Norse settlements was extremely limited although the larger estuaries appear to have attracted one or two farmsteads, for example, Kirkiboll near Tongue, Eriboll, and Arnabol on the shore of Loch Hope. On the west coast evidence is even more slight with Unapool, one of the few settlement names in this area. It would seem that most settlers favoured the islands for establishing their new homes rather than the mainland of North-West Sutherland. It might be tentatively suggested that the very limited areas which the north-west mainland offers for agriculture were already settled by active Gaelic farmers capable of defending their land against newcomers and that the opportunities for new settlement were easier on the islands. This would have been even more true after several of the early groups had carved out new farms for themselves.

Finally, on place names, it must be stressed that modern maps record very few of the names of the pre-clearance clachans in Sutherland but an initial study of a selection of 18th century maps does not suggest any great variation from the pattern outlined above and the remarkable contrast to Caithness, despite the obvious environmental differences, is outstanding.

The Archaeological Evidence

Whereas in the north-east of Scotland, any man-made mound of unknown antiquity tends in popular parlance to be called Pictish, in Sutherland it is called Viking or Norse or Danish. In reality there is no evidence whatsoever to assign many of the grass covered knolls often called Viking graves in Sutherland to the Norse period. In fact the archaeological evidence of Norse settlement is even more sparse than the place name evidence, and despite extensive field work by the Archaeological Division of the Ordnance Survey in recent years no domestic settlement which can be assigned to the Viking Age has so far been located. Finds are limited to a few graves and a handful of unstratified objects.

A grave near Dunrobin Castle produced two typical oval 10th century Norse brooches indicating a woman's grave (Greig, 1940). Both brooches are in poor condition. A further grave near the castle produced what may be the socket of an iron spear-head while the discovery of a corroded iron axe and iron ring on the shore nearby may represent a third grave. Near the standing stone to the east of Ospisdale House an oval brooch along with an " urn " was discovered in the mid 19th century indicating another grave. The only other grave find is recorded in Durness parish. Unstratified finds which cannot definitely be related to graves or any other structure are a pair of iron forge tongs and an iron knife both from the Dunrobin area and an iron ploughshare, possibly of Norse origin from Swordale near Bonar Bridge. All these finds were made in the 19th century, and while their distribution reflects the settlement pattern suggested by the place names, there can be no doubt that their survival and documentation is largely due to the presence of Dunrobin Castle and its powerful and acquisitive owners. With the lack of communications to the more remote parts of the country until relatively recently, many finds have probably gone unrecorded and unpreserved.

Viking Traditions

Tales of violence and acts of heroism have attracted the story-teller as much in the past as they do at present. Many of these tales are recorded in Sutherland; some, such as the burning of Frakork, probably being factually accurate. The exact location of this incident somewhere in the upper part of the Helmsdale valley is disputed but the *Orkneyinga Saga* describes the arrival of Sweyn son of Asleif, with his troops by a route over the mountains surprising Oliver and Frakork in their houses. Oliver escaped over the river but his men were either slain or driven into the houses which were then burnt along with all the inmates including the old hag Frakork.

Many traditions, however, can be shown to be totally inaccurate. The Vikings, for example, are accused of burning the forests over much of Sutherland accounting for the lack of timber in many parts of the country today. The evidence for this is said to be the many blackened logs discovered in peat bogs. Such logs are found in many North European bogs in areas never visited by Vikings and modern dating techniques show that they belong to phases of climatic deterioration during the prehistoric period. It would seem therefore that a tradition of the Vikings burning forests in some small part of Sutherland has been enlarged to cover the whole country. Other prehistoric features sometimes attributed to the Vikings include the introduction of peat as a fuel although peat had been used since Stone Age times, and the use of rotary querns for grinding grain which had been known from the Iron Age. It is even suggested that the bagpipes were introduced by Danes As Worsaae (1852), in his tour discovered . . . if anything, whether good or bad, be of doubtful origin, it is frequently attributed to " the Danes ".

CONCLUSION

In the light of the current state of knowledge it would seem that the impact of the Vikings on mainland Sutherland and also the extent of their actual settlements is much less than local oral tradition would suggest. The somewhat circumstantial evidence of the political situation coupled with the more precise archaeological and philological material support this view. However, it is too early to write a definitive account of Viking Sutherland. Documentary sources, with particular reference to Sutherland, have never been fully abstracted and assessed; the remoteness of much of the District, the rapidly escalating costs of excavation, as well as the need to conserve sites means that it will be decades before the many mounds and knolls which tradition associates with long forgotten battles and the burial places of earls and chieftains can be scientifically con-firmed or discarded; and the pre- 19th century maps of the country, almost all in single manuscript copies along with early documents have still to be combed for " lost " place names and early forms of those still known today. Only when these fields of research have been exhausted, will it be known with any certainty whether the pattern of settlement outlined in this chapter is a true picture of the Viking Period.

Chapter twelve

THE MIDDLE CENTURIES

A place without people is a dead thing; it has no history. The turbulent history of Sutherland consists of two closely related themes, that on the one hand of a Gaelic province under assault, on the other the savage, interminable struggle for land. Together they generated a complex saga of blood, strife and political intrigue.

The first Earl of Sutherland on record is William, son of Hugh, son of Freskin, a member of the de Moravia family which held lands in West Lothian and Moray during the reign of David I. It is generally held that the earldom was carved out of Caithness, being " created " about 1235 by Alexander II. If so it was the first such creation, as opposed to royal recognition of an existing native title, in Scottish history, and the only one in the whole of the 13th century. Wherever possible Scottish kings favoured peaceful methods of insinuating their influence, such as intermarriage between incomers and natives, as, for example, in Caithness and Orkney, and later, Strath Naver, whose heiress, Joanna, married another member of the de Moravia family. Both the *Orkneyinga Saga* and the 12th century Scottish tract, the *De Situ Albanie*, testify that Caithness comprised two districts divided by the Ord of Caithness. John of Fordun states that in 1196 William the Lion crossed Strath Oykel and subdued " both the provinces of the Caithnessmen ". The saga discusses the exploits of the clan Moddan who occupied Kildonan. One of the Freskins possibly married into this family of native mormaers, so acquiring their title. The fact that the Gaelic name for Sutherland is *Cataibh*, an area containing such names as Braechat, suggests that Sutherland was regarded, in a sense, as the bulk of the old earldom of Caithness, under another name. Furthermore, the earl's Gaelic title, *Morair Chat*, reminiscent as it is of mormaer, has an antique look about it.

The emergence of the earldom coincided with the reorganisation of the diocese of Caithness under another of Earl William's relatives,

Gilbert de Moravia. The church's experience in the north had not, hitherto, been a happy one. Disputes with their flocks led to the mutilation of Bishop John and the murder of Bishop Adam, roasted, it was said, in his own kitchen. Gilbert transferred the see from Halkirk to the ancient ecclesiastical site at Dornoch where he established a new cathedral (Plate 25), modelled on the constitution of Lincoln. The parish churches of the diocese were assigned to maintain the bishop and nine canons. Thus such Sutherland parishes as Dornoch, Clyne, Creich, Kildonan, Rogart, Lairg, Golspie and Loth were recorded for the first time. Those of Farr, Durness and Reay were not part of the earldom at that date. A major achievement for the diocese and the de Moravia family alike was the canonisation of Dornoch's founder. As hard-headed and pragmatic a saint as he must have been a bishop, St Gilbert's attributed miracles include the restoration of incinerated account books and the rescue of a local salmon fisher from bankruptcy.

It has been truly observed that the house of Sutherland reached its greatest height in the time of David II. After initial hesitation it committed itself to the cause of independence to be impressively rewarded by the son of Robert Bruce. Following his marriage to Princess Margaret, the king's sister, William fifth earl was granted almost kingly powers when his earldom was erected into a free regality in 1345. He also received extensive lands elsewhere in Scotland. When David was captured at the battle of Neville's Cross William became one of the negotiators for his release, then a hostage in England for payment of the king's ransom, and latterly an ambassador between the Scottish and English courts. What impression this Gaelic magnate made at the court of Edward III is not recorded but safe conducts survive allowing the earl himself, as well as his *garcionis* (grooms), his *vallettus* and his *scutifer* (esquire) to travel back and forth between London and the far north. Unhappily for the earl (but in terms of his marriage contract), when his wife died without heirs he lost his powers of regality as well as many of his other lands.

The earls and such cadet families as the Sutherlands and the Murrays, did not, of course, monopolise landholding in the north. The mid 13th century Bodleian map notes of the wilds of Assynt and Strath Naver, " *hic habundabant lupi* " — " here wolves abound ", and " wolfish " was one of the less charitable adjectives which *Morair Chat* might have applied to the human inhabitants of these areas. David II had granted " the four davach lands of Assynt

with the fortalice in the isle thereof " to Torquil MacLeod of Lewis
for the service of one ship of twenty oars. When Alexander Stewart
Earl of Buchan, more familiarly known as the Wolf of Badenoch,
was made lieutenant of the country between the Moray and Pentland
Firths, he granted Melness and Hope to Farquhar Beaton, the king's
physician who later received the Little Islands of Strath Naver
from the king himself. Between these two areas, at " the outmaist
boundis of Scotland " lived the Mackays. Just how or when they
arrived in the north is a secret locked in Celtic mists but one of
the more attractive hypotheses is that the Mackays (*Mac Aoidh*)
had some connection with the MacHeths of Moray who supplied
several rival claimants to the Scottish kingship in the 12th century.
After one MacHeth rising Malcolm IV is said to have " removed
them all from the land of their birth, as of old Nebuchadnezzar,
king of Babylon, had dealt with the Jews, and scattered them
throughout the other districts of Scotland, beyond the hills ". It may
be therefore, that the Mackays arrived in the north about the same
time as the Freskins.

The Wolf of Badenoch whose commission as lieutenant obviously
threatened Sutherland power, deserted his wife in favour of one
" Mariota filia Athyn ", Athyn possibly representing a valiant attempt
to render the problematical Aoidh. About 1395 Robert, sixth earl,
attempted to break the Wolf/Mackay alliance by arranging a reconciliation between Mackay and himself at Dingwall Castle in the
presence of the Lord of the Isles. The dirk was preferred to
diplomacy for Robert murdered both Mackay and his son. Surviving
Mackays feuded with the MacLeods of Lewis who ravaged Strath
Naver and Braechat, interference in the latter area bringing the
earl down on their heads, and the near annihilation of their force
at the battle of Tuiteam Tarbhach in Strath Oykel. Following his
defeat at Harlaw in 1411, Donald of Islay, Lord of the Isles, much
in need of allies, married his sister to Angus Mackay of Strath
Naver. Five years later Donald granted to Angus and his son,
Neil, the lands of Strath Halladale and Creich.

The star of the house of Sutherland fades somewhat in the
course of the 15th century. The seventh earl is said to have won
his spurs in France but otherwise he and his successors maintained
a strangely low profile. At the century's end Earl John was,
tragically, the subject of a brieve of idiotry, driven mad, perhaps, by
the endless clan feuds which exhausted the participants as they
weary the reader. Angus Dubh Mackay amused himself by attack-

ing Sutherland allies, notably the Murrays of Culbin. Arrested with his son and the Lord of the Isles at Inverness when James I decided to tame the Highlands, he was soon released though Neil was imprisoned on the Bass Rock. Angus's cousin and ally, Thomas Neilson Mackay, feuded with the Mowats of Freswick, but he was betrayed by his own brothers who divided his estates in Creich, between them. The Murrays, with Sutherland aid, attempted to exploit Angus's consequent vulnerability but they reckoned without one of the great heroes of Mackay historians. By his second wife, a daughter of Alasdair Carrach MacDonald of Keppoch, Angus had a son, Iain, known as *Abrach* through being fostered in Lochaber. When, in 1433, the Murrays invaded Strath Naver, young Iain commanded the clan at the battle of Drum nan Coup on the slopes of Ben Loyal. At this " Bannockburn of the Mackay's " old Angus was killed. His successor, Neil of the Bass, with Iain Abrach's help, pursued Mackay feuds in Caithness. His son, in turn, allied with the Keith family against Clan Gunn, only to be burned to death in Tarbat church by the Rosses of Balnagowan. Revenge was sought and obtained when John Reoch Mackay and William Dubh mac Ean Abrach smashed the Rosses at Aldicharrish in 1487.

It is no exaggeration to state that James IV changed the course of Highland history through his forfeiture of the Lord of the Isles in 1493; the *Gaidhealtachd* would never be quite the same again. That same year John Reoch Mackay obtained royal remission for his part in the battle of Aldicharrish. In 1504 he received a gift of the non-entry lands of Strath Naver, Strath Halladale, Creich, Assynt, Rogart, Eddrachilles, the Little Isles of Strath Naver, a part of Strath Fleet and other estates. Two years later the 1415 charter of Donald of Islay was registered in the books of the lords of council. Mackay was thus well rewarded for his assistance in subjugating the lordship of the Isles. The same authority which conferred respectability upon the Mackays, however, was also indirectly responsible for one of the most notable pieces of skullduggery in the annals of the north, namely, the Gordon usurpation of the earldom of Sutherland. King James made George Gordon, Earl of Huntly, sheriff of Inverness and lieutenant of the north.

Much of the complexity and obscurity surrounding the history of Sutherland is to be attributed to its greatest historian, Sir Robert Gordon of Gordonstoun (Plate 26) whose *Genealogical History,* completed in 1630, strives to depict the acceptable face of the earldom. Sir Robert (1580 - 1656) was learned, far-travelled and deeply involved in the political affairs of his day but the advice which he gave his nephew, John thirteenth earl, whose tutor he was, warped his own historical judgment. " Let a Gordones querrell be your own . . . preferre your surname to your nearest allyance ". Throughout his work the Gordons are glorified at the expense of their neighbours and rivals. He possessed the Gordon antipathy towards 'Gaelic barbarism' and he urged his nephew to suppress both the language and the Highland garb. 'Cause the inhabitants of the countrey to cloith them selfs as the most ciwill prowinces of the kingdome do . . . The Ireishe langage cannot so soone be extinguished. To help this plant schooles in ewerie corner in the countrey to instruct the youth to speak Inglishe'. To him history was a quarry of materials which would justify Gordon activities in the present or the future.

John, ninth earl of Sutherland, inherited his father's mental trouble. At his succession his brother Alexander was somehow prevailed upon to surrender his claim to the earldom. Their sister, Elizabeth, had married Adam Gordon, son of the Earl of Huntly. Adam, aware of his brother-in-law's malady initiated an enquiry at Perth which resulted in the execution of a brieve of idiotry against John who, apparently of his own volition, being 'weak of natural intellect and . . . afraid lest his estate be alienated or squandered', named Adam as one of his curators. A month later the earl mysteriously died. In 1514 his sister was served heir and very soon Adam Gordon was styling himself Earl of Sutherland, in right of his wife. The succession was challenged by Alexander Sutherland who held Dunrobin and who was obviously regarded by many as the legitimist claimant. For some five or six years he resisted Gordon claims. In 1520 the last of the house of Freskin was killed on the coast near Kintradwell. 'His head wes careid to Dounrobin on a spear and placed upon the height of the great tour', wrote Gordonstoun. 'So ended the bastard Alexander Sutherland, with all his hye pretensions and clame to this earldome, whose presumptious and overweaning maid him have a tragicall end'. He was not quite the last for the Gordons took care to despatch his son John some thirty years later. Of Alexander's bastardy there was, and is, no proof; it may be that the presumption was all on the part of the Gordons whose presence in the north from now on dictated the pattern of local politics. Indeed the experience of Sutherland in the 16th century constitutes a veritable microcosm of contemporary Scottish history.

By the 1520s rumbles of reform had already been heard throughout Scotland. Following the agony of Flodden two distinct parties gradually emerged. The pro-French Huntlys belonged to that which favoured the extension of the Auld Alliance. The other broadly supported some kind of accommodation with the Auld Enemy. Gordon support for the French party virtually dictated Mackay adherence to the pro-English faction which, in time, became identified with religious reformation as well. Iye Dubh Mackay and Bishop Robert Stewart of Caithness both became 'assured Scots' who sought to promote marriage between the infant Mary, Queen of Scots and the future Edward VI of England. Another was the remarkable John Elder, 'borne in Caitnes', who wrote to Henry VIII advocating Anglo-Scottish union. John Gordon, tenth earl of Sutherland, on the other hand, was very thick with his kinsman, Huntly, and both were staunch supporters of Cardinal Beaton.

Although there were occasional efforts to settle northern differences peacefully as in 1549 when temporary agreement was reached between 'the big four' — the earls of Sutherland and Caithness, the bishop of Caithness and Mackay — the feuds were not quenched. Indeed, the reverberations of religious and political conflicts which affected the whole of Europe were echoed in local feuds which simply assumed a new dimension. During Sutherland's absence in France Mackay unsuccessfully attempted to exploit popular discontent caused by the heavy-handed administration of the earl's brother, Alexander. More ominously Bishop Robert Reid of Orkney effectively bastardised Aoidh Mackay by finding fault with his grandparents' marriage. When Aoidh refused to answer a summons to appear before Mary of Guise at Inverness, Sutherland was granted a commission for both his arrest and the reduction of his estates. Aoidh was captured after the seige of Borve and sent to Edinburgh.

Earl John was appointed hereditary bailie of the diocese of Caithness in 1553. During the next few years he acquired a great deal of church land so that by 1560 he was paying over £330 Scots in feu duties for those lands, roughly half the annual rental of his entire earldom. He was also made hereditary constable of the episcopal castle of Scrabster and of the palace at Dornoch which were said to be situated 'in Irish country among fierce and untamed Scots'. These substantial holdings of church lands made him uncertain as to which side to support. Protestantism would no more safeguard possession than would conformity guarantee confiscation.

A brief flirtation with the Reformers ended when Mary Queen of Scots returned to Scotland but hopes of advancement were dashed when he was forfeited and exiled for his part in Huntly's rebellion while Mackay received a royal pardon for his earlier activities.

The Mackay ascendant and the declining fortunes of the Sutherlands were both checked through Mary's tortuous domestic intrigues. When she became estranged from Darnley she bought the Earl of Huntly's support with a grant (among others) of the superiority of Strath Naver. Sutherland was restored with a new grant of all his lands *'in unum integrum et liberum comitatum'*, of which free earldom Dunrobin Castle (Plate 24) was designated the principal residence. Following Darnley's murder Bothwell divorced his countess, Lady Jane Gordon, Huntly's sister. Sutherland attended the royal wedding. Bothwell and Mary parted forever on the field of Carberry on 15 June 1567. A week later Sutherland and his wife were poisoned at Helmsdale by the earl's aunt. His son Alexander narrowly escaped the same fate. He survived to take as his second wife Bothwell's discarded spouse, Lady Jane Gordon, the mother of Sir Robert Gordon of Gordonstoun.

The Mackays invaded the earldom wasting Skibo, firing Dornoch and rampaging in Strath Fleet to resist the ever-tightening Gordon stranglehold. Huntly sued for peace and Mackay was infefted in Strath Naver on payment of 300 merks.* He would shortly have to acknowledge not only a Gordon, but a Sutherland superior. Meanwhile Alexander, eleventh earl, had his own problems. George Sinclair obtained powers of justiciary from Portnaculter to the Pentland Firth as well as the wardship of the fifteen year old Alexander whom he married to his own daughter Barbara, aged thirty-two and rumoured to be Mackay's mistress. Caithness occupied Dunrobin. The people north of Strath Oykel now entered the most dismal period in their history as the cynical struggle for land and power increasingly resembled a local civil war.

Alexander was extricated from Caithness's clutches and promptly sued for a reduction of the latter's powers of justiciary so successfully as to be appointed royal lieutenant and justice-depute within the bounds of Sutherland and Strath Naver. Widespread suspicion of his Roman Catholic sympathies did not prevent his territorial aggrandizement. He gained more lands from the Bishop of Caithness and annexed the estates of the Rosses of Balnagowan. From Huntly he received the superiority of Strath Naver and the

---

* Merk, an old coin worth 13/4d (c.67p).

sheriffship of Sutherland. The Caithness feud was rekindled with renewed intensity. To add to the chaos the Murrays were engaged in separate feuds with the Mackays and with the MacPhails. Perhaps the most tragic, and ultimately the most damaging, of all the internecine strife which disfigures the history of the far north was the disputed chiefship among the Mackays which split the Abrachs from the main clan. Black Hugh of the Battle-axe allied with Caithness and the Robson Gunns against the Abrach Mackays, the MacLeods of Assynt and the Earl of Sutherland. Private deals and overtures caused further rifts between these allies resulting in naked treachery and blood in the heather.

When Earl John succeeded in 1594 he and Caithness each had to find caution of 20,000 merks to guarantee peace in the north. The long struggle for supremacy ended (if the feuds did not) when John received a fresh grant of his earldom and other possessions from James VI in 1601. The old grant of David II was revived and the earldom was recognised as a regality. The earl was appointed hereditary Sheriff of Sutherland. His estates were entailed to ensure that, failing heirs, they would pass to a son of the earl of Huntly; no other family would be permitted to exploit the device by which the Gordons had obtained the earldom a century before. For the first time Sutherland was defined by the boundaries which have survived to the present day; it now included Strath Naver.

Earl John devoted much time to domestic affairs. He achieved reconciliation with the Rosses. If the north remained an undeniably wild place the blunt finger of the law was increasingly evident in its affairs. In 1567 Huntly had enquired in Parliament 'be quhat means all Scotland be brocht to universal obedience, and how may McKy be dantonit?' More and more often the privy council was taking notice of what was happening in Sutherland. For example, in 1608, three brothers named Pape, two of whom were ministers at Dornoch and Rogart — the third was sheriff-clerk of Sutherland — were attacked at Dornoch by two MacPhails and a Murray. In this 'Pape Riot' the sheriff-clerk was killed. The Earl of Sutherland was charged by the council to bring the murderers to trial though, in the event, they fled to Lewis. The privy council also took a keen interest in the activities of Arthur Smith the counterfeiter who received shelter from the Earl of Caithness and saturated the north in false coinage. His prosperous career ended when he was slaughtered by Sutherland's agents at Thurso. By such unpeaceful means order was gradually brought to the north.

19. Braegrudie Stone 'Circle', near Rogart   *(D. Omand)*
20. Hut Circles, Invernaver   *(B. Kenworthy)*

21. Dun Dornadilla Broch, Strath More   *(D. Omand)*
22. (left) Long cist Pictish burial, Dunrobin *(J. Close-Brooks)*
23. (right) Pictish Symbol Stone, Dunrobin, discovered in 1977
               (A. Smith)

24. Dunrobin Castle   *(B. Kenworthy)*
25. (left) Dornoch Cathedral   *(J. Campbell)*
26. (right) Sir Robert Gordon (artist unknown)

27. The Kildonan Gold Rush *(The Northern Times)*
28. Strathy *(J. Campbell)*

Few of the Sutherland earls started out with greater advantages than John Glas. His father's efforts secured his patrimony and during his minority the earldom was in the secure hands of Gordonstoun who advised him on a comprehensive range of subjects including marriage, education, religion and justice (which should be 'blind and friendlesse') as well as the management of his house hold and estates. 'Let your kinered and allyes bee welcome always to your table; ewer further them in all ther honest actions by word, liberalitie or industrie; for by that meanes you shall double the bond of nature. Bee a neighbour to their good as weill as to ther blood'. If the earl purchased lands in Strath Naver he should use the natives kindly and so alienate them from Mackay. It was important to treat the Mackays as vassals rather than companions — 'because they are usually proud and arrogant, let them know you are their superior'. Gordonstoun urged friendship with the MacLeods of Assynt and all Highlanders ' for it is comunly sein that wher ther is neerest vicinitie ther is farthest distance of harts, neir neighbours are seldom frie from jarres and quarralls' — as the history of Sutherland so unhappily, but neatly, demonstrated. The earl should maintain spies in Caithness and Strath Naver and he should take special care with the Earl of Caithness for 'a little matter will kindle a hid spark of malice bred and rooted in both your hearts'.

Gordonstoun also foreshadowed the calamities which were to engulf 17th century Scotland. 'Few noble men in Scotland', he observed, 'can frie themselffs from robbing of the church in some degrie'. The large Sutherland holdings of church lands were threatened by Charles I's Act of Revocation in 1625 which insisted that such lands be surrendered to the crown. Gordonstoun warned as well that Charles would seek to curb the power of the Scottish nobility. 'He may when he listeth dantone the proudest and mightiest of you all'. Because of the antiquity of his title Sutherland claimed precedence among the Scottish nobility. Such considerations explain why Sutherland was the first to subscribe the National Covenant in Greyfriars church, Edinburgh, in 1638 at the outbreak of the Scottish Revolution. Thereafter he played a prominent part in the covenanting leadership though local preoccupations excluded him, perhaps fortuitously, from most of the military activity in the south. He figured inconspicuously in the battle of Auldearn when Montrose and Alasdair mac Colla brilliantly defeated the army of the covenant.

Relations between the Mackays and the Gordons improved

somewhat in the early 17th century since Donald Mackay was the grandson of Alexander, Earl of Sutherland. Donald's advancement was in part due to the efforts of his uncle, Gordonstoun; he was knighted by James and created Lord Reay by Charles I in 1628. Donald created a scandal when, in 1616, he eloped with his pregnant mistress although already married to the daughter of Mackenzie of Kintail. His infatuation was short-lived and he returned to his wife but the debts incurred through this adulterous adventure forced him to sell 'the lands of Edderachillis by-west Laxford'. As Ian Grimble sensibly points out, 'Sir Donald, the first chief to obtain a title other than that of Mackay, the first to write letters in English and to possess Gordon blood, was also the first on record as having treated *Duthaich 'Ic Aoidh* as a disposable asset, to be sold in lots in order to pay personal debts incurred far beyond its borders'. He also earned the displeasure of his Gordon kinsmen when he refused to support an attack on Caithness and it is probable that Gordonstoun, eager to be rid of one who was more of a liability than an asset, actively encouraged Donald in the exploit for which he is most famous, namely the raising of Mackay's Regiment for service in the Thirty Years War. His active recruitment gave rise to the Gaelic saying, 'Everyone that is down in his luck shall get a dollar from Mackay'. Many a Strath Naver man also received an unknown grave in a far off land.

Donald's military expeditions did little to relieve his financial embarrassment which was exacerbated by further amorous adventures. In 1633 parliament ratified Charles's grant to Earl John of the 'free and separate sheriffdom of Sutherland' which included Strath Naver, Eddrachilles, Durness, Strath Halladale and Assynt. Donald's impoverishment forced him in 1642 to sell part of Strath Naver to Sutherland. His impecuniousness and instincts alike led him to support Charles against the covenanting Sutherland. As usual, the small stage of Sutherland displayed a local version of the drama currently rocking the entire nation. The Mackenzies, under their chief, the Earl of Seaforth, had designs upon Assynt. In 1646 they attacked the Macleods in alliance with the Mackays who, from time to time, continued to loot Sutherland corn and cattle in the time-honoured fashion. Donald died in Denmark in 1649, having encouraged Montrose to launch his last expedition from the north. Montrose was surprised and defeated at Carbisdale in Strath Oykel by a force of Monros and Rosses under Colonel Strachan. Ignorant of the alliance between Sutherland and Neil MacLeod of Assynt,

Montrose stumbled up Strath Oykel to capture at Ardvreck. The stories of Neil's treachery are without foundation; he was as much a prisoner of circumstance as his captive. He was to lose the struggle to fend off Seaforth and the long line of the MacLeods of Assynt came to an end.

Earl John Glas was also hard pressed. His support for the covenant brought him debts of £50,000. Faced with demands from Charles II, and later the Cromwellians, he excused himself with illnesses real and imagined. While Glencairn initiated his royalist rising in Sutherland 'the old good Earle of Sutherland who was most eminent for religion and did great services for it in his country' co-operated with the English army of occupation. Gordonstoun had commended the wisdom of having a son 'bred in England' but the cost of John's two sons' education in London caused him much anxiety. He attended the Restoration parliament of 1661 and the following year he resigned his earldom to his son. George, fourteenth earl, saw little of his estates, spending most of his time in England and abroad. The earldom was troubled by 'brigandage' and the Earl of Caithness still instigated the odd cattle raid though George himself was preoccupied elsewhere. He joined the growing opposition to James VII and II and, at the 'Glorious Revolution' in 1688 he gave his support to William and Mary. One of William's generals was among the most distinguished military men of his day — Major General Hugh Mackay of Scourie. Mackay was resoundingly defeated at Killiecrankie by the Jacobites under Viscount Dundee. Another soldier and Dundee's brother-in-law, was the future fifteenth earl of Sutherland. He was another whose main interests were far from home. In 1706 he unsuccessfully attempted to trade his vote in favour of the Treaty of Union for a commission as lieutenant-general.

In the 17th century an anonymous writer on Strath Naver observed, 'It is a habit common to all those districts where the ancient language is spoken, that they revere, court and love their chief in the highest possible degree; fight and readily lay down their lives for him in dangers; and in addition to the usual burdens of their farms, whenever necessity arises, as when the chief is giving his daughter in marriage, or paying his debts, or redeeming mortgaged estates, or acquiring new ones, they contribute willingly by way of extraordinary dues the fourth or fifth cow, all cheerfully without distinction of wealth or poverty'. The greatest tensions in Sutherland arose through the earls' dual roles as powerful local chiefs and great nobles of Scotland, much involved in national affairs. Yet according to Gordonstoun the traditional role was in evidence when, in 1609 'the inhabitants of Sutherland' contributed ' a tenth part of their frie goods' to Earl John while later his son was supported at university for five years from the same source.

The earliest surviving Sutherland charter (circa 1211) records Hugh Freskin's grant of the lands of Skelbo, Creich and Invershin to Gilbert, archdeacon of Moray, future bishop of Caithness, and to those of his kin (*parentela*) to whom Gilbert should grant them. By 1512 the comital lands were divided into the *proprietas* and the *tenandria,* that is, the property lands held by the earl himself, and the tenandry lands held by the earl's free tenants or tacksmen. The former, often measured in davochs, the old Celtic agricultural unit, included Lairg, Golspie, Dunrobin, Loth, Kildonan and Brora, 'almost all the best lands of the southern and eastern part of the country'. Among the tenandry lands were Eddrachilles, Coul, Clyne and Rogart. The tacksmen included Sutherlands, William Clyne of Clynelish, a Dunbar, a Kynard and Mackay who held the Ord of Caithness. The rent of the property lands amounted to £103.4s.8d. as well as various quantities of barley, beef, poultry, sheep, oats and iron. The tenandry rents were £147.13s.4d. and seven chalders* of barley. In 1546 the annual rental of the earldom was £66.13s.4d. A glimpse of the agricultural wealth of the area is given by Ross of Balnagowan's raid on the lands of Achany in 1593. He was accused of carrying off fifty work horses each worth £40, forty four mares in foal valued at £60 each, one hundred and eighty cows in calf valued at some £3,200 in toto, seventy oxen worth £20 each, two hundred and fifty ewes at £3.10s., two hundred wedders at £3, two hundred she-goats at £3 as well as pigs, plaids, wool, weapons, utensils and cash. In 1646 the Mackays were accused of looting five hundred cows and oxen, six hundred sheep, two hundred horses and mares, and three hundred goats. The basis of the Sutherland economy was thus pastoral agriculture though there was some attempt to diversify in the 16th and 17th centuries.

Gordonstoun boasted that Sutherland abounded in corn, grass, woods, fruits, wild fowl, deer, fish and 'all other commodities which are usual in the kingdom of Scotland or necessary for man'. The province's exports included corn, salt, coal, salmon, beef, hides, wool, linen, tallow, butter, cheese and plaids. The straths were well manured while freestone, limestone, iron-ore and slate were among

---

* Chalder, an old measure of 16 bolls, or 1 ton.

the area's natural resources. He advised his nephew to develop the burghs, suggesting a Saturday market at Dornoch. ' Perswade the inhabitants of that towne to builde wessels and shippes of their owne to transport from thence such commodities as the countrey yeelds, and to bring thither from other parts such merchandise as is requisite for the weill of the countrey. Erect it in a burgh royall if you can'. Through his own efforts Dornoch became a royal burgh in 1628. Charles I's charter described it as the only city of the earldom 'to which, beyond the memory of man, the inhabitants of that country resorted as to a common emporium in order to purchase the necessaries of life'. Because the people of Sutherland were 'for the most part barbarous and uncultivated mountaineers' the burgh would be 'of great advantage in reducing them to a state of civilisation'. In 1601 James VI had erected the Inver of Broray into a free burgh of barony and regality 'to be called the burgh of Innerbroray', giving it power to elect the usual officials, to hold markets, to build a tolbooth and to encourage various merchants and craftsmen. The coal deposits at Brora are first mentioned in 1529 but it was not until 1598 that Jane, Countess of Sutherland, actively attempted to exploit them. Her son, Earl John, who, before his early death displayed a great interest in economic development, sunk a small shaft on Brora links and developed the associated salt pans. He also received a gift of admiralty giving him rights of salvage on shipwrecks and the right to claim such valuable commodities as stranded whales, fourteen of which were once washed up at Dornoch. Throughout the 16th and 17th centuries considerable attention was paid to salmon fishing but there is little evidence of much attempt to harvest the rich coastal fisheries. By the 1620s a search had also been made for deposits of silver and gold.

When Patrick Sellar visited Sutherland in 1809 he discovered an area untouched by modern developments. Backwardness, however, is in the eye of the beholder. Throughout the long period when fifteen earls of Sutherland held sway, their territories were open to many external influences. The earliest charter to be dated at Dunrobin Castle (1401) indicates that some English was spoken in the vicinity of Backies at that date. When John Elder wrote to Henry VIII in 1543 he challenged the prevailing view that the Gaelic lords of Scotland were a 'wilde, rude and barbarous people, brought up without lernings and nourtour' by asserting that, on the contrary, they surpassed the Lowlanders in faith, honesty, policy, wit and civility. In 1544 certain letters read out in the baillie court at Dunrobin in the presence of the earl had to be explained to the tenants with the aid of a Gaelic interpreter. After the Reformation it proved difficult to obtain Gaelic speaking ministers though some are on record, and Alexander Monro, minister at Strath Naver in the 1630s composed Gaelic poetry. Although Gordonstoun looked forward to the suppression of Gaelic through English speaking schools, he told his nephew, 'it is requisite that you learn to speak the vulgar language of the country that you may truly understand and uprightly judge the complaints of the poor ones', which suggests that not all of the Sutherland earls felt compelled to learn Gaelic. In 1660 the fourteenth earl recommended 'a good young man who hath the Irish language' as tutor to the family of Gordon of Embo, in the hope that he might also be employed in some of the local churches. Despite such passing interest it seems clear that the earls were moving apart from their Gaelic tenants in the course of the 16th and 17th centuries. It was a Gordon failing for the same was true of the Huntlys. The documentary curtain rarely parts to afford a glimpse of the Gaelic face of the earldom. The seventh earl had sons named Thomas *Beg* and Thomas *Mór*. In 1602 the twelfth earl's MacKean harper perished in a snow storm and with him there died the last real evidence of Sutherland allegiance to traditional society.

Much more representative of Gaeldom were the Mackays. Two of Mackay's pipers were present at the killing of Smith the counterfeiter — a MacCrimmon of the well-known Skye family and one, John MacRory. When the Mackays recovered part of their lands after the Restoration John Mackay reconstructed an almost aggressively traditional household at Durness. There Lord Lovat visited him for a sporting holiday in 1669. They indulged in hawking, hunting, sea-fishing, archery and wrestling. There was music and dancing, Lovat supplying a Chisholm fiddler while Mackay retained a piper, a harpist (*clarsor*) and an *amadan*, or fool. At his departure Lovat received a shelty, firelocks, bows, an antique sword and a pair of deerhounds. Lady Reay presented him with a silk plaid, a doublet and trews. In that 'northern outpost of Gaeldom' there survived values and traditions already ancient when the Freskins first arrived in the north five hundred years before. They survived through half a millennium of tragic feuding, bloodshed and political intrigue. In that struggle the native clans had more or less held their own. Sutherland's greatest tragedy lay in the future.

APPENDIX — THE CASTLES OF SUTHERLAND.

The earliest, and possibly the most impressive 'castles' of Sutherland are the numerous brochs which adorn its landscape. Traditions which relate that the vitrified fort at Dun Creich was built 'with a strange kind of mortar by Paul Macktyre' may suggest that the site was reoccupied as a defensive structure at some time during the Middle Ages. In 1630 Sir Robert Gordon recorded the existence of a number of castles of which little or no trace now remains. Among these were Pulrossie, Ospisdale, Cuthill, Aberscross, Golspie Kirkton, Golspie Tower, Clyne, Kintradwell, Crackaig (built towards the end of the 16th century by Lady Jane Gordon), and Durness close to Balnakeil. Castle Uain (Clyne parish), a hunting seat of the earls, was in existence in 1769. The old house and castle of Embo, a Gordon residence, was destroyed by fire at the end of the 18th century to be replaced by the modern house.

To judge from the surviving motte sites two of the oldest Sutherland castles must be Invershin or Duffus ' near by the place where the River Shin empties itself in the sea', and Proncy, both of which belonged to the Sutherlands of Duffus. Both estates are first recorded in 1211 though 'Proncy Castletown, Tower and Fortalice' are not documented until 1562. Helmsdale Castle occupying its spectacular site on the south bank of the river was built by the Countess of Sutherland in 1488. It was there that the earl of Sutherland and his wife were poisoned in 1567. Helmsdale was 're-edified and repaired' in 1616 by Sir Alexander Gordon of Navidale who also built the castle at Torrish, in Kildonan, in 1621.

Another castle, recorded in David II's grant to Torquil MacLeod, was the fortalice of Assynt which probably occupied the same site as Ardvreck Castle built by the Macleods of Assynt about 1590. The fragmentary ruins of this keep, possibly once some four stories high, still impress. At the south-east end of Loch Assynt the Mackenzies built Edderachalda or Calda House, now also ruined, in the 1660s. Farther north Mackay dwelt at Borve, perched on a splendid sea rock at Farr. Little of the building remains, this once impressive stronghold being largely destroyed in an engagement of 1544. The Mackays moved to nearby Tongue which became 'their special residence'; it was rebuilt and enlarged in 1678 and again, in 1750. One of the most puzzling and intriguing sites in the northwest is Castle Varrich on the Kyle of Tongue. The Royal Commission Report on the historical monuments of Sutherland (1911) said of this square, roughly built, two storey structure, 'a great antiquity has been attributed to the castle which the character of the structure does not warrant'. Nonetheless it has been suggested that Varrich was the Beruvik of *Orkneyinga Saga* while others have claimed it as an episcopal castle belonging to the Bishop of Caithness.

The greatest concentration of castles was, of course, in the south-east of the district between Dornoch Firth and Strath Fleet. Skibo originated as the residence of the bishops and St Gilbert himself may have occupied it. It survived as an episcopal stronghold until the 16th century when Dornoch Palace was built. Thereafter the Gray family became hereditary constables of Skibo. The castle was renovated in 1769. It was purchased in 1895 by Andrew Carnegie who used a little of his colossal fortune to erect the modern building.

Skelbo, on its commanding position overlooking Loch Fleet, was yet another castle acquired by the powerful Sutherlands of Duffus in the 16th century. The late Dr. Douglas Simpson considered it to be a motte and bailey castle with a square keep, probably dating from the 14th century. There was an earlier castle on this site, however, for it was here that the English and Scottish commissioners learned of the death of the Maid of Norway in 1290. Dornoch Palace or Castle was in existence by 1557 though the new building was partially burned by John, Master of Sinclair and the Mackays in 1570. In the early 17th century it passed to the earls. Like Skelbo it was occupied by the Jacobites in 1746. It was renovated in 1812 and served, for the next forty years, as a court house and jail. The castle was then converted into public buildings and is now used as a hotel.

Dunrobin (Plate 24) on its strong, defensive site may have been the headquarters of the earls from the beginning. There was certainly a castle or keep there by 1401. A good deal of rebuilding apparently took place towards the end of the 16th century, a highly active period of castle construction in Sutherland. Early in the following century Earl John added a mansion house. The extravagant modern building, incorporating the older keep, was erected by the second Duke of Sutherland between 1845 and 1851.

Chapter thirteen

THE 18th & 19th CENTURIES

In the 1790s the only parishes in the old earldom of Sutherland which were wholly in the Sutherland estate were Kildonan and Loth. Elsewhere other heritors had substantial holdings — for example, Carrol in Clyne parish, Uppat in Golspie, Embo and Skibo in Dornoch, Langwell and Lettie in Rogart parish, Gruids and Achany in Lairg. Beyond the bounds of the old earldom, within the County and sheriffdom, the Sutherlands had purchased the whole of Assynt parish in 1757 "with a view to enlarge the property of the Family of Sutherland in that Country where the Family Estate lies"; otherwise, they owned in 1800 only two properties in Creich parish and the barony of Strath Naver in Farr, and there was no Sutherland family land at all in Lord Reay's territories in the north and west of the District, the parishes of Eddrachilles, Durness, Tongue or in Strath Halladale which lay in the Sutherland part of the parish of Reay.

Professor R. J. Adam comments in his edition of *Papers on Sutherland Estate Managements, 1802-1816* that there was no concerted policy by the Sutherland family to purchase the remainder of the lands within the District in the first twenty years of the 19th century; yet by the mid-1830s little of it was not in Sutherland hands. In 1812 Carrol and Uppat were taken over, making the family sole heritors in Clyne and Golspie, parishes close to Dunrobin Castle. In 1813, with the purchase of the lands of Armadale, Ardbeg and Strathy on the northern coast, the entire extent of Farr parish came into Sutherland control. In 1828 the Reay estate was added to the family holdings, probably signifying a deliberate reunification of the former Sutherland properties; and by 1834 only "two small patches" of Rogart parish remained outside Sutherland ownership. But in the mid-1830s, substantial portions of Lairg still lay in the estates of Munro of Pointzfield and Rose of Achany, heritors whose principal lands lay in Ross-shire; and in the parish of Creich, Dempster of Skibo was still the leading heritor in a group of five, with less than a quarter of the valued land there in Sutherland owner-ship. Nonetheless, in the period with which this chapter is concer-ned, the family of Sutherland and the policies it carried through in its estates dominate the history of the District.

It was a period in which the management of Highland estates underwent everywhere some remarkably eventful changes. In the course of the 18th century the old relationship between clan chief and clansmen which was based on military service was converted into a landlord-tenant, rent-paying relationship. The Jacobite rebel-lions each helped to speed up the introduction in Highland proper-ties of a Lowland-style 'feudalised' land-tenure system; and the after math of the '45 — with its effective disarming of the clans, the for-feiture of rebel estates which placed large tracts of country in government management, the end of heritable jurisdictions — en-sured that the new landholding structures would be adopted sooner rather than later. If a Highland estate was no longer going to be valu-able to a landlord for the prowess which its military capabilities could provide, then it would have to prove its value in other ways — by offering a sufficient and secure income which would allow him to vie with other aristocrats or gentry in the political and social life of London or Edinburgh or Bath or wherever.

The ability to improve the returns from the estate, by the ex-pedient of increasing the rents or otherwise, became important, not only because a still greater income would enhance the land-owner's status but because periods of inflation (as in the 1740s and 1780s) tended to whittle away their real value. The need for a big-ger income could arise for many different reasons: for instance, the appointment of Earl Gower — who had married Elizabeth, Countess of Sutherland, in 1785 — to the costly honour of ambas-sador to France in 1790-92, adding a further drain on resources al-ready stretched by the expenditures of attendance at the London court. But raising rents, or as in this case granting wadsets of land, was only one element in the 'improvement' of estates under the new system. When in the early 1770s, the tutors to the child-Countess (who had inherited in 1766 at the age of one year) called for a series of surveys into the family's properties, another major issue came at once to the fore — the need to reduce, preferably to halt, emigration.

It was at that time a commonly-held principle that a thriving nation (and, similarly, a thriving estate) required a stable — and, better still, an increasing — population, if it was to 'progress' rather than stagnate and if it was to have a labour force ready to take advantage of the new economic possibilities open to a civilising and improving community which could then exploit its resources in order to provide a better standard of living for its members. Many organisations were at work as stabilizing and civilising agencies in the Highlands — the Church in providing increasing numbers of presbyterian ministers in Highland pulpits, and the missionaries and catechists employed under the Queen Anne's Bounty scheme; the school provision activities of the Society in Scotland for Propagating Christian Knowledge; the better communications with the southern part of Scotland offered by General Wade's roads; the work of the Forfeited Estates Commissioners and the British Fisheries Society; and so on. But would large-scale emigrations, mainly removing those of initiative among the Highland inhabitants, undo all their good work? What, then, was causing the emigrations and how could they be halted?

A survey in Assynt in 1774-75 reported that there had been substantial removals in 1772, after there had been two successive years of poor crops — "famine was a real element in the situation"; and in the eastern part of the estate matters seemed to be even worse, with public works in treeplanting and dyking being introduced and large quantities of imported grain being released to the tenants — without affecting the impulse to emigrate.

The crisis of 1770-72 put a very severe strain on the estate: for example, arrears of rent rose from £2500 in 1770 to £4000 in 1774, and in 1772 alone the cost of meal which was distributed to the needy throughout the holdings was more than £2000. Professor Adam rightly points out that one major problem facing the tutors was that they "had no investment capital or property in the Lowlands" to offset their expenditure, and they were finding difficulties in meeting their obligations. One reaction was to remove inefficient or ineffective factors from their posts, and this was done. They also looked very hard at the position of tacksmen and wadsetters in the estate organisation, for two of the most frequent reasons given for emigrating related to the tacksmen in particular — increased demands for rent (which indicated that the tacksmen were rack-renting their tenants) and oppression by tacksmen in demanding a very wide range of feudal services. The response of the tutors in Assynt, applied elsewhere too, was to limit the power of sub-letting in future leases: in 1775, under a new set for Assynt, very few tacks-

ment held more than one modestly-populated farm, this being introduced as one way of reducing or removing the abuses.

The survey on Assynt showed one development which was to
have implications for later improving policies in the estate. Some
68% of the total population of the parish lived on coastal farms,
which took up a little over half the total area of the inland farms,
but supported twice as many inhabitants. On these coastal farms,
the tenants achieved a bare subsistence from the arable that they
worked and paid their rents from the proceeds of selling their black
cattle; significantly, the survey stresses the importance of coastal
fishings as an extra source of income and employment and approves
the few instances of potato cropping that were found. The coastal
areas, therefore, were relatively heavily populated and — in the
editor's words — were "pushing up against the limits of their resources"; yet the inhabitants there had a ready-made support against
disaster in the fact that they were not wholly dependent on cattle-
rearing (as were the inland tenants) nor even on the land — popu-
lous as the coastal region was "there was no class of landless squat-
ters to be found there".

If we turn to the parish minister's commentary on Assynt in
the *Old Statistical Account*, (OSA), written in 1793, he notes that
those who lived "in the lower parts of the parish" usually had sufficient provisions to see them through ten months of each year
" and with a good herring season the whole year may pass tolerably
well "; but those living inland could subsist only for six or seven
months at most. How was the land to support its population, especially since the minister believed it had increased by one-third
since he entered the parish church in 1766? His own responses were
too limited: long-term storage of grain to offset price rises in times
of scarcity, and the encouragement of outsiders — "people of enterprise and credit" — to promote fisheries and manufacturers. The
OSA indicates that Assynt was by no means the only Sutherland
parish which could hardly feed itself even in the best years. Dornoch reported "barely enough victual in ordinary seasons", as did
Farr; Lairg could produce no more than "8 month's bread", while
in Edrachilles " even in the best seasons the crops are not sufficient for two-thirds of the inhabitants" who were normally supplied
(as were other parishes in the north) from Caithness. In Sutherland,
Creich and Golspie alone exported grain and/or potatoes "in tolerably good years".

Thus, if emigration in the 18th century was caused by the oppression of tenants by tacksmen, some remedy at least lay in the hands of the landowner and her factors. But what could be done, or so readily done, to combat poverty and privation, and the intermittent dearths which produced a restlessness that led so often to the decision to leave for America? In seasons that were affected by bad weather, and in those which immediately followed, disaster was close at hand. The early 1740s had been terrible years; there were sporadic bad times in the 1750s and 1760s. As we have seen 1771-72 were particularly severe, and the *OSA* reports are full of comment about the hard times experienced in 1782-83 and in 1792. In all these times, large numbers of cattle had been lost through starvation and disease and, as a result, vast arrears of rentals had been built up, with further sums owing for imported grain purchased by the estate for its tenantry. The poor and the small tenants flocked to join those already on the sea coasts, to keep alive on the cockles and mussels they could find there and any fish that was to be had. Potatoes seemed to be a more reliable crop than grain and, especially on the smaller lots, more and more land was given over to them: the *OSA* reports that in Clyne half of the tilled land was under potatoes; in Dornoch they had become the principal article of food and the chief subsistence of the people for a third or a half or in some instances for two-thirds of the year; Durness was marginally self-sufficient, it was said, only because of the great quantities of potatoes grown in the parish.

There is no doubt that, apart from a genuine humanitarian impulse to improve the living standards of the smaller tenantry and the growing need to reconstruct agriculture in the estate in order to increase the returns from rents (and these were not seen as necessarily exclusive), a definite stimulus was given to plan for agricultural reform and improvement in order to combat the readiness of starving tenants to emigrate. Paradoxically, by the 1850's when the Sutherland family were convinced that emigration was a sound solution to the desperate problems of subsistence that faced their tenants, it was their agricultural improvements — including the clearances and the settling of tenants from the interior straths on the coasts — which were being blamed as the prime *cause* of the destitution and the mania for emigration that occurred following the failure of the potato crop in 1845-46.

Many observers in the later 18th century, residents in Sutherland or visitors, saw the essential problem of the Northern Highland estates as one of capitalizing sensibly on the available resources, however scarce they were — of the land, of the rivers and coastal seas, of the labour potential of a settled population — in order to offer their inhabitants something better than a hard-fought, bare subsistence punctuated by periods of misery, privation and abject poverty that blunted their resilience. If a rising population was to be maintained in reasonable circumstances, and if the estates were to provide better returns in rent to their owners, then there had to be a significant reconstruction of the local economy. Where an estate had a seaboard, particularly one with good natural harbours, then there were special advantages for owner and tenants alike. The Assynt survey of 1774-75 indicated as much to the Sutherland tutors; thereafter, the removal of inland populations to coastal settlements was frequently discussed, became in due course the (initially hesitant) estate policy of the early years of the 19th century, and was later a by-word of James Loch's direction of Sutherland affairs from the 1820s to the 1850s.

In 1774-75, as we have seen, some 68% of the Assynt population was already to be found on the coastal farms, occupying there less than half the ground allotted to the inhabitants of inland farms; with only slightly more infield, the coastal tenants were producing considerably more grain for their own feeding — even if this too often was still too little for their needs — and had additional and often vital food supplies from their fishings (supplemented by a few potatoes). There was a more stable living to be gained on the coast; and in bad times it was common enough for inland families to move there. Not only in Assynt did this happen, but in Dornoch in the east, Tongue in the north and elsewhere in the District. In these coastal areas in the mid-1770s, so soon after the bad years of 1771-73, it was notable that the tenants were paying more rent than their inland counterparts, and were paying it more regularly. These were facts which then, and subsequently, would not be lost on the Sutherland and Reay families.

The need to develop fishing is, indeed, a common plea made by the ministers in the *OSA* reports. The accounts for Clyne and Loth, for instance, complain that it was the "industrious southerners" from Moray and Ross who were most active and energetic in fishing off their parishes, and proceeded to "carry home full loads" and with them the income which might otherwise have gone to support the needy natives of Sutherland. The *OSA* reports offered the hope that the development and extension of coastal fisheries in Sutherland, together with the emergence of fishing and other manufacturing villages, would reduce the need for young men and women to go to find temporary work each summer in the Lowlands — in factories sometimes, more often in general agricultural labour or perhaps in service, most frequently for harvest work. These temporary migrations certainly provided good wages, very often a vital element in the payment of rents or in the ability to buy additional feeding for humans or cattle or to purchase next year's seed — especially in years when cattle prices were low or crops were affected by bad weather. But they underlined the ultimately *dependent* nature of the local parish economies in Northern Scotland — their dependence on outside (mainly Lowland) sources of income, seeming to make it almost impossible (unless some substantial changes took place) that the northern parishes would achieve even a modest self-sufficiency. Not all was lost, however, according to the minister of Tongue, in these temporary sorties to the south country, for sometimes the young emigrants "returned to their native soils with more skills, and more free of that Highland pride which makes them disdainful of hard labour". Most others, however, agreed rather with the minister of Creich that the young men tended to return, fresh from their worldly experience and with relatively high wages, "somewhat in the style of gentlemen", all too ready to laze the winter away until it was time for them to go south again.

In the later 18th century, Highland proprietors were just as susceptible as other landlords to ideas of "progress", and to those currently assertive economic theories which demanded an end of runrig farming, promoted the enclosure of fields and the introduction of 'balanced' rotational systems, and prompted the removal of cottars and 'supernumerary' subtenants into villages where a new spirit of morality and industry would "civilise" them. A very real problem, however, was that large-scale agrarian improvements and the development of manufactures needed capital for investment. In later 18th-century Sutherland this was more often provided by southern companies and 'outsider' enterpreneurs than by local enterprise — for instance, we find a Peterhead salmon-curer at work in Durness, and Dempster of Dunnichen's group of "Glasgow gentlemen" underwriting the cotton mill at Spinningdale, etc. As we have noted already, the Sutherland family had no cushion of property or investments outside their landholdings within the District on which to fall back in hard times or in moments when investment was called for. Developments in the 18th century had to be supported, by and large, from the too often ill-paid rents which formed the heritor's main income — and there was then, accordingly, "very

little alteration or improvement . . . on the Sutherland estates"
(Richards, 1973). Wadsetting (mortgaging tracts of land for limited
periods) was, at best, a short-term expedient for raising income;
it was to prove a disadvantage in general estate planning, and usually
wadsets were granted for political purposes only. The Sutherland
family seem to have hesitated, in most instances anyway and rather
more than other proprietors, to raise their rents regardlessly. Thus,
not until Earl Gower, as Lord Stafford, inherited his English fortune
in 1803 was substantial capital for improvement going to be available — and most Sutherland leases did not run out until 1807. But
in 1806 an early clearance, of some 77 families from upper Strath
Naver to the northern coast, did take place; by 1808 there was increased activity in planning for future improvements; and in 1809
two Moray men (of wide reputation as improvers there) argued in
favour of a project which would open up trade with the Northern
Highlands by packet boat from the Moray coast. These two —
William Young and Patrick Sellar — "brought with them an assortment of panaceas for the economic problems of the Sutherland estate and soon began to exert a major influence on the Countess"
(Richards, 1973).

Young and Sellar did not plan at this time to include any emphasis on sheep-farming; on the contrary, they stressed the importance of flax cultivation and land drainage, with the building of
threshing, flax and woollen mills — "If your Ladyship can lead the
people from destroying the soil, and from every starving creature
on it, to settle in villages . . . and get the sons and daughters of the
present generation into the employment of those who can teach
them industry ... Sutherland may enjoy as many comforts and pay
fair rents as any of her neighbours". Bouyantly optimistic about
their own ideas, they were very critical of earlier "improving"
clearances because these had not removed the people into prepared
new holdings "pointed out for their industry"; resettlement, not
clearing, under a 'complete plan' was to be the policy. In 1810, when
Young became the factor for the Sutherland estates, the full-ahead
was given to the substantial improvements which he considered
most appropriate — the tempting of supernumerary inland crofters
on to coastal moorlands on advantageous improving leases; the
plans to create "fishing stations in which mechanics will be settled,
inland villages with carding mills".

Crop failures and dearth in 1802-4 had sharpened interest in
improving policies for the Highlands just before the Stafford money

was made available for use in the Sutherland estates; another crisis brought on by bad weather in 1812, showing once again the very narrow division there was between subsistence and famine in Northern Highland properties, hurried along Young's great plans for the reconstruction of the Sutherland economy. It was in 1812-13, too, after having been opposed to the large-scale introduction of sheep-farming, Sellar — and with him Young, no doubt — was converted to it as improving policy. (Sellar took out a lease himself on a proposed sheep-walk in Strath Naver in an area marked out for clearance.) Meanwhile, Young had been invited to report on the English estates of Lord Stafford and stunned the new commissioner of those estates, James Loch, by specifying (November 1812) "that everything that differed from Moray was wrong and everything was to be improved by the total eradication of the present tenants and the introduction of Scotch farmers ..." This is important for it shows that Young's Highland policies were not specific to the situation that obtained there; to him, his improving policies were *generally* valid, and he wished to apply them as much in Staffordshire as in Sutherland. There was, it seems, no peculiar vindictiveness on Young's part towards the Highlanders; in his attitudes and actions, he showed himself as insensitive to the claims of an English "tenantry of 200 years' standing" as he was to the Sutherland tenantry in Kildonan and Strath Naver in 1813 and 1814, the years in which the most renowned of the 'Sutherland clearances' took place, leading in due course to the trial and acquittal of Patrick Sellar in 1816. Trumped up as the charge of murder may have been, engineered by the personal antagonism of Sheriff-substitute McKidd, Sellar never recovered from the trial; he became an embarrassment to the Sutherland family and resigned, under pressure, from his factoring partnership with Young. And Young, the wayward enthusiast who showed too little concern for the ever-increasing financial outlays he was forcing on the estate, was also persuaded to resign. Thereafter, from 1816 until his death in 1855, James Loch was to be in charge of the policies of improvement carried through in the Sutherland estate.

It is as well, perhaps, to reaffirm here that the introduction of large sheep farms was not an early development in the Sutherland family's property — certainly not to anything like the extent which it has so often been popularly assumed. In comparison with those clearings for sheep which took place in neighbouring Ross-shire estates or on Lord Reay's land in Edrachilles, Durness and Tongue, the earlier Sutherland family removals were few in number and extent. Too many of the families who were evicted from Strath Naver in 1806, for instance, were found to have emigrated to America, and the fact that 140 of these emigrants were lost in a shipwreck off Newfoundland merely increased the dislike of enacting policies which so clearly prompted emigration. At that time there was still only a hesitant readiness among the Sutherland's factors and agents to accept that the introduction of very large sheep-walks could prove the essential answer to Sutherland improvement. What is interesting, indeed, is that in the early 1790s there was more immediate, and even unhesitating, support among the parish ministers than among the estate managers for extending sheep husbandry — thus in the *OSA* account for Edrachilles we are told that "the nature of the country looks more adapted to the rearing of sheep" (than cattle); the hilly part of Creich was "excellent for sheep"; Lairg was "peculiarly suited" to sheep, although it was not necessary to remove the present possessors from these lands, "merely convince them to change their stock management"; in Dornoch, however, while large tracts of land were lately (1791) covered by sheep, "the ardour for sheep-farming has hardly yet commenced here". The *OSA* returns show, taking averages for the Sutherland parishes as a whole, a holding in each of some 2000 cattle, 2500 sheep, 500 goats and 600 horses. Sheep were, therefore, by no means unknown — but the new and improved Lowland breeds, the Lintons and the Cheviots, were still few or non-existent. What is clearly to be seen is that, even in the more favoured parishes, the demands on available pasture (and on winter-feeding for cattle and sheep and goats and horses alike) were very great indeed.

It is difficult, indeed, to escape the impression — in the *Sutherland Estate Papers*, and especially from Dr Richard's *Leviathan of Wealth* — that a major part of the eventual attractiveness of sheep-farming to the Sutherland policy-makers was not entirely or predominantly their assessment of the high rentals that could be charged for sheep-walks; but rather that it allowed them, more easily than with any other improvement that could be brought in, to remove complete townships of inland tenants on to the coasts — and hence to meet James Loch's deepest conviction: namely that the dependent, impoverished and indolent inhabitants of the straths would, almost at a stroke, be converted into independent, prosperous and industrious crofter-fishermen, a credit to themselves and to their rentaller-landlord, if only they could be persuaded to settle in and work the prepared lots on suitable coastal strips. They would almost at once become much less of a burden — indeed, hopefully, soon no burden at all — on the estate, achieving a new self-sufficiency by a judicious combination of agriculture and fishing; and the lands they vacated would not only bring in a good rental, but also at the same time produce the raw material for woollen-based manufacturers of various kinds, for the thoroughly gainful employment of the 'supernumerary' population for whom adequate lots could not be found. Sheep became a vitally important part of the 'grand design', not so much for themselves perhaps, but for forcing that restructuring of the settlement areas in Sutherland which economic theorists like Loch believed was essential, if not for the immediate then for the ultimate benefit of tenants and landlord alike.

And this 'grand design' for Sutherland, at least according to the reports published in 1845 in the *New Statistical Account* (*NSA*), many written in the later 1830s, seemed to be working out reasonably well. In Clyne, for instance, three quarters of the coastal area on which families cleared from the interior had been settled had by then been taken in from waste — about a quarter of the whole parish was in arable; and the bigger farms, enclosed by stone dykes, grew "luxuriant crops" of barley, oats and turnips. In Creich the small farmers were said to be imitating their superiors, who were rapidly reclaiming waste land and carrying forward schemes of drainage or irrigation. In Durness, run-rig was "wearing out", townships had been lotted out in regular divisions and stone cottages were being built. The minister of Rogart, with no little satisfaction, wrote that "Travellers must regard the cottages of our working classes with pleasure; no part of the northern Highlands has so many well-built, neat-looking cottages as the county of Sutherland". And in Golspie it was reported that the "small tenants now live in decent cottages with glass windows". In Loth the "removed cottagers" were to be found trenching and improving the formerly waste ground with great industry — and, as was remarked with some pride, "not a single sixpence of rent was not paid on the last rent day". In Farr, however, it was commented that a "better system of husbandry" was still needed among the lotters; and in Tongue the system of crofting was said to be "decidedly bad" with more cattle being kept than could be properly fed, and only the potato crop giving "a really remunerating return".

On the other hand, the hoped-for expansion of fishing had not always come up to expectations. In Clyne there were still only three regular crews of fishermen while the "other inhabitants had not taken to the sea". In Dornoch, there were no regular fisheries, even the fishing colony at Embo restricting itself to meet purely local demands. In Tongue what had been anticipated as "an extensive herring fishery" had turned out to be a wildly ruinous speculation. Nor had matters gone easily in Durness whose minister wryly commented that it was "not to be expected that a people who had led chiefly a pastoral life were to be soon reconciled to a change which placed them in crowded hamlets on the shore". Yet in-shore fishing was thriving in Edrachilles and also in Farr (where agriculture was reportedly so backward); and the more carefully planned fishing communities at Helmsdale and Portgower in Loth had both developed well. It is worth noting that there seems to have been in Sutherland no such general opposition to fishing or to combining fishing and crofting (or such a crippling lack of adaptability on the part of the cleared crofters) as was sometimes suggested in the 1830s or has been claimed since. It is clear that, frequently, in parishes where *local* fishings were being ignored, large numbers of young men would go nonetheless to Wick, to the Moray coast and elsewhere to work for a summer season at the herring, at sea as well as on land. It has been reported, for instance, that in 1839 in addition to its inshore boats Edrachilles had 24 larger vessels which were owned by crews scattered throughout its coastal townships and which all made the annual trip to Caithness for the herring fishing season.

It appears that the older hankering after seasonal employment still remained strong among the Sutherland tenantry — with the main direction shifting from the now reducing opportunities for agricultural employment in the south to the expanding demands for work in fishing and on fishing stations in the north and north-east. Rents were still frequently paid from incomes which were gained outside the District. At any rate, and for whatever reasons, the great Sutherland plan to develop local fishings — apart perhaps from those based at Helmsdale — did not work so smoothly as it might have done. What is rather more remarkable is that, as well as these temporary and seasonal migrants, increasing numbers of Sutherlanders became emigrants, often moving north into Caithness to establish themselves as crofter-fishermen in parishes such as Latheron, and led there to severe congestion in the coastal agricultural areas as farms were broken down into smaller units to accommodate them. The question remains why these men and their families found it more congenial to take up crofting/fishing in Caithness in the 1820s and 1830s rather than on the Sutherland coasts; and there is no obvious answer to it in the evidence so far available to us; the move out of the country was, in many instances, the first stage in an eventual emigration overseas.

The ministers who wrote the *NSA* accounts had favourable things to say on other matters. The improvements in Sutherland roads were, for example, universally applauded — "no fewer than 480 miles (772 km) of road, mostly by the means, wholly through the instrumentality of the Duke of Sutherland, throughout Sutherland" (Edrachilles); "the finest roads in the kingdom" (Clyne), with no tolls; they "have completely opened up the county to new sources of industry, travellers and speculations of the capitalists" (Durness). There was less absolute dependence than once had been the case on the local fairs, for the improved roads meant that the permanent retail shops at Dornoch or Golspie or Bonar Bridge were more readily accessible; and at major fairs in the District (e.g. at Brora and at Golspie in October) "shopkeepers come from a fair distance and set up tents to display their commodities and usually meet a ready sale". By mid-century, therefore, Sutherlanders had begun to enjoy an ease in communication that had been unknown before — soon to be added to when the ducal family supported the establishment of the east coast railway in the later decades of the century.

Yet the air of well-being which occurs in some sections of the parish accounts of the 1830s and 1840s is offset by a sense of foreboding in others. Herrings and potatoes had certainly become the dominant articles in diet — increasingly so as the numbers of cattle decreased and the keeping of goats all but disappeared as pasture lands were retained for the grazing of sheep. Oatmeal and barleymeal were still important articles of food but they often had to be imported in quantity, even in years of reasonable harvests. Meanwhile the population of Sutherland continued to increase, always adding to the considerable difficulties in maintaining an adequate subsistence for its inhabitants, especially when the coastal lots on which they were placed might be further and further subdivided. In a survey of the Sutherland estate taken a little later, in 1852, it was discovered that there were only twelve large tenancies, with a total of 120 holdings in the District, contributing £25,258 to the annual income of the estate. At the same time there were no fewer than 2785 "small tenants" whose rentals totalled only £5,933. These tenancies accounted altogether for some 80% of the total population — the remaining fifth being cottars (with rent free cottages and patches of ground for potatoes) who had to seek employment or sustenance where they could.

Table 11b summarizes the general pattern of increase and decrease in population in the Sutherland parishes, taken in fifty-year periods, from Webster's account of 1755 to the series of government censuses in the 19th century.

A more detailed breakdown of these population returns, decade by decade, is given on an adjoining page. As that shows, if we had chosen to divide the 19th century figures at 1841 rather than 1851, then the "half-century" contrast between the general increases in population in the earlier 19th century and the general decreases in the later 19th century would have been even more notable. In many parishes there had been marked losses of population in the 1831-1841 period, reflecting the difficulties of the years of dearth in the mid-30s. These losses were mostly attributed to emigration, some to absences "in search of employment" at the time the 1841 census was taken. By 1837, indeed, the minister of Assynt had been emphatic in his warning that emigration was the only sure way out of the continuing troubles in his parish, whose occupants were "generally in straitened circumstances, though rents are not high ... Unless emigration on a large scale takes place, soon there will be a painful crisis". By that date James Loch had already indicated a greater willingness than before to consider emigration as part of his general policy; subletting seemed to be a distinctive threat to the success of his plans for the coastal settlements — and this he strictly forbade after 1833-34, in so doing actually stimulating emigration from the districts which were to suffer badly in the years that followed.

The Assynt minister was being descriptive rather than prophetic in 1837 because in 1836 there had already begun a catastrophic period of distress from crop failures in the Highlands, the worst in Assynt, for example, for almost 30 years. In 1836-37, too, there had been an almost total failure of the now essential potato crop. And, to cap all, in 1835-37 the fishings had been very poor.

The crisis hit very generally in the north and west, and was frequently met by an extraordinary response from sympathetic landowners who provided their tenants with reasonably-priced meal, offered them clothing and allowed the building-up of arrears of rent. The Sutherland family seemed to have been notably generous in their treatment of their tenantry at this time. In addition to the landlords'

efforts there were the highly successful fund-raising activities of all
the Gaelic Societies and also much support offered in cash and in
kind by the Established Church (in a relief campaign mainly organi-
zed by the non-intrusionist wing of the church which was so strong
in Northern Scotland). Once again, famine had shown how close to
disaster the whole Highland area was, with a population (despite
emigration) which was clearly outrunning all its resources. On this
occasion, however, a new danger became uncomfortably apparent to
the landlords and their factors: for Macleod of Macleod, in an attempt to save the lives of (and to bring the most modest comfort to)
the people of his Skye estates in the later 1830s, so overreached his
resources that he went bankrupt. The lesson was clear (and was to
be underlined by the experience of Mathieson and Mackenzie of
Seaforth in Lewis): there was no advantage to a landlord, nor in the
long run to his tenantry, to attempt to support artificially a population which an estate could no longer maintain even in normal circumstances. The minister of Tongue, a late contributor to the *NSA*,
writing in 1841, had seen the difficulties of the most recent years of
dearth when he concluded: "If there are no plans for change, then
soon there will be no alternative but emigration at the expense of
either government or landlord, a poor law by assessment, or a summary and universal ejection". Certainly landlords and their factors
seem, in the later 1830s and early 1840s, to have been readier to accept the fact of emigration — if only because, as a means of making
their lands more capable of supporting their inhabitants, it appeared
sensible to initiate still more clearings and to tempt the removed
tenants to try their luck abroad. But it was to take another, even
more serious, period of famine finally to convince both landlords and
government of the need to throw aside older hesitations and to be
active in promoting schemes of assisted passages for emigrants.

In 1846-48 potato disease was rampant; there was a poor harvest
in 1849 and this was exacerbated by a failure of the herring fishery.
In 1850-51, after the shortest respite, potato blight struck again, and
incomes were badly hit by a fall in cattle prices; and the fishing was
poor. In Sutherland, the second Duke responded at once, no doubt
in an effort to cut his losses, by wondering whether he should sell
Assynt — an estate which appeared to have defied every costly attempt at improvement. Instead, the factor there cleared whole townships, with a view to their resettlement on the more acceptable basis
of a much reduced population or to prompting the emigration of the
displaced people. It is said, for instance, that one-sixth of the whole

TABLE 11A – POPULATION IN SUTHERLAND 1755–1901

		1755	1790s	1801	1811	1821
(A)	ASSYNT	1934	'3000'	2395	2479	2803
	CREICH	1705	1730	1974	1969	2354
	LAIRG	1010	1350	1209	1354	1094
	ROGART	1761	2000	2022	2148	1986
	Total	*6410*	*8080*	*7600*	*7950*	*8237*
(B)	DORNOCH	2780	2508	2362	2681	3100
	GOLSPIE	1790	1600	1616	1391	1036
	CLYNE	1406	1793	1643	1639	1874
	Total	*5976*	*5901*	*5621*	*5711*	*6010*
(C)	LOTH / KILDONAN	2626	2735	2814	2904	2573
	REAY (pt)	?	?	865	861	1057
	FARR	2800	2600	2408	2408	1994
	Total	*5426*	*5335*	*6087*	*6173*	*5624*
(D)	TONGUE	1093	1493	1348	1493	1736
	DURNESS	1000	1182	1208	1155	1004
	EDDRACHILIS	869	1024	1253	1147	1229
	Total	*2962*	*3699*	*3809*	*3795*	*3969*
	TOTAL	20774	23015	23117	23629	23840
PERCENTAGE INCREASES						
	(A)		26.05%	−5.94%	4.61%	3.61%
	(B)		−1.26%	−4.74%	1.60%	5.24%
	(C)		−1.68%	(14.10%)	1.41%	−8.89%
	(D)		24.88%	2.97%	−0.37%	4.58%
	ALL SUTHERLAND		10.79%	0.44%	2.21%	0.89%
	CAITHNESS		11.65%	−8.84%	2.39%	26.06%
	SCOTLAND		20.60%	5.40%	12.30%	15.80%

1831	1841	1851	1861	1871	1881	1891	1901
3161	3178	2989	3178	3006	2781	2551	2386
2562	2582	2714	2521	2524	2223	2013	1836
1045	913	1162	961	978	1355	1169	1081
1805	1501	1535	1439	1341	1227	1195	1105*
8573	*8174*	*8400*	*8099*	*7849*	*7586*	*6928*	*6408*
3380	2714	2981	2885	2764	2525	2404	2794*
1149	1214	1529	1615	1804	1556	1451	1665
1711	1765	1933	1886	1733	1812	1713	1724
6240	*5693*	*6443*	*6386*	*6301*	*5893*	*5568*	*6183*
2471	2782	2928	2742	2499	2526	2356	2221
1013	1067	1073	1089	1019	994	893)	2557
2073	2217	2203	2103	2019	1930	1857)	
5557	*6066*	*6204*	*5934*	*5537*	*5450*	*5106*	*4778*
2030	2041	2018	2077	2051	1929	1925	1783
1153	1109	1152	1109	1049	987	960	870
1965	1699	1576	1641	1530	1525	1409	1418
5148	*4849*	*4746*	*4827*	*4630*	*4441*	*4294*	*4071*
25518	24782	25793	25246	24317	23370	21896	21440
4.08%	−4.65%	2.76%	−3.58%	−3.09%	−3.35%	−8.67%	−7.51%
3.83%	−8.77%	13.17%	−0.88%	−1.33%	−6.48%	−5.52%	11.05%
−1.19%	9.16%	2.27%	−4.35%	−6.69%	−1.57%	−6.31%	−6.42%
29.71%	−5.81%	−2.12%	1.71%	−4.08%	−4.08%	−3 31%	−5.19%
7.04%	−2.88%	4.08%	−2.12%	−3.68%	−3.89%	−6.31%	−2.08%
18.33%	5.25%	6.51%	6.21%	−2.72%	−2.82%	−4.34%	−8.90%
13.00%	10.80%	10.20%	10.20%	9.70%	11.20%	7.80%	11.10%

TABLE 11B – PERCENTAGE INCREASES/DECREASES IN POPULATION IN SUTHERLAND			
PARISH	1755–1801	1801–1851	1851–1901
ASSYNT	+24%	+25%	−20%
CREICH	+16%	+37%	−32%
LAIRG	+20%	−4%	−7%
ROGART	+15%	−24%	−28%
Total	*+19%*	*+11%*	*−24%*
DORNOCH	−15%	+26%	−6%
GOLSPIE	−10%	−5%	+9%
CLYNE	+17%	+18%	−11%
Total	*−6%*	*+15%*	*−4%*
LOTH / KILDONAN	+7%	+4%	−24%
REAY (pt)	?	+24%)	−22%
FARR	−14%	−9%)	
Total	*+12%*	*+2%*	*−23%*
TONGUE	+23%	+50%	−12%
DURNESS	+21%	−5%	−24%
EDDRACHILIS	+44%	+26%	−10%
Total	*+29%*	*+25%*	*−14%*
ALL SUTHERLAND	+11%	+12%	−1%

population of Scourie left the parish for overseas. Certainly in the 1850s, and for the first time, the people of Assynt were being *urged* to emigrate.

Between 1841 and 1851, however, only the northern and western parishes of Assynt, Farr, Tongue and Edrachilles actually declined in population, these alone failing to replace by natural increase those who removed. The Duke was now ready to provide free (or very extensively assisted) passages for his distressed tenantry, but this actually did little to reduce the burden of dependent tenants and cottars. As Eric Richards has pointed out, it was in the aftermath of the famine of the 1840s that Loch's long-standing policy — of promoting coastal fishing settlements — was to be rejected: the people on the coast did not, by and large, survive the crisis any better than the inland tenants. In 1852-53 Loch was to be found admitting that the sheep walks established in the previous thirty years or so had been too large — though he was still claiming, as a distinct success, the rise in acreage under arable on the estate, from 13,420 acres (5,429 hectares) in 1807 to 32,237 acres (13,048 hectares) in 1852.

Yet, oddly enough, in the 1860s, almost at the moment when things looked particularly bad, when the 'grand design' seemed to have failed — following the attacks on Sutherland clearance policy, in the writings of Hugh Miller and (more surprisingly) *The Times*, in the 1850s by Karl Marx and Sismondi, and Donald Ross, and in the 'gloomy memories' of Donald Macleod among others in the aftermath of Loch's death in 1855 — the wool market became buoyant, prices rose, and by the 1860s a new 'sheep mania' (as James Hunter described it) took place. In 1853 the total number of sheep in the District was 168,000; by 1875 this had risen by 40% to 240,000. Landlords and greater tenants made fortunes as wool returns increased (the numbers of sheep farms in the parishes of Assynt and Durness more than doubled in the period) and were able to drive up the rentals too — by 30% between 1860 and 1880. Had the policy been a correct one after all?

Perhaps it seemed so at first to the ducal family, to the factors and to the Lowland sheep farmers. It was much less obvious to a tenantry who were able to share very little in the economic upturn. For them, there were still clearings to contend with; and the returns from following the herring along the east coast continued to be the surest way to pay their rents. The fortunes that were made by the sheep graziers were not being ploughed back into Sutherland.

In the period of 'mania', the intensity with which the land was being pastured by sheep began to take its toll. In the 1870s it was stated that grazings were obviously deteriorating and were declining in the numbers of sheep they could support; sheep diseases increased and weakened the stock; in some areas it was noted that cattle were being reintroduced to slow down the destruction of pasture. Meanwhile shepherds' wages more than doubled in the years 1850-1880. Then, in 1879-80, came a winter in which the weather was so severe that losses in sheep stocks amounted in value to two or three years' rental. And that calamity was followed by a greater one still — in the face of increasing Australian competition wool prices collapsed on the home market. The sheep graziers pulled out in large numbers, and returned to the Lowlands.

Many tenancies were not renewed when they fell in; leases were ended prematurely by emigration; and it became very difficult to find new tenants. Even the offer of rent-free tenancies was often not enough to persuade tenants against emigrating. Increasing numbers of Sutherland farms had to be taken into the family holdings — in 1876 the family had farmed c.2,000 acres (809 hectares), in 1886 it had 175,000 acres (69,000 hectares) in its immediate control. The level of rents on the estate certainly fell: arable lands brought in £11,000 in 1881 but only £8,750 in 1891; hill grazings returned £31,000 in 1879 and less than £16,000 in 1892. By a cruel (or apt) turn of fate, the more exclusively a farm was given over to sheep the more it dropped in revenue.

Yet, another turn of fate was to bring some respite from these difficulties. As James Hunter has put it: "With no obvious agricultural alternative to sheep, and with commercial forestry still in the future, it is hard to see what profitable use they (the landlords) could have had for the lands vacated by sheep farmers if the sporting market had not been available ... The sporting boom ensured the survival of land-lordism". And this at the very time, in the 1880s, when Highland landlords were under particularly severe attack. This was the decade of rent strikes, the "crofters' war" in Skye and the Napier Commission; of the new and vital political force which the enfranchised crofters could exert once they had been given the vote in 1884 — in Sutherland the District voting list was increased from 374 to 3180. And in 1886 the Crofters' Commission began its work, destined to bring even more serious financial crisis to landlords in the North-West Highlands and the Islands, when it frequently reduced the existing rentals.

After 1884, with the Crofters Party well to the fore and the

Liberal Party ready to join any bandwagon against the landed nobility and gentry, with the cruel mistakes and misfortunes of the
land policies since 1800 exposed by the Napier Commission, with
a pan-Celtic movement that was only too ready to equate the
heinousness of Irish and Highland landlordism, the Sutherland
family and their factors were again the target for attack. In a period
of intensifying nationalism in which absentee landlords were especially condemned, when the campaign for land nationalization
(often associated with the name of Henry George) extended into
Scotland and was particularly directed at Highland estates, there
were published such books as Alexander Mackenzie's compilation
on *The Highland Clearances* to add fuel to the smouldering fires of
clearance-consciousness. And the extension of deer forests into old
sheep walks merely added new insult to earlier injury. If there was
some respite for the landlord by introducing or extending deer
forests, there was none for the tenantry: the agricultural depression
merely accentuated the unending problems of subsistence farming
on very limited croft lands. Security of tenure, even reduced rentals,
could not overcome the difficulties of poor markets for produce,
and the intermittent ravages of bad weather. Poverty abounded on
the Sutherland estates, as elsewhere in the North-Western Highlands and Islands. And as government began, in the later 19th century, to adopt a more rigorous state-supported system of social welfare, the strain on landlords' incomes became still greater. In Sutherland this was especially hard to take: the ducal family had over-
spent income, in carrying out Loch's policies between 1833 and 1845,
by some £175,000; in the thirty years before 1883 they had spent
£1¼ millions, almost £¼ million beyond rental income from the
estate; yet despite such support from the family's English properties and investments, what real progress had been made?

Gradually more land did become available to those who for-
bore to emigrate. The Crofters' Commission prompted applications
for the enlargement of crofts, with a view to making them more
viable units, and persuaded landlords to release appropriate lands.
The attachment to their native soil seems to have remained es-
especially strong in Sutherland and its inhabitants took particular
advantage of the opportunities offered by the Commission — one
quarter of all applications for enlargements coming from Sutherland
(see Table 11c).

Government policies, especially perhaps in the payment for public services provided through parliamentary legislation, seems in the

TABLE 11C – ENLARGEMENTS OF CROFT HOLDINGS 1886–1912

	Population in 1911	Number of applications received	Total area assigned		Applications per population as in 1911	Average area assigned	
			Acres	Hectares		Acres	Hectares
ARGYLL	70902	222	4864	1979	1 in 319	22.0	8.9
CAITHNESS	32010	232	1466	593	1 in 138	6.3	2.6
INVERNESS-SHIRE	87272	1614	18910	7660	1 in 46	11.0	4.4
ROSS & CROMARTY	77364	726	13608	5519	1 in 106	18.7	6.7
SUTHERLAND	20179	1069	31733	12962	1 in 19	29.7	12.0

TABLE 11D – RATIOS, PER 1000 OF POPULATION, OF REGISTERED POOR IN 1906

	Total poor	Paupers aged 65+
ARGYLL	16.4	9.4
CAITHNESS	20.9	14.4
INVERNESS-SHIRE	21.9	12.3
ORKNEY	16.1	9.4

	Total poor	Paupers aged 65+
ROSS & CROMARTY	25.0	13.2
SHETLAND	21.4	14.5
SUTHERLAND	29.4	19.6
ALL SCOTLAND	12.9	5.2

19th century — as, indeed, later — to have been made with the rateable valuations of Southern Scotland (or perhaps Southern England) in mind. What might easily enough be paid for out of a 2d rate in, say, Midlothian might need a levy of 1s 6d (7½p) in the £ in Sutherland. The problems of distance and dispersal of population over a very large area of land, the higher costs which these involved, made the inequalities in such a situation even more marked: for instance, it cost 8s 4d (c.42p) per week to keep someone in a poorhouse in Sutherland, but only an average of 4s 9¾d (24p) in Scotland as a whole. And if we take poor relief and the provision of poorhouses as an example, centrally-directed policies were often not acceptable in Sutherland because they did not fit the local situation sufficiently well. Thus in 1910 the poorhouse which Sutherland had to provide by law offered places for 114 inhabitants, but only 27 were filled: Sutherlanders had a strong aversion to "putting away" their poor, whether they were relatives or not, and disliked intensely sending them away a long distance from their own home districts; and the local parish authorities, recognising this, continued to give out relief to the needy and to give it in the locality, at the same time that Highland 'neighbourliness' kept very low the numbers of 'declared poor' in any case. But emigration left Sutherland with a curiously imbalanced age distribution in its population which not only meant that it tended to have, relatively speaking, a higher proportion of 'ordinary poor' but also a distinctly higher proportion of listed aged paupers (see Table 11d). It is not surprising that once the Liberal government introduced old-age pensions paid from central funds in 1908, in Sutherland especially the burden of supporting the local poor was considerably lightened.

But Sutherland landlords and tenants, who as elsewhere shared equally the rates burden for these public services, found themselves with unavoidable expenditures in, say, the provision of schooling and the caring for lunatics in suitable accommodation. The very wide dispersion of population made the support of public schooling after 1872 a particularly heavy drain on resources that were to be increasingly limited as the depression wore on in the 1880s and 1890s. The maintenance of the insane in asylums was, so it appears, an extraordinarily heavy burden in Sutherland — whereas in 1911 Inverness-shire and Ross & Cromarty each supported only 1 in 95 of their populations in asylums, Argyll 1 in 79 and Shetland 1 in 36, Sutherland found itself with as many as 1 in 27 of its inhabitants

as declared lunatics. (No explanation has been given for these amaz-
ing discrepancies in the census returns for 1911.) Perhaps the only
direct benefit that came in social welfare from central government
policies was in the extension of medical services. The Poor Law
Amendment Act of 1845 required the provision of medical attendance for the workhouse poor, to be supplied from local rates with
the support of a government relief grant after 1847. And parochial
authorities in the Highlands, supposedly in order to provide for the
paupers, supplied medical services for the whole community in this
way — many patients being attended to entirely free of charge.

The Education Act of 1872 increased the number of 'regular'
schools in Sutherland, and brought many school boards to the brink
— or over the brink — of bankruptcy in meeting the high demands
in the quality of the schoolhouses which had to be built. By 1912
there were altogether 52 public schools in the thirteen parishes, with
122 teachers for a total of 3499 children aged 5 to 14 years of age.
In 1834 Sutherland had supported at least 23 schools; in 1838 as
many as 36, if not more, in the thirteen parishes. In 1838, indeed,
in addition to the parochial schools — at least 12 of the 13 offering
Latin, 10 Greek, 2 French, 9 Mathematics and 3 book-keeping —
there were 11 General Assembly schools supported by the funds of
the Church of Scotland, 5 SSPCK schools (one partly paid for by the
Duchess of Sutherland), 5 schools endowed by the Glasgow Gaelic
Society and 1 by the Edinburgh Gaelic Society, and at Baligill in
Strathy a subscription school paid for entirely by the inhabitants.
The coming of the new 'national' system in 1872 no doubt brought
schooling closer to hand for many townships: what is very doubtful is that it even maintained the existing opportunities to study the
higher branches of school instruction and to keep open the access
to university study that the old system had achieved — at least until the Scotch Education Department belatedly took a more favourable view of its duty to provide 'secondary' education in Scotland.

Religion has played an important rôle in the past two centuries
or so in the lives of the inhabitants of Sutherland and it may be fitting to close our review with some comments on it. In fact, for all
the great strength of religious affiliation in the last two hundred years,
the presbyterian Church was weak in Sutherland until well into the
18th century. Loth and Rogart were still paying stipends to episco-
palian ministers until 1720; only in 1728 did Assynt get a presbyterian
into its pulpit. In 1717, indeed, a report from the presbytery of Tain
claimed that the Northern Highlands were "overrun by the spirit of

atheism and infidelity". Superstition abounded (as Donald Sage declared that it did still in the 1830s); at any rate, in 1716 the Rev. John Mackay of Lairg thought it worthwhile to report to his presbytery a mark of his success — that his kirk session had begun to meet regularly to ensure church attendance on Sabbath worship and the general good behaviour of the community. And he may well have had something to crow about, for as late as 1727 there were only two elders to be found in the entire presbytery of Tongue. It is worth noting, in this context, that for many years patrons and people took so little interest in exercising their rights to appoint parish ministers after the Patronage Act of 1712 that presbyteries were left to fill the vacancies.

In the course of the 1730s and 1740s, however, a popular evangelicalism spread quickly into the District, bringing with it that special brand of lay influence in church matters which became so notable in the 'fellowship' prayer-meetings and the emergence of "The Men". In some areas of Sutherland, disputes between ministers and these prominent laymen led to separatist movements in which members of congregations refused to attend their parochial churches. Generally speaking, however, there was in Sutherland, right up until the Disruption of 1843, a very great distaste for secession from the Established Church. During the 18th century, once it came to be used, patronage seems to have been exercised with a good deal of discrimination — thus it served to appoint men eminent for piety and zeal in Lairg, Dornoch, Rogart and Creich, for example. The appointment of Skeldoch of Farr was, in all probability, the exception — for he was described as a "capitalist farmer in a large scale" whose wide range of worldly activities brought him intermittently before presbytery and synod, and he was thought to rack-rent his tenants. In the later 18th century, indeed, there may have been some lessening of standards among the ministers who were appointed to Sutherland charges: there are indications that pastoral work declined, with less family visiting and catechizing, and that secular pursuits were making increased demands on ministers' time, e.g. Ross of Clyne was said to be "a farmer, cattle-dealer, housekeeper and first-rate sportsman, and knew how to turn all these occupations to profit". Moderatism had arrived, at least in some parishes.

Yet the more general, as well as the more internal and particular, issues in Church politics in the later 18th and early 19th centuries seem not to have troubled Sutherland very much. It is notable that Donald Sage (who removed from Achness mission station to Aberdeen Gaelic Chapel in 1820) was surprised, on his move to the south, to discover for the first time the extent of Moderate-Evangelical divisions and party-politicking in the Assembly. This 'remoteness' from church politics was soon to end, however. The increasing bitterness between Evangelical and Moderate groups in the Church in the 1830s, followed by intense campaigns on both sides to gain support throughout the country, brought leaders of both parties into Sutherland.

The desire of congregations to obtain the 'warming' sermons of Evangelicals made Sutherland a ready target for the attentions of Thomas Chalmers and the non-intrusionists — those in the Evangelical party who wished to weaken the hold of the patrons over ministerial appointments by giving a veto in these elections to the communicant members of congregations. What made the non-intrusionist Evangelicals even more attractive to Sutherlanders was that they became increasingly anti-landlord, as their attempts to reform the patronage system were rebuffed by Peel's government in the early 1840s, openly with the intention to maintain landlord influence and interest. In the Sutherland of that time — with clearances, removals and emigration still very much live issues — the crofters allied themselves to Chalmers and his party, against government intervention in church affairs, 'for people's rights against patron's rights'. As a result of the confrontation with government in 1842-43, in May 1843 the 'Free Protesting Church of Scotland' was founded: and in Sutherland, although only 8 out of the 18 parish ministers 'came out' into the new Free Church, it is estimated that at least 18,000 and probably more out of a total population of roughly 25,000 joined the new church. At once the existing tensions and divisions between crofter-tenants and the Duke, his factors and the Lowland graziers were intensified: they now worshipped in different, very antagonistic, though still presbyterian Churches. And, to make matters worse, in the immediate aftermath of Disruption, the Duke refused — at least in the terms that the Free Church rather arrogantly wanted — to grant sites for new church buildings. In fact, he willingly agreed on sites for all parishes in Sutherland within the year, by July 1844, but the damage had been done. Pamphlet after pamphlet condemned him for his action, pamphlet after pamphlet recalled all the old sores of the early clearances — and the Established Church, now associated with the hated landlord and his factors, enjoyed its share of the vilification too. The rivalries and hatreds of the Disruption period and later, the new element of religious and sectarian antagonism, did a great deal in the later decades of the 19th century to keep aflame the fires of landlord-tenant dispute and suspicion — for the local community divided each Sunday into its rival groups, a small 'superior' band of worshippers in the Auld Kirk, the huge new Free Kirk filled with its host of crofters and cottars.

By the close of the 19th century it was clear that the 'economic miracle' promised to the Sutherland family by Young and Sellar and schemed by Loch, had not come to be. For all the efforts that had been made, for all the money that had been spent, the eventual achievement was very disappointing. Good-will and bad management, sensible policies and senseless actions, had provided frustration and irritation for the landowners, and deep suspicion and determined opposition among the tenants. Grand designs for improvement failed elsewhere — but not with the public clamour that attended the Sutherlands. It is a nice, and unresolved, question whether the early clearings and the great increase in rental incomes in the 1820s and 1830s enabled the estate to support its tenantry more effectively in the famines of the late 1830s and mid 1840s in a way that would have been impossible otherwise — if not the 'Great Hunger' would have devastated Sutherland as it did Ireland? There is much still to be discovered about Sutherland in the 19th century and the recent decision to deposit a large portion of the Sutherland estate papers in the National Library of Scotland in Edinburgh, opening them up to all scholars in due course, is very welcome indeed.

In the first pages of this chapter it was noted that the Sutherland family only gradually came into its near monopoly-holding of properties in the District, in a typical piece of family aggrandizement that can be matched many times elsewhere in Scotland. Perhaps it should end in 1897, with the announcement of a sale by private treaty, by Messrs Watson Lyall and Co. of London, of substantial parts of Assynt (including Culag House and Lochinver, Inchnadamph Hotel), Durness, Eriboll, Kinloch, Rhifail and Skelpick in Strath Naver, Armadale and Creich: for that really signified the end of the dream of the Marquis of Stafford and the Countess-Duchess.

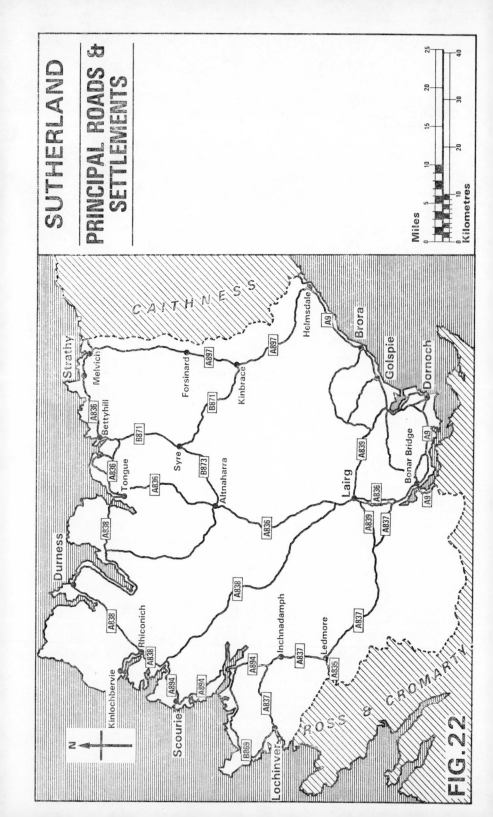

SUTHERLAND

PRINCIPAL ROADS &
SETTLEMENTS

FIG. 22

Chapter fourteen

20th CENTURY
DEVELOPMENTS

Take a District of 525,248 hectares (1,297,914 acres), with a population of about 13,000, giving an average of 40 hectares (99 acres) to one person, compared with 0.44 hectares (1.1 acres) per person for Britain as a whole, the lowest population density of any Scottish District. Take a District with the largest acreage of peat bog in Scotland, with vast tracts of moorland, bounded on three sides by water, with unsurpassed scenic grandeur of mountain, river and loch, whose only arable land is a narrow strip along the east coast. Take such a District and you have Sutherland — a land of crofting, of sheep and store cattle, a tourists' paradise, which has yet to see its natural and indigenous resources fully exploited so that it can reach the stage where the flow of people is travelling northwards and insidious persistent depopulation is at last halted.

From 1900 onwards the cry has been for more small industries to be introduced into the District which has most of its sparse population concentrated on the coasts particularly the eastern one (Fig. 22), and its vast interior given up to sheep, cattle, deer, loch and river fishing. Here, the number of human inhabitants are few.

Any upsurge of population looks like being dependent on the bridging of the Dornoch Firth which will bring East Sutherland within easier travelling distance of the fast developing Easter Ross and hopefully a more direct share in the burgeoning oil industry. In the meantime, we have to be content with seeing a large part of our manpower, upwards of 400 at the peak, travelling daily to the oil production platform industry at Nigg, a round journey for most of c.160km (100 miles). For Sutherland there is the population danger that these workers will set up home nearer their place of work.

Now oil is being tapped only 19 km (12 miles) off Helmsdale — B.N.O.C.'s Beatrice Field — with no prospect of its being piped ashore in East Sutherland, which is frustrating when at one time it seemed that quite a substantial oil-related industry was to be established at Inverbrora using a labour force of 80-100 people.

Once that has been said, it would be wrong for Sutherland not to boast about what has been achieved inside its boundaries since 1900. Perhaps the most outstanding achievement was its new school building programme in the second half of the century, unmatched, relatively speaking, by any other District in Scotland. There were other substantial achievements in the earlier years, mostly through private enterprise and through private money which put Sutherland on its path to progress, however modest. The Sutherland Technical School and the Lawson Memorial Hospital, at Golspie, the Wool Mill at Brora, a hospital for infectious diseases at Cambusavie, Dornoch, and the branch railway line from the Mound to Dornoch were all established in the first few years of this century.

Private enterprise also saw Captain Thomas Murray Hunter leave Wick in 1901 to revive the wool mill at Brora and run in conjunction with it the local coal pit and brickworks. In 1913, he launched the Brora Electricity Supply Company which resulted in the village being acclaimed as "The Electric City", its streets, houses and shops taking advantage of this new form of lighting. For 25 years Hunters supplied the public with electricity.

Road reconstruction has been a prominent feature of the second half of the century, with schemes being completed, particularly in the west, along with the £500,000 bridging of the Kyle of Tongue by a firm of local contractors the now defunct Alexander Sutherland, Ltd., of Golspie.

Crofting too, came into its own, the crofters making more or less full use of grants and subsidies at their disposal through the Crofters Commission, evidenced by the vast improvement in the quality of their livestock, particularly in the young beef field. Of course, the crofters need ancillary industry to keep them viable, but all things being equal, Sutherland crofters are not doing badly, although many of them could profit from more arable land. With new Parliamentary legislation they now have the opportunity of being landlords themselves.

Land use, of course, is the big problem in Sutherland, and it will be interesting to see how the Baird Brothers of Forsinard Estate fare in their bid eventually to reseed 8090 of the 12140 hectares (20,000 of 30,000 acres) which recently came into their possession. In this context it is interesting to note that the Highland Development Board say that they are going to take a firmer line to ensure better land use.

The founding of "The Tech" in 1903-04 was a triumph for the late Duchess Millicent, wife of the fourth Duke of Sutherland and grandmother of the present Countess of Sutherland. Her farsightedness in bringing about the birth of this residential school for crofters' sons was acclaimed by the Government of the day and it proved that Duchess Millicent was far ahead of her time in educational thinking. The building no longer serves its original purpose but is used as an annexe of Golspie High School.

For Sutherland, perhaps the most striking development in the second half of the century has been in the general educational field. The former Sutherland Education Authority's building programme was quite phenomenal. It started quietly enough with a new school at Helmsdale in the 1950s. From the 1960s came the avalanche with new secondary schools at Brora, Golspie, Dornoch and Farr (Betty-hill) and new primary schools at Altnaharra, Unapool, Tongue, Kinlochbervie and more recently Melvich. Substantial reconstruction and improvements of primary schools such as Kinbrace, Bonar Bridge, Rosehall, Scourie, Stoer, Durness, Lochinver and Rogart took place. At the moment there is only one six-year senior secondary school in Sutherland taking pupils to university entrance standard — Golspie High School. After the 2nd World War there were two, but Dornoch Academy was controversially downgraded to four-year and subsequently to two-year status. Before the War, Brora, Helmsdale, Bonar Bridge, Scourie and Lairg also presented pupils for their Higher Leaving Certificate.

Now (1978) there is a proposal to build a four-year secondary school at Scourie in North-West Sutherland, which will also cater for the parish of Assynt. A condition of this development would be a vehicular road bridge at Kylesku to supplant the existing ferry service and thereby help to solve a serious transport problem.

Sutherland has vast mineral deposits (see Chapter I) particularly in the north and west (e.g. dolomite) but even in 1962 only two minerals, the coal and brick clay of Brora were being worked and both of these industries have since gone out of existence.

With such a magnificent deep water anchorage at Loch Eriboll on the North Coast the way might be open there for the establishment of a large industrial complex, e.g. a petro-chemical works.

But now Eriboll seems to have gone into the background with Easter Ross reaping all the benefits in the way of oil platform construction, with possibilities of an oil refinery and petro-chemical industry.

Because of the depopulation trend Sutherland County Council were among the first to call for a Development Board for the Highlands, and in the event they got their wish. Yet, the earlier hopes for Sutherland are far from being realised. The ideal is for small industries to be started in all the townships round Sutherland's vast coastline in much the same way as Brora developed. Brora indeed was the ideal model for it boasted a distillery and a wool mill in addition to the brickworks and coal pit.

Will Sutherland, then, have to reconcile itself to taking no direct part in the oil and other major industries? It certainly looks that way. A major step to progress would seem to be the bridging of the Dornoch Firth. Then, more industries might be attracted to set up business in the District.

Sutherland County Council helped to lead the way in craft industries when, in 1964, they acquired an Air Ministry camp at Balnakeil, near Durness, for only £3000 and converted it into a craft village. Gradually small craft enterprises started up all round the coast, and today there is a very formidable list, with some quite outstanding developments at Bonar Bridge, Lochinver, Achmelvich, Achins, Golspie, Helmsdale and, of course, Dornoch, where the County Council, before local government reorganisation in 1975, also set up an industrial estate. Balnakeil and Dornoch are now run by the Highland Regional Council, who are also preparing another industrial site at Brora.

Golspie, and Sutherland as a whole, is greatly indebted to Alexander Sutherland, Ltd., the building contractors, who before their tragic collapse were the biggest employers in the area with a peak labour force of 600 workers. Golspie, as other parts of Sutherland, had indeed been fortunate in its family businesses. James Sutherland & Son, builders, also played an important part in the village's economy, and now J. & J. Nicol, joiners and carpenters for well over 100 years, and in more recent times building contractors, are rapidly taking over the mantle of Alexander Sutherland Ltd.

When the third Duke of Sutherland built the stretch of railway line from Golspie to Helmsdale in 1872 he decided to open an engineering shop at Brora to give employment to the local people. Some 18 years later the plant was removed to a smaller building and the original structure was converted into a weaving factory, leased to a firm from Yorkshire and finally taken over by Captain Hunter in 1901.

The brickworks eventually went out of existence because of lack of labour in the 2nd World War — although production was ultimately revived by other parties before closing again following the Conservative Government's three-day week. When Hunters had no further use for coal as a source of power for the wool factory they gave up the pit. Fortunately, the wool mill (Plate 35) has gone from strength to strength. After the War the American market was largely exploited, and today this forms an important part of the company's business. In the early days there were only 20 to 30 workers in the mill, but today that number has increased to well over 140, and Hunters are now the biggest private employers of labour in the District.

The original brickworks were founded by the Marquis of Stafford in 1818 and reopened by the third Duke of Sutherland in 1873. He ran them for 10 years on his own account and then they were leased out to other operators. In 1873 the annual production was 57,000 bricks and that was eventually stepped up to 355,000. Fire bricks, drain pipes and tiles were also produced.

In 1914, the brickworks were taken over by Brora Wool Mills, who also ran the coal pit at that time, and both industries were carried on by this firm until 1940 when the brickworks were dismantled because of labour difficulties. When the kilns were worked by T. M. Hunter, they produced two million bricks a year at their peak and employed upwards of 20 men with a market from Inverness northwards. Then in January, 1954, Sir David Robertson, M.P. for the constituency, who had taken over Brora coal pit in 1949 when it was threatened with closure by the National Coal Board, announced an agreement for the revival of the brick-making industry.

In July, 1966, the Highland Development Board financed the proving of a new coal field at Brora at a cost of over £100,000. The bores were put down to the west of the existing abandoned pit shaft in an area where a National Coal Board engineer estimated there were eight million tons of coal reserves. Now the old pit chimney and shaft superstructure have been levelled and the new mine abandoned.

The industrial history of Brora goes back some 400 years. Coal was discovered there by the 10th Earl of Sutherland, who died in

1567. The brickworks started in 1872, the wool mill in 1890 and the electricity supply company in 1913.

Another family business of importance to Sutherland employment is that of Peter Burr, grocers, general merchants and haulage contractors of Tongue. Burrs of Tongue began business there in May 1913. The " Tongue Empire " is still an integral part of the economy of the north coast.

Dornoch's biggest private employers are Grant & Sons, butchers and farmers, who were established in 1847 and now employ around 100 staff. Their refrigerated vans travel the length and breadth of Britain.

The publishing company of *The Northern Times*, whose first issue appeared in 1899, contains some of the most modern and versatile printing plant in the country. A link-up with Mr. Carmichael's Method Publishing Co. Ltd., which moved to Golspie from the south in September, 1968, further increased the company's facilities and enabled *The Northern Times* to offer the Highlands a commercial print service as creative and as polished as any in the country.

Sutherland Transport and Trading Company, Ltd., of Lairg, which has contributed much in the way of local employment, has now branched out as building contractors. Before 1926 Sutherland Transport was known as the Sutherland Motor Company, a business that had been in existence before the turn of the century. The company's buses served most of North and West Sutherland, but now uneconomic runs in the more remote areas are catered for by Post Office minibuses. The inaugural run by a Post Office minibus carrying passengers as well as mail was marked by an official ceremony at Kylesku in September, 1972. This, the first service to be operated in the Highlands, covered the route from Kylesku to Elphin. The plan, said the Post Office, was to cater for rural areas where there was no public transport, and so they would be replacing their usual vans with minibuses to give facilities which the public of the area did not enjoy at the moment. A parallel service was later provided on the Scourie/Kylestrome route and from Scourie to Laxford Bridge to link up with the Durness mail bus in the morning.

The original Clynelish Distillery at Brora was founded in 1819 by the Duke of Sutherland with the object of providing a convenient market for the grain produced by the tenants on his estate. In 1846 the partnership of George Lawson and Sons obtained a lease of the premises and carried on the business until 1896 when the distillery passed into the hands of Ainslie & Company. The company was dissolved on the retirement, in 1912, of Mr. James Ainslie and Mr. Thomas Ainslie, leaving Mr. John Risk as remaining and sole partner. This event was the forerunner of the Clynelish Distillery Co., Ltd., registered on December 18, 1912. In 1930 the company's capital was acquired by Scottish Malt Distillers, Ltd., and in 1968 a new and larger distillery was built on adjacent ground.

No praise could be too high for the North of Scotland Hydro-Electric Board for their efforts in the 1950s to bring light and power to Sutherland, despite the terrific cost of installation, particularly on the rocky west coast. It was indeed a great social service achievement and perhaps has not been properly recognised publicly.

The Sutherland chapter of the Hydro Board's story began soon after the Board were set up by Parliament in 1943. In the first assessment of potential water power resources many areas in the District were listed for examination, the principal one being the catchment of Loch Shin. In 1946 the Board appointed civil engineering consultants to carry out a preliminary survey. By 1947 they had prepared plans for a distribution scheme for North Sutherland.

The most spectacular job tackled by the Board was the construction of the Shin scheme (Plate 33) with its two large dams and its four power stations. This scheme was published by the Board in 1951 and approved by Parliament in 1953, the first contract being placed a few months later. The start of work was marked by a ceremony on the site of the Lairg dam in July, 1954. Present was the late Tom Johnston, chairman of the North of Scotland Hydro Electric Board, and former Scottish Secretary of State. Over 1000 workers were engaged on the construction of the Lairg scheme, including many local men.

In February, 1955, the Shin scheme secured press headlines with tunnellers driving a 4.9 m (16 ft) diameter tunnel through the granite between Achany and Inveran. They advanced the tunnel by 66 m (215 ft) in a week, achieving a British tunnelling record. Following the dam construction phase the power stations at Lairg and Invershin went into production in January, 1959. The completion of the Cassley and Duchally power stations on the west shore of Loch Shin, near Overscaig, and other associated works followed. The electricity generated by the two western stations was fed to the Cassley sub-station from which the Durness district was sup-

plied. The Board decided to erect a 132,000-volt line from Beauly
to Loch Shin to be extended later to the Pentland Firth, linking
Sutherland and Caithness to the water power schemes and other
parts of the Board's area. A second circuit was added later and
this line was eventually extended to Lybster and then on to Thurso.
Into the main collecting point at Inveran went electricity produced
by the Shin scheme. An additional major supply was commissioned
near Brora to augment the supply along the eastern seaboard. Then
came part of a super grid back-bone of the Board's system which,
when completed, stretched from Dounreay to Fife, carrying electricity to meet the ever increasing demand. Into the northern terminal
eventually went the output of the United Kingdom Atomic Energy
Authority's prototype fast reactor. Thus Sutherland shared in a
major Scottish achievement — the development of water power
resources and the electrification of a great stretch of country. Electricity supplies had been extended to remote places and provision had
been made for the development of the future.

Because he did not want returning ex-Servicemen to leave their
homes in search of employment after the 1st World War the fifth
Duke of Sutherland presented as a free gift to the Government the
4,856 hectares (12,000 acres) sheep farm at Borgie in North Sutherland, for dividing up into small holdings. Eventually 50 families
were to benefit from the experiment. Over and above he sold the
farms of Eriboll, Shinness, Armadale, Achnabourin and Keoldale to
the Government for the purpose of resettling ex-Servicemen.

On Shinness houses were built and the farms broken up into
holdings given to ex-Service applicants. On Eriboll, however, this
did not happen. No houses were built on the farm. The plan had
been to let the farm to the already existing smallholders who were all
ex-Servicemen, but they were unable to meet the terms. Borgie
Farm was a different proposition in so much that the arable area
was small and large portions of the hill ground were poor, being
composed mainly of black heather and bogland. The Duke therefore
decided to incorporate forestry in his scheme, in order to provide
steady employment for the holders and to ensure them a living
whatever the post war years might bring. A crofter, the late Mr John
George Mackay, of Borgie, said in an article in " *The Northern
Times* " of July 30, 1965: " If the Government had taken serious
notice and if these schemes for the Highlands had been put into
proper operation then there would be thousands more living in
their native land than there are today."

Indeed, it was the Duke's contention that in view of the unemployment problem some of the large sheep farms in the Highlands should be put to better use by displacing the tenants and paying them compensation before the expiry of their leases. Then the farms could be divided into smaller economic units and offered to ex-Servicemen who were anxious and appeared to have the ability to earn their living from the soil. " But though many of these Highland farms were on my own estates," said the Duke, " I personally was powerless to act in this way. Most of the existing leases still had many years to run before I would be free to do as I wished with the farms." He had explained that these sheep farms were let on long leases to tenant farmers who had " no need financially of so great an acreage and who, in many cases, neither employed sufficient labourers to get the best out of their land nor had the slightest wish to do so. Some of them would probably have been perfectly happy to have sold their leases and invested the capital or perhaps to have reduced the size of their holdings." But a scheme such as he proposed, said the Duke of Sutherland, needed to be comprehensive and must have Government backing and not be dependent upon private individuals. He had urged the Government to introduce a special Bill for Scotland giving themselves the power to take over the farms and develop small holdings on payment of compensation. Each holding, he had suggested, should comprise about 10 hectares (25 acres) with outbuildings and a three-bedroom cottage. The Servicemen should be trained in agricultural matters and provided with sufficient capital to allow them to stock their farms adequately and to tide them over for a certain period until they were able to make their holdings self-supporting and earn a reasonable livelihood. As a result of the Duke's efforts a special Land Settlement Bill for Scotland had been introduced later in the year and became law early in 1920. As a " *Glasgow Herald* " writer stated at the time of the Duke's publication of his autobiography: " Looking back ", the Duke had " worked persistently and often successfully for the Highlands."

The Highlands and Islands Development Board, in 1969, made a detailed survey of the Strath of Kildonan to establish a land use plan for comprehensive development. The Board's specialists investigated the Strath's potential for tourism, river fishing and for commercial sea fishing by boats based at Helmsdale. The Forestry Commission and Department of Agriculture surveyed the estates of the Strath to determine agriculture and forestry potential. The results of these studies have been drawn together to form the basis of a draft report. But at the time of writing nothing effective has been achieved.

In the last 25 or so years crofting in Sutherland has improved out of all recognition, and this has been largely due to quite generous Government subsidies. One has only to visit the annual weaned calf sale at Lairg to see just how well Sutherland crofters, all things being equal, have been doing on the livestock side. The quality of the beef calves which they rear is quite outstanding and their products are eagerly bought by Aberdeenshire feeders among others (See Chapter 15).

When Mr Lloyd George, at the time Chancellor of the Exchequer, spoke in October, of 1913, about repopulating the Highland glens and growing corn where there were now deer forests the 5th Duke of Sutherland took up the challenge. He offered to sell to the Government 85,000 hectares (210,000 acres) at 46p per hectare (22/6d. an acre) in the parishes of Eddrachilles, Durness, Tongue, Farr and Lairg. He was also prepared to sell the fishing rights at a price to be fixed by arbitration. But Lloyd George's reply was that the conditions of the offer " make it impossible for the Government to accept, but if the Development Commissioners see their way to make any use of the land it will doubtless remain open to them to avail themselves of it."

People are looking again at the possibility of reclaiming the vast acreage of peat bogs in the Highlands. It has been argued that these reclaimed bogs could become the winter feed reservoir for Sutherland and grow potatoes and other vegetables as they do in Ireland.

The extent to which fish farming will develop in Sutherland is not yet clear, but in March, 1975, the way ahead was shown by the Montrose firm of Joseph Johnston and Sons Ltd., when they set up such a project at Badcall, Scourie. Sutherland's first fish farm is based in this 110-year-old salmon house at Badcall, and the firm's objective is to instal a salmon smoking plant and refrigeration facilities.

Small industries using Sutherland's indigenous resources can aid the salvation of this depopulated and neglected area. e.g. the old Drill Hall at Helmsdale has been converted into a white fish process-ing factory; another building by the harbour has been turned into a lobster processing factory; a new mussel factory in the same area has been established. A furniture and toy making business, leather-craft work and the distribution depot of a brewery company, all will provide much-needed employment in the village.

Tourism was a dirty word in the days of the old Sutherland County Council of the 1950s. Then the fear was that crofting would be neglected. Certainly it was recognised that in a District of such natural scenic beauty tourism must have its place, but woe befall the councillor who was thought to have his mind too much in the tourist trade! Now it is seen that crofting and the tourist industry are inextricably woven together. The crofters themselves soon realised that here was a golden opportunity, if only for two or three months in the year, to supplement their income. The crofters were not hard to convince that if they were to make the most of this growing tourist trade they must improve their houses, and this they did, with the help of grants available for the purpose. Now theirs is an important contribution to the District's bed-and-breakfast facilities which are being used more and more by touring motorists.

The truth is that Sutherland must remain a great attraction for people in the south who want to escape the rat-race in their own urbanised areas and who find the relaxation, recreation and restfulness they want here. Perhaps Dornoch is the one place in Sutherland where the tourist industry could be developed in a meaningful way. It is a pity that the schemes so far presented have been on a very large scale which conjured up inordinate expenditure in providing public services.

In September, 1968, Professor Grieve, Chairman of the Highlands and Islands Development Board said after a tour in Sutherland: "Make no mistake, the north and north-west is the toughest area the Board have to deal with. Why this is so we do not know. It is clearly to do with some feeling that this is away up at the top end of the United Kingdom — like the Arctic Circle. This feeling has got to be broken down."

But there has been difficulty in persuading industrialists to move north. The Board could not direct them. But if it could not then the answer was that the Board itself had to prime the pump just as it had built hotels in the west. It might also have to do this with industry. The need for self-help in the Highlands has been reiterated all this century. For example, in 1959, Lord Forbes, Minister of State for Scotland, who was on a tour of West Ross and West Sutherland, said: "The Government can do a certain amount, but enthusiasm has to come also from the people themselves. There must be a co-operative effort in agriculture, forestry, fishing and other lines."

So far as forestry was concerned, in 1950 the late Duke of Westminster launched a 1215 hectares (3000 acres) planting scheme at Loch More. By the beginning of 1965, after 15 years, approximately eight million trees had been planted. Crofter-fishermen were the source of labour. Their peak strength was 132, and draining and fencing were the first jobs on most difficult terrain. There were 113 km (70 miles) of deer fence and about 113 km (70 miles) of sheep fence. This new-found employment was a great boost for the parish of Eddrachilles and beyond, for the estate brought in workers by bus from Stoer round to Melness. The employment force at that time numbered 40. On the east coast the Skibo Estate and the Sutherland Estate promoted afforestation schemes, the latter's being very substantial, covering a wide area from the Mound to Littleferry, to the slopes of Ben Bhraggie, along Dunrobin Glen and at Uppat, Brora. But the role of forestry is another story and for it the reader will have to refer to Chapter 17.

Part three

GENERAL

Chapter fifteen

_____

AGRICULTURE

In terms of agricultural production, Sutherland comes last of all the mainland Scottish Districts. A glance at the physical geography (Fig 6) of the District explains why very clearly Along the south-east coast from Bonar Bridge to Helmsdale there is a low-lying, fertile ribbon of arable land varying from under 0.8 km ($\frac{1}{2}$ a mile) to a little over 3.2 km (2 miles) wide. Along the north and west coast there are patches of cultivable ground as there are in the deep Straths that divide the District, but otherwise Sutherland is a land of mountain, wasteland and water with only very limited agricultural value.

Four distinct eras of development can clearly be seen on examining the farming history of Sutherland. Firstly, there were the primitive forms of agriculture that persisted almost unchanged right up to the dawn of the 19th century and certainly long after they had been superseded by more enlightened methods elsewhere in Scotland. Then there was the introduction of the Chviot sheep that transformed the pattern of rural life with such brutal abruptness only to be followed by a lingering decline that was not halted until the Second World War. Finally, came the post-War period of relative prosperity, albeit at a lower level than elsewhere in Scotland.

FARMING BEFORE 1800

Nowadays it is difficult to imagine how completely isolated Sutherland was from the rest of Scotland before the Act of Parliament of 1803 provided for aid in the construction of roads and bridges in the Highlands of Scotland. Certainly, so far as land tenure and cultivation were concerned, little had changed in a thousand years.

Under early Celtic feudalism the land was considered to be owned not by the King but by the people themselves, the Chief being merely the spokesman and leader, demanding and receiving an obedience fostered by affection rather than power or fear (Symon, 1959). With the passage of time some of the Celtic ideas about succession and ownership of land were modified but the underlying relationship between those who occupied the land and their Superior remained, and this explains to some extent the attitude of disbelief and resignation that characterised so much of the later Clearances.

The most significant development in land tenure in Sutherland was that of the tacksman (middleman) system whereby instead of the landlord receiving payment in cash or kind directly from all who occupied his land he leased large portions of it to tacksmen who were very often close relatives and who in turn obtained rent from the other occupiers as sub-tenants. Clearly, to be profitable, the tacksmen had to raise more rent than they paid the owner and, in unscrupulous hands, it led to a system of rack-renting that made the life of the common peasant one of abject penury and extreme privation.

Land settlement in Sutherland took place along the fertile eastern seaboard and up the deep straths and was characterised by a mode of life conditioned by subsistence farming that was heavily reliant on livestock and therefore subject to wild fluctuations depending on the severity of the winters. The type of housing changed little over the century, dwellings being built of turf and roofed with the same material, latterly on top of a wooden frame (Symon 1959). Humans and stock lived under the same roof and entered by the same door. Wherever possible the house was built on a slope with the family occupying the higher end where a fire was placed in the centre of their living quarters. The floor was of bare earth and when the accumulation of waste made the place un-inhabitable another hut was erected nearby and the old home abandoned and used as a supply of manure for the next crop. In 1780 an English traveller on seeing these houses remarked " the people here make their houses of the grass and feed their cattle on the stones," (Henderson 1815) which is perhaps as much a commentary on the quality of the livestock as on the living conditions of the natives.

Bere and oats were sown wherever there was enough soil and were grown in succession until the crop failed through an accumulation of disease and weeds. Only the most primitive cultivation implements were used; indeed, the caschrom or digging spade was in general use in the parishes of Assynt, Eddrachilles, Durness and Tongue right into the 20th century. Elsewhere, the Highland plough was used from early times. It was made of local birch or alder with a thin plate of hammered iron on its bottom. It was usually drawn by four garrons yoked abreast preceded by a driver walking backwards striking the animals in the face to urge them forward. Donald Sage, recalling his youth in Kildonan about 1795, recalls a scene 'scarcely less primitive than that which Virgil might be himself familiar in his boyish days at Cremona' when the plough was pulled by three horses and a cow which 'groaned most pitiously' while the ploughshare was pressed down into the furrow by the hands of two attendants (Sage, 1976). The only cultivation instrument in general use was a wooden harrow with wooden peg teeth attached to the unfortunate garrons by their tails.

Livestock was the basis of the economy, sheep and cattle being kept in almost equal numbers and goats making a significant contribution to the household diet. Sheep were of the old Kerry breed with good wool but were very small, the carcase only weighing between 11 kg and 15 kg (25 lb to 35 lb). There was virtually no external trade in sheep, the produce of wool, mutton and milk being entirely for home consumption. The custom was to herd and tether the sheep by day, keep them in folds by night and house them in the winter. Furthermore, the need to keep them close at hand for milking meant that large areas of hillside were never grazed at all. The cattle were mostly of the small Black Skye type and were renowned for their hardiness and much sought after in the south. They were bred throughout the District but where the conditions were particularly poor in the north and west the calves were frequently sent to the east coast after weaning, where they were kept until ready for sale at the age of three or four years by which time they would still be less than 225 kg (500 lb) live weight (Macdonald and Blackwood 1880). Beef cattle were really the only saleable commodity produced and were sold in July and September at the great Kyle Market held at Bonar Bridge before being taken south over the old drove roads to Crieff and Falkirk.

1800 - 1875 — THE CLEARANCES

By the beginning of the 19th century the social conditions within Sutherland were moving rapidly to an explosive climax. The potato had been introduced as a crop in the 1750's and had rapidly become part of the staple diet. This, coupled with the calmer times following the '45 Uprising, led to an increased population from 20,000 to 23,000 between the First Statistical Account of 1795 and the end of the century and it continued to climb despite a swelling tide of emigrations to the New World.

Under the pressure of over-population and an over-dependence on the blight-prone potato, starvation became a very real threat throughout the District and in many cases severe winter weather reduced tenants and their families to absolute dependence on their landlord and other superiors for sufficient food to sustain life. Into this scene in 1806 the Cheviot sheep was introduced by two Northumberland farmers, Messrs. Marshall and Atkinson, who had obtained a lease from the Duke of Sutherland on almost 40,468 hectares (100,000 acres) in the centre of the District. Their success was immediate and began a stampede of sheep farmers from the south. In that year and again in 1807, as if to make way for a new order of things, scab and rot killed the majority of native Kerry sheep that had formerly grazed on straths and mountain sides along with the black cattle (Macdonald and Blackwood 1880). The Duke of Sutherland, the owner of nine-tenths of the District that bore his name, quickly realised the unique potential that lay in the interior of his estate and through his agents, William Young, Patrick Sellar and James Loch began the systematic eviction of his vast tenantry from glens and straths to the coast in a manner that by contemporary accounts was unprecedented in its brutality and has clouded judgment on his stature as an agricultural pioneer and reformer to this day (see also Chapter 13). The success of the Cheviot sheep can be gauged by the following table:-

TABLE 12

NUMBER OF CHEVIOT SHEEP (Macdonald and Blackwood 1880).

YEAR	
1808	5,000
1811	15,000
1820	118,000
1830	156,000
1860	200,000
1874	240,000

The system of sheep husbandry adopted was that known as "ewe and wether flocks". This was a system of self-contained flocks that sold each year a crop of cast ewes and of three year old wethers. Ewes were maintained on the improved lower ground left by the departing tenants and the wethers grazed on the higher ground.

Extensive sheep farming and crofting were quite incompatible and so for undisturbed stretches of land sheep farmers were prepared to offer very much higher rents than crofters. Indeed the valuation of Sutherland trebled in fifty years. However, the incomers did not have it all their own way. The dispossessed natives turned to sheep stealing and in the two years of 1815 and 1816 eleven farmers were said to have lost no fewer than 3,187 sheep and were obliged to form the United Association of Noblemen and Gentlemen of Sutherland and Caithness for protection of their property (Macdonald and Blackwood 1880). However, it was not only livestock husbandry that was revolutionised at this time: the tide of reform also swept over the arable land on the east coast. In 1810 Sellar took over the lease of Culmaily and Morvich farms and in the next ten years he reclaimed some 100 hectares (250 acres). He introduced a system of six course rotation incorporating three years of temporary leys, two years cereals and one of turnips using principles of cultivation and stock management that were hardly improved upon until this century.

Farther down the coast George Dempster was experimenting with improvements of a very different character on Skibo and Pulrossie. A man of great humanity, he was appalled by the human misery and suffering arising from the Duke's " reforming zeal " and was determined to prove that there could be another solution. He built a weaving mill at Spinningdale and offered his employees as much land as they could improve at a nominal rent. Their successors were then to have the holding valued and the agreed rent fixed for their lifetime. Unfortunately, his industrial enterprise failed and the scheme was abandoned before it had hardly begun (Macdonald and Blackwood 1880).

1875 — THE LONG DEPRESSION

In the last quarter of the 19th century, in common with the prices of other agricultural products, those of mutton and wool declined and hill sheep farming entered a period of profound depression. Even before the onset of this depression the stocking capacity of the land had begun to decline alarmingly. Some farmers reckoned that in the late 70's only two-thirds of the numbers maintained about 1840 could be supported. The chief cause was the deterioration of the grazings, particularly on the green or old croft land made available by the Clearances; but other factors contributed, not least the absence of cattle which allowed more aggressive plants to get out of hand and encouraged the natural process of the reclaimed land to revert to heather. To maintain their numbers, farmers were obliged to send their young breeding stock away to winter in Morayshire and Nairn which greatly added to their costs; indeed it was reckoned that in the five years preceding 1880 most sheep farmers in Sutherland had lost money.

The winter of 1878/79 marked a watershed in the fortunes of the sheep farmer. For four months snow lay over Sutherland east of a line from Loch Eriboll to Loch Shin. Twenty-five per cent of the sheep stock perished and many more would have done so if they had not been moved to Caithness and there fed on hay supplied in train loads every second day from Ross-shire and Inverness. Even so, some of the losses were appalling. On one farm 500 ewes reared only 50 lambs and another 200 ewes died at lambing time. On another all 500 young wether lambs were lost in the snow (Macdonald and Blackwood 1880). Many of the lambs that did survive were weak and prices were well down on previous years although twice what they were to fall to in the next decade.

The depression in sheep farming was accompanied by a rising demand for moors for sporting purposes and with landlords quick to seize any opportunity of maintaining their income, history repeated itself in the Highlands but this time it was the sheep and not the people who were cleared off the land. Indeed between 1880 and the outbreak of the Second World War the total number of sheep in Sutherland declined by 40% and many former sheep runs were given over to deer forests. For instance, the Duke of Sutherland sold off Reay Estate to the Duke of Westminster and thus in one move 70% of the Parish of Eddrachilles was reserved for sport.

Fortunately, for the peace of mind of those engaged in farming, the long depression that lay ahead was not appreciated and the new wealth brought into the District by the Cheviot sheep was used to support a number of agricultural innovations, quite the most important and most spectacular being the land reclamation undertaken by the Duke of Sutherland at Lairg and Kildonan between 1873 and 1882. The Lairg improvements, for instance, resulted in an area of some 725 hectares (1,800 acres) between Loch Shin and the River Tirry being reclaimed by means of giant ploughs so that hay and turnips could be grown for winter feed. The whole work was supervised by Mr Kenneth Murray of Geanies and cost £100,000. At the height of the operations, fourteen giant steam engines could be seen in use at the same time (Loch 1820).

The long period of depressed prices that continued from the opening up of the American Corn Belt until 1939, with only a brief period of profitability during the Great War, affected the arable farms on the east coast of Sutherland less than might have been expected and certainly far less than the wheat growing areas in the south. This was largely because of the high proportion of grass and fodder crops in the six course rotation that had been universally adopted since Patrick Sellar's work at Culmaily and Morvich provided the cheapest form of feeding for stock and maintained fertility of the soil with the minimum of outside expenditure.

Table 13, overleaf, demonstrates the remarkable stability achieved, with only barley virtually disappearing from cropping, although it is significant that it was not replaced by an increase in oats but rather by an extension of the grazing acreage.

THE POST-WAR YEARS

One of the main problems facing farmers in Sutherland has always been, and remains, the distance from the large consumer markets in the south. It was the reason why cattle were virtually the only saleable commodity until the coming of the railway and indeed it is doubtful whether the explosive growth of the sheep industry could have taken place without the same railway system to take the wool and mutton south. The 1947 Agricultural Act, by guaranteeing minimum prices for almost all agricultural products, not only reduced the farmers' risk dramatically but went a long way to reducing the risks attached to marketing in remote areas and resulted in a quarter of a century of stability that has seen dramatic improvements in technology right across the industry. In the arable sector along the east coast, while the names of the farms remain the same and most farmers still follow a rotation that is not so very different from Patrick Sellar's innovation of 150 years ago, almost everything else has changed. Fields have been enlarged to help mechanisation, modern steadings have been built on almost every farm, initially provided by the landlord, but increasingly now modernised with tenants' capital. Rotational grass, the most important crop on the farm, is more and more intensively managed.

Farm mechanisation is perhaps the most obvious area of change to the passing stranger. In 1945 there were still a thousand working horses in Sutherland; today there are virtually none, the tractor having taken their place. One result of mechanisation has been a

* Statistics obtained from the Department of Agriculture for Scotland.

TABLE 13 – AGRICULTURAL STATISTICS FOR SUTHERLAND* 1850–1940

	1850	1870	1880	1914	1920	1930	1940
BARLEY (Acres)	3,600	2,000	2,250	650	600	200	150
OATS (Acres)	6,800	6,000	8,000	8,000	8,000	6,000	6,000
POTATOES (Acres)	2,500	1,700	1,900	1,300	1,300	1,000	950
TURNIPS (Acres)	2,000	2,500	3,200	3,000	2,700	2,400	2,000
CATTLE (Numbers)	12,500	10,000	12,300	5,000†	3,500	3,900	4,200
SHEEP (Numbers)	160,000	216,000	200,000	84,000††	84,000	92,000	100,000

† Breeding Cows only   †† Breeding Ewes only   * See text   Note. 1 Acre = 0.4 Hectares

TABLE 14 – AGRICULTURAL STATISTICS FOR SUTHERLAND* 1945–1975

	1945	1955	1965	1975	
BARLEY (Acres)	160	320	1,300	2,000	
OATS (Acres)	5,600	4,700	3,400	1,500	
POTATOES (Acres)	900	600	500	150	*Note:*
TURNIPS (Acres)	1,700	1,700	1,700	1,000	*1 Acre =*
BREEDING COWS (Numbers)	4,500	4,500	4,000	6,000	*0.4 Hectares*
BREEDING SHEEP (Numbers)	100,000	94,000	110,000	98,000	
HORSES (Numbers)	1,000	300	–	–	
AGRICULTURAL WORKERS	650	550	300	190	

severe reduction in the number of agricultural workers employed, from 650 immediately after the War to under 200 today. Apart from the effect on the farms themselves in terms of vacant cottages and an absence of relief help in times of crisis, the social effect on the District through the loss of some 1,500 persons has been serious and is one of the major factors contributing to the population decline. The combine harvester was still viewed with scepticism in many quarters as a realistic means of securing the harvest in Sutherland as late as 1960. Today, it would be hard to find a binder on any farm and even the majority of those crofters who still grow grain will have it harvested by combine.

On the cropping side the changes have been just as dramatic. Table 14 shows that potatoes have virtually ceased to be grown as a commercial crop in Sutherland and, indeed at present, there is only one farm with an appreciable acreage. Perhaps the most remarkable feature has been the revival of barley where the acreage has come up from virtually nothing to 800 hectares (2,000 acres) and continues to rise at the expense of oats which are now more or less confined to croft ground. There are two main reasons for this: the development of a local market for malting barley and the changeover to the combine harvester which requires a crop to be some two weeks riper than was necessary with the binder, where final ripening could take place in the stock. So far, it has proved impossible to breed an oat that will mature anything like as soon as the earlier barley varieties so that although barley requires a higher standard of cultivation and manuring than oats if it is to give a comparable yield, the need to get the harvest in before the equinoctial gales has proved decisive in the choice of cereal. The total acreage under cereals has halved since the War. This reflects the change in winter feeding from hay and turnips to silage which is now made on virtually all farms although hay and, to a lesser extent, turnips have held their own on smaller holdings and crofts because of the very high capital cost in machinery required in making silage.

Advances in science and technology cannot alter the basic nature of Sutherland which is still predominantly a livestock area; even the most fertile farms still derive the bulk of their income from livestock sales. The Cheviot sheep has held its position despite a period of some fifteen years from the mid 1950s to the early 1970s when lamb prices remained virtually static. Certainly, some of the larger flocks owned by absentee landlords were dispersed but in the main farmers and crofters, particularly those in Sheepstock

Clubs, soldiered on because of the complete lack of any alternative enterprise to turn to. Nowadays, the sheep are kept in regular ages and almost all the lambs are sold as stores for further fattening at the big August and September sales held in Lairg and Rogart. Indeed, the August sale in Lairg is the largest one day sale in the United Kingdom. Despite a very high standard of stockmanship throughout Sutherland, sheep farming remains the least developed of any livestock enterprise. There has been very little change in the way in which sheep are herded on the open hill ,with virtually no land reclamation this century, and there are still many flocks that only receive winter feeding in extreme conditions. This is not so much through any lack of technical knowledge as through a lack of capital and confidence in the future. However, perhaps the only bright prospect for farmers in the North as a result of our member-ship of the European Economic Community is in a new market for sheep on the Continent. If these hopes are realised then we may yet see sheep numbers approaching the figures of one hundred years ago.

Breeding cow numbers at 4,000 remained almost unaltered from the beginning of the century until 1972; then, in response to an ex-pectation that more beef would be required in Europe there was a dramatic increase with most farmers enlarging their herds and some new ones being established on hill farms that had seen vir-tually no cattle since the Clearances. Unfortunately, these expecta-tions have not been realised and there is every indication that cow numbers are declining, perhaps even faster than they built up. Cer-tainly, there is no way in which cattle can be kept economically in the District unless the majority of winter feed stuffs can be grown on the farm. This very much limits the herd size especially on the poorer soil outwith the eastern seaboard. Except for the more fer-tile farms, calves are usually born in the Spring and sold at the calf sales in the late Autumn. Lairg and Rogart both have cattle sales but, unlike sheep, a significant number of calves and cast cows are sold in Dingwall which is the nearest weekly market for all farmers in the District, except for those few on the north coast for whom Thurso is the normal outlet.

CROFTING

No chapter on agriculture in Sutherland would be complete without a description of the crofting system. We have seen that in Sutherland the relief, soil and climate determine a pastoral system of farming where cropping is only done to provide food for the cultivator and winter feed for his stock. To support any considerable population holdings must, of necessity, be small and cultivation of the available ground intensive. This, in essence, is the reason why crofting prevails in the Highlands. In the past, crofting was the pattern of farming for the whole of Sutherland with the exception of a few larger farms and small estates on the east coast belt. For centuries the coastal fringe and straths were cultivated by a proud and independent people who carried on a way of life that hardly changed from generation to generation. They were true crofters in a sense that they were totally self sufficient. Milk, oats and barley cakes were the staple diet supplemented by fish for those who lived on the coast and by mutton for those in the Strath. Every scrap of in-by land was carefully cultivated and stock were herded on common grazings associated with each township. By any standard life was almost unbearably hard and yet a contemporary 17th century traveller reported with some envy that they were "frugal and temperate in their habits; in Spring and Harvest they laboured hard and the Summer and Winter were passed in ease, poverty and contentment" (Macdonald and Blackwood 1880). The system had begun to break down by the time of the Rebellion of 1745. Over-population and therefore pressure on scarce food resources was the principal reason. As we have seen already, between 1755 and 1798 the total population of Sutherland rose by 10%. Even the Clearances failed to halt the rise. Although many evicted families emigrated (from Foindle and Ardmore in Eddrachilles, almost 1000 people emigrated to North America in 1806 alone — Adam and Rankin 1964) by 1845 the population had reached a peak of 25,500. The introduction of the potato about 1756 had staved off immediate disaster and it quickly became the staple diet in most households but, in the end, its liability to blight plunged the whole of the North of Scotland into famine in the terrible years of 1845 and 1846. Only emergency relief measures instituted in the cities in the south prevented mass starvation, but even so another wave of emigration took place and the long decline in population which began continues to this day.

According to the Royal Highland Agricultural Society of Scotland there were 2,680 crofters in Sutherland in 1853. Each had an average of 1.6 hectares (4 acres) of arable land and 14.4 hectares (36 acres) of outrun and owned 2 cows and 5 sheep. A quarter of a century later the only material change was in the housing conditions which had been considerably improved, thanks to timber and lime being supplied free of charge by the Duke of Sutherland. What he was not prepared to do, however, was to offer his tenants leases and so, lacking security, there was no inducement to the crofter to improve his land. The agricultural depression that overtook the whole area in the last quarter of the century bore most heavily on crofters and tenants of holdings of an uneconomic size. It was no longer possible to exist on the croft alone and so the practice of multiple occupation that is so much a feature of modern crofting came into being. Initially, it was the herring fishing that attracted both men and women who would move south to begin work as soon as the crops had been sown in the Spring.

As the agricultural depression continued, so the condition of the crofter worsened and the demands for security of tenure, fair rents, more land and better communications began to be aroused. Could it be right that a system that produced so many fine soldiers, doctors, scientists and clergymen should be allowed to decay and pass away? The Government appointed the Napier Committee whose report in 1884 was accepted and two years later the Crofters' Holding Act and the Congested District Act were passed. A Crofters' Commission was appointed and security of tenure and fair rents were assured. The Nation, however, failed to identify a policy of cheap food and free trade as the main cause of the agricultural depression and rural depopulation. Crofting continued to be uneconomic, the acreage of cultivated land continued to decline, so did cattle numbers, and the exodus from the countryside into the villages continued. Today, the problem has not changed — indeed in many respects it has worsened — as the young men leave home and those remaining grow older and a way of life that was always fragile, struggles to survive against the pressures of inflation and agricultural techniques that demand a larger scale of enterprise.

It is hoped that the new Act that allows the crofter to buy and develop his croft will find enough young men prepared to accept the challenge and keep alive the priceless heritage that is more truly Sutherland than anything else the District can boast.

Chapter sixteen

FISHING

It is likely that there has been sea fishing round the north and west coasts of Sutherland as long as there has been settlement. Not all townships, of course, lay beside a calm loch in which small boats could easily and safely operate. But for those that did, there was a variety of fish to be caught quite reliably by hand-line and there was, particularly in the latter half of the year, at least the chance of herring to be caught by net. Use of simple and cheap equipment gave a useful if uncertain supplement to the food raised on the small-holdings which served nearly every family. For the most part, we can only speculate how well and how widely the people were equipped for these tasks but from the records that begin to accumulate for the late 18th century, it is clear that there was a general use of fishing opportunity. In Home's 'Survey of Assynt' considerable groups are shown to be in some sense dependent on fishing. In one settlement, the surveyor finds at least at the season of his report, 'most of the people employed at the Fishings'; in another were 'Sub-tenants consisting of upwards of a Score of Families whose great business was at the Fishing'. Moreover, these groups were well distributed along the coast; 'Fishings are become an object worth attention on any part of the Coast' (Adam, 1960). Not least were they to be found on the open unprotected stretches south of the Point of Stoer and fishing was evidently sustained even in arduous situations where boats had to be hauled over open beaches. It is notable too that the fishing communities were reasonably well provided with land; certainly there was no landless class and averages for settlements ranged between 1.6 and 4 hectares (4 and 10 acres) per family, far more that was to be typical of a later time. The way in which small-holders might organise for fishing is shown for the areas farther north in a report on the parish of Eddrachilles made in 1793. They were excellent boatsmen, we are told, but "there is no person whose sole business is fishing, consequently no fish is sold except herring; yet everyone is a fisher and fishes for himself. Every village and almost every house has a boat, nets and all sorts of fishing tackle." (*Old Statistical Account — O.S.A.*).

In Assynt too, about the same time, we find that every farm had one, two or three boats (*O.S.A.*).

Much of the fishing was for immediate consumption but some also was for sale; fishing had become at least intermittently a commercial operation. In a country so remote from any possible markets, fish for sale had to be cured and curing implied the intervention or service of the merchant. Particularly did sales depend on a capitalist intermediary in the curing of herring; pickling, the simpler of the two main types of process, required much salt and many barrels. It was unlikely, particularly when the salt laws were so repressive, that these would be provided by the fisherman himself, and reddening required even more elaborate and expensive capital in the shape of 'smoking houses'. In fact, outside capital was already playing some part in the development of the local effort of herring fishing. Partly this was because the north and west coasts of Sutherland formed the backdrop to the operations of large sections of the main fishing fleet of Scotland. Every year in numbers that on the whole were increasing since mid-century, a fleet of vessels — known as 'busses' — was fitted out with salt and barrels to journey in the second half of the year to the promising fishing grounds which generally proved to be in the sea lochs of the north-west. In fact, they operated by the lowering of small boats so that sheltered water was essential. As many as eighty of these vessels might be found at a time in the Sutherland lochs (*O.S.A.*). Nominally, until 1786, they were not allowed to buy herring from the local boats but it is clear that in fact they did so and after 1786 the trade was legitimised. Any large onset of herring shoals — which occurred capriciously and by no means every year — would attract the fleet which would thus constitute a reasonably dependable market for the produce of the local fishermen. There were instances, too, of curers setting up land establishments within the area both for pickling and for reddening. 'By the side of Loch-Inver is the fishing station of Culag, built at the expense of £2000 Sterling, by John-Joseph Bacon, Esq.; of the Isle of Man and one Donald Ross partner, for a certain share of that sum. Of late years the lease and buildings have been all transferred to other adventurers' (*O.S.A.*).

29. Bonar Bridge looking West, c.1913   *(D. McGregor)*

30. Bonar Bridge, 1978   *(A. Smith)*

31. Golspie, Ben Bhragaidh in background   *(B. Kenworthy)*
32. Helmsdale   *(A. Smith)*

33. Lairg, with Shin Dam   *(J. Campbell)*
34. Salmon Fishing on the Naver   *(J. Campbell)*

35. Finished Fabric,
Hunter's Wool Mill, Brora
(J. Macrae)

36. Clynelish Distillery,
Brora
(J. Campbell)

Commercial opportunities, then, were drawing the inhabitants, particularly of the west coast of Sutherland and most of all in Assynt, into sporadic ventures in herring fishing. The other main possible form of commercial operation, line-fishing for cod, proved much harder to establish although conditions seemed favourable. Stranger boats made good catches of cod nearby, particularly from the bank that stretched at a short distance offshore along the north coast. And authority favoured cod rather than herring fishing as an engine of improvement. Herring, with its chance of sudden gain for little effort, offered no incentive to 'habits of industry'; sudden excesses of money solved no underlying problems; the arrival of stranger fleets and the establishment of commercial relations with them demoralised the inhabitants. Or so it was thought. Cod fishing, on the other hand, offered a reasonably steady if modest gain for the sustained effort — an altogether more reliable base for social improvement. Even the merchants sought to encourage cod fishing. Yet the people evidently thought otherwise. Their investments and their efforts were mainly for herring fishing.

The whole arrangement in which a population, well settled on the land, was generally prepared for fishing, drew a useful subsistence from it and was involved more sporadically in the excitement of a big and profitable herring fishing, was to be swept away by two gathering forces. One was reorganisation in several of the landed estates of Sutherland, the other the emergence and long-term consolidation of a new and greatly successful form of herring fishing in Caithness. Both had profound effects on the fishing arrangements of Sutherland.

The plans for the human engineering of the estates of the Countess of Sutherland had become notorious but this was not the only tract of land in the district in which people were forcibly moved to fit the schemes of authority. The Reay estate, indeed, provided something of a model for imitation by the planners of the greater estate and the Bighouse and Armadale estates in the north also saw many movements of the tenantry (Loch 1820). The common idea was to lay the lands of the interior in sheep farms and to resettle the displaced population on the coasts, where it was supposed it might learn new habits of industry and a more secure form of livelihood in fishing. Thus many hundreds of families were decanted along the western and northern coastlines — a long stretch, but one which the choicer spots were already occupied. Land, of course, was still accepted as a necessary support, even in communities designed for fishing as a main activity. There could not be much land where occupation was already so complete; and in any case the planners of the new order held it to be desirable not to allow enough land to distract from the main business of fishing. Two arable acres (0.8 hectares) came to be accepted as a rough standard in accommodating these settlers and even in the older settlements immigrants brought congestion and a breaking down of the traditional standard. Thus, in 1820, in almost every part of the western and northern coast which was at all capable of settlement, there existed a swollen population crowded on minute and often infertile fragments of land and driven therefore to look to fishing for relief. The exact nature and potential of the fishing to which it did turn was determined by the fishing growing to the east — in Caithness.

The fishing of Caithness was based on a simple organisation; for it, curers laid in stores of salt and barrels, ready to cure rapidly the highly erratic landings of a fleet of small open boats — unlike the busses on which hopes had rested in the 18th century — which nightly moved distances of up to 24km (15 miles) to the fishing grounds. The curing stations were fixed for the season and boats were engaged to the curers at given locations. The fishing was emerging by 1790 but remained small in scale, employing about 200 boats till around 1810; then sudden expansion took the numbers to over 1,000 in a very few years, and thereafter, till late in the 19th century, such numbers would regularly congregate on the Caithness coast for the period from late July to mid-September. Boats were engaged by curers to fish for them at a price per cran fixed in pre-seasonal bargaining.

The attraction of this Caithness fishing tugged at the populations of the coast and even inland areas all over the Northern Highlands and Islands. Sutherland, so close geographically and with such need to find a lucrative form of fishing, was at least for a period, the most deeply affected. There were in fact two ways in which money could be made by seasonal immigrants to Caithness. The simpler and easier was to tramp to one of the Caithness stations and engage as a hired hand in one of the big boats owned by the east coast men, for it was customary for boat owners, who were usually formed in partnerships of two or three, to complete the crew by hiring men who had no direct share in the boat. It was strictly a seasonal arrangement, although sometimes links were formed that would manifest in recurring hirings by the same owners.

The reward was based on an annual bargain, the principles of sharing being different between different crews and sometimes over different seasons, but generally it would be in some way tied to the size of the catch. It was liable to fluctuation, then, but through the first half of the century returns generally settled at between £4.10s. and £6 for six weeks' work. The numbers employed ran into thousands, not only in Caithness, but also at the stations that had burst into action after 1815 along the southern Moray Firth and the east coast of Aberdeenshire. Most of the seasonal migrants went to Caithness and this remained a substantial if variable means of earning a living.

The harder way to share in Caithness earnings was to join in a crew which would take its boat to one of the Caithness stations. This was hard because it involved an arduous feat of self-equipment based on substantial earnings. By 1830 the standard fishing boat capable of being used with advantage in Caithness conditions was of forty-foot (12m) keel and would cost, along with a fleet of nets, over £100, a very far cry from the fourteen-foot (4.3m) skiffs with their few nets that had been the traditional equipment of west coast fishermen. There were, it is true, ways of abridging the expense: to buy secondhand from successful east coast men, or to use a sub-standard boat. But at the very least a big expenditure was needed and what help the west coast fishermen might get from the curer or merchant carried with it substantial burdens and obligations. Yet it is reasonably certain that considerable numbers did make the transition from small- to large-scale fishing. In 1840 Eddrachilles had twenty-four large boats, valued at £30 each, a figure suggesting they were probably smaller than those owned by Caithness and east coast men but still considerably larger than any previously owned on the west coast (*New Statistical Account —* N.S.A.). With its fleet of nets such a boat might well be valued at over £100. By 1855 there were 106 Class I boats (i.e. boats of over thirty-foot (9m) keel) on the north and west coasts as a whole (British Fisheries Annual Report 1855, 1856).

In the early 1840's another opportunity opened to the owners of sufficiently equipped boats; a Minch fishing, arranged on the Caithness model — and indeed run by east coast curers — was based on fishing stations along the east coast of Lewis, commencing annually in May and lasting until late June. It could therefore be exploited by crews additionally to their activity in the later summer fishing of Caithness. So it continued year after year, and the dependence together with the scale of the rewards in these forms of fishing is shown in a report made in 1869 (Commissioners Report on the Employment of Children etc.). In that year, the parish of Assynt had forty-four boats, each of which went both to the Lewis and to the Caithness fishings. Every coastal township had at least one, and some had several. The average gross takings for a crew were £96 to be divided between five or six men and to meet costs of equipment and depreciation; one boat made £181 but one made as little as £13, which certainly did not cover costs. At the best, in this particular year, which was probably typical enough, individual gains were not outstanding and in several cases they were disastrous. The gross takings from active fishing were somewhat greater than those made by the migrant hired hands but in terms of net gain, the hired men probably had the better of it, with a clear return of about £5 per head. Dependence on this form of fishing was well-nigh universal, with an average of two members of each household engaged. Thus there were 259 houses in the district, something over 200 hired hands, and probably well over 250 members of crews. Dependence on fishing was not quite so widespread in the parish of Eddrachilles but of much the same order of individual commitment. The north coast parishes of Durness, Tongue and Farr sustained still smaller groups of fishermen operating in the same way as those of Assynt (Commissioners' Report on the Employment of Children, etc). Apparently then, herring fishing at distant bases pursued for about three months in the summer had, for some fifty years, proved the mainstay of the coastal population with its scanty resources of land; to that extent the plans laid before 1820 had succeeded. Yet it was a success with deep flaws. The returns were fluctuating and often scarcely enough to meet costs; the equipment was second-rate compared with that of the east coast men and, indeed, it was only by buying second-hand boats from the east coast crews that the owning partnerships of working fishermen, which was still the system in Sutherland, could continue to act.

Moreover, by 1870, the Sutherland distant water fishing — big boats making their annual migrations to fish for the secure markets offered by the curers — was beginning to decline. By 1886 the number of boats with the capability of off-shore fishing was down to forty-six and by the end of the century the whole industry had virtually disappeared with the number of first-class boats down to five (Fishery Board for Scotland, *Annual Reports* 1886, 1900). Explanations can be given in terms of the increasing capital demands of herring fishing in the new conditions of the time. The decked boats that were widely adopted in the seventies, the continued increase in size, the use of steam capstans, the further extension in the scale of the drift of nets made for rapid increase of capital costs; by the eighties, a herring boat fully equipped with nets cost about £500 or £600 and by the end of the century it cost around £1,000. It was just too much to ask of a fishing population which continued to operate within a vicious circle of poor equipment and low returns and therefore of inability to make further improvements. Yet a people in very similar circumstances, that of parts of Lewis, did manage to step up its efforts and to particpate even to an increasing degree in the main herring fishings (Gray, 1973). Perhaps its advantage was that it had a fishing in its own locality; it could operate initially from home bases. No fishing station was set up in Sutherland as a base for the Minch fishing (as opposed to the very different fishing within the sea lochs of the coast).

The herring fishing in the open water pursued from distant bases rose to play a dominating, if annually uncertain, role in the coastal economy and then fell to leave behind severe social problems. Other forms of fishing, more modest and less spectacular, were sometimes more durable. Cod fishing, it is true, went through the same cycle as herring fishing although with far less of an expansion. Great faith was placed in cod fishing as an engine of reform, a means of securing steady incomes on the basis of stern effort. Yet, aspiring cod fishermen never fully or securely surmounted the difficulties that surrounded the operation. For one thing, line fishermen did not collect centrally at the ports where they could be sure of sale of their catch. They operated in the stormiest months of the year from the beaches of their own townships, which in many cases in Sutherland were exposed and dangerous. Difficulties of marketing, too, were chronic (Gray, 1973). Never were secure and comprehensive long-term arrangements made by merchants to purchase and cure the catch of an extensive population. Thus we find fishermen having to send cod on their own account to main markets at Wick or Aberdeen; or, more often, giving up, helpless to secure the full gains of their effort. In fact, merchants who did sporadically start in the business of curing cod developed an extensive credit and barter system through which they supplied the fishermen with general goods and fishing gear and purchased probably more products than the fish in which they were mainly interested. There might be profit for them in these sidelines but there was also the risk of being left simply with bad debts. In any case, for fishermen it was profoundly discouraging and might well end in complete withdrawal. Thus the cod or line fishing never seriously challenged the supremacy of herring and, like the distant water herring fishing, it faded away in the final years of the 19th century. Trawlers from a distance were blamed for devastating the fishing grounds but this was simply a final blow at a faltering system.

The loch fishing for herring followed a path of growth and decline very different from that of any other fishing. This was an activity in the tradition of the 18th century when the arrival of herrings in the loch would touch off a feverish but highly localised activity. Small boats would be launched in their dozens and large catches might be made for a brief period. So, essentially, it continued through the 19th century. But this local fishing was evidently never a rival to the fishing in distant waters, although, with a possible period of fishing extending through the winter, fishermen back from the east coast might well participate. Above all, it remained desperately precarious, depending upon occasional visitations by the shoals and upon the chance arrival of curers or vessels with curing stores to give value to the catch. In the last quarter of the century the exploitation of passing opportunity became potentially more efficient. Steam vessels began to arrive with curing stores or to carry away fish to larger curing centres. Larger boats eventually powered by paraffin motors allowed crews to travel greater distances to the shifting centres of fishing (Gray, 1973). But the increased capital cost of such participation had also by this time begun to cut into the numbers of participants. The larger catches that were made were by the efforts of a comparatively small minority which scarcely even replaced the crews that had once depended on Caithness and Lewis fishings.

In fact, from 1880 onwards, fishing in nearly all its forms was shrinking to a small and occasional effort. One standby remained to give income from the sea — the lobster fishing. This was already of some importance early in the 19th century. It was an ideal form of fishing for peasant by-employment as an account from Durness in 1845 shows (N.S.A.). The boats were small, of fourteen-foot (4.3 m) keel, each being manned by a crew of two men. They worked at night, close inshore. Brought ashore the lobsters were closed in perforated floating chests till called for, weekly, by welled smacks. Activity like this seems to have been steadily pursued as a background to the more absorbing but also more precarious tasks of herring fishing. Thus in 1869 when Assynt sent forty-four boats to the herring fishing, twenty-four were engaged, at the same time of year, in lobster fishing (Fourth Report on Women in Agriculture). It is true that the latter only gave a return less than one tenth of that of the herring fishing but in the end it was to outlast herring fishing, a durable and rewarding form of enterprise even to the present day.

The east coast of Sutherland had no ancient tradition of seamanship and fishing. The more spectacular then was the rise after 1810 of a station for curing an appreciable portion of the catches made at the summer fishing of the east coast. Indeed, here the coincidence of the two forces of redeployment of population and of the growth of the successful herring fishing is even more striking than on the west and north coasts. The area at the mouth of the river Helmsdale was chosen for the settlement of the dispossessed from the interior. Small-holdings were being laid out betwen 1811 and 1816 and along with the feus for houses without land provided the basis at Helmsdale for a mixed community of farmer-fishermen together with some who fished full-time (Adam, 1972). There were other ingredients in the new fishing community making another part of the plan to substitute industry for agriculture. Skilled families from the old fishing communities were attracted, for example from Fraserburgh, to set an example for the native settlers who had no experience of the sea (Loch, 1820). The third element in planning was the physical equipment of a port with shelter for the boats and buildings for curing. Authority, it seems, was learning from the spontaneous experiences farther north and was deliberately creating the material framework as well as assembling the human sinew of a major fishing station of the new model and of a community that would exploit its facilities. Indeed, the standard of provision for curing yards was outstandingly high, far better than the yards farther north, which were often open and unsheltered stances (N.S.A.). The port became one of the stations to attract boats from outside and well into the 19th century fishing persisted on a fairly modest and rather fluctuating scale. Some resident full-time fishermen, probably the descendants of the immigrants from farther south, fished the year round. These developed cod and haddock fishing with which to occupy the gaps between herring fishing seasons.

An underlying weakness manifest in relatively poor equipment and in continuing debt eroded the ability of at least the farmer-fisherman to meet the conditions of the last quarter of the century.

By that time the expensiveness of first-rank boats had so increased that only fishermen already debt-free and with the income that came from equipment of the highest order could continue to hold shares as independent fishermen even nominally owning the boats that they worked. Many of the Helmsdale men, then, sank to become the wage-earners to the more successful and most of them would have to go to a strange centre to find such work (Report of the Departmental Committee on Sea Fisheries in Sutherland and Caithness, 1905). This they combined with a local haddock fishing in small boats through the rest of the year. Even more compelling was the adoption after 1900 of steam drifters which were so enormously more expensive. Ownership then came to be concentrated in a few centres and increasing bodies of fishermen all along the coast — particularly those in the lesser centres — ceased to have any share in the boats. This was, it is true, a tendency rather than a drastic and complete change. Helmsdale did have some steam drifters on the register, but they were owned by curers and made available to fishermen on a hiring basis. Moreover, sailing vessels were still extensively used up to 1914. Helmsdale in fact shows the varieties of adaptation to these circumstances with some owners, mainly of sailing boats, but with a growing majority who had shares in neither boats nor nets.

By 1914 fishing had so shrunk as to consist on the north and west coasts of only a lobster fishing and an occasional herring fishing in one or other of the lochs, this being exploited by outsiders as much as by residents: on the east coast it now comprised a haddock fishing by local fishermen coupled with sporadic efforts at herring fishing mainly by the local fishermen acting as wage-earners. The hard experience of fishing after 1918 obliterated more of the residues of once widespread fishing. Little was left by the 1930's on the west coast except a mere handful of motor boats and a somewhat greater array of even smaller craft; they made nothing from herring fishing, a few hundreds of pounds from miscellaneous inshore fishing, and most of all from lobster fishing. The loch fishing for herring had died out completely in the 1920's. The 1950's, it is true, brought greater activity into the area in the shape of boats, mainly from the Moray Firth, coming to sweep the prolific Minch with seine nets, the catch being of white fish. Landings were made at Lochinver (Plate 2) and Kinlochbervie on Loch Inchard and the fish were taken by road to east coast centres while crews would return to their homes at the weekend. In fact, the west coast lochs served as little more than landing stages. Helmsdale sustained more of a local effort. By 1923 there were no steam drifters on the register and a herring fishing now in great travail had little to offer. But the use of seine nets on motor boats, of which in the 'thirties over a dozen were operating from the port, successfully replaced the less productive line fishing for haddock. Fish were entrained to reach the Glasgow market in good condition. However, the creeks along the coast south to Embo, which had once contained substantial clusters of fishermen and boats, ceased to have either. Helmsdale, with a fishing far below the great days of the 19th century herring fishing, alone remained to pursue a modest and steady effort.

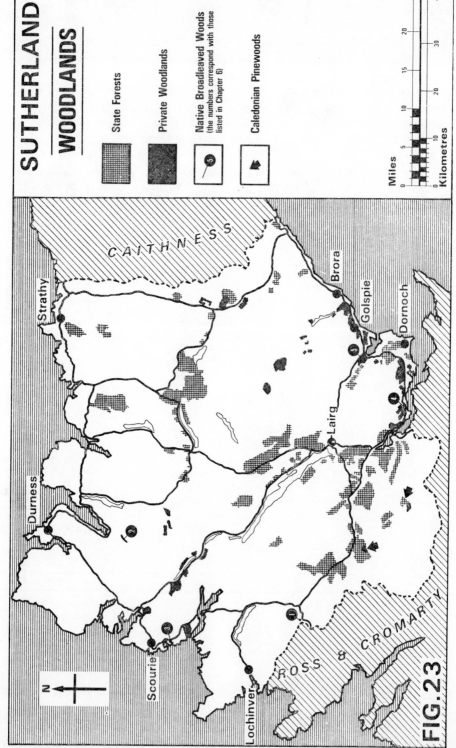

SUTHERLAND
WOODLANDS

State Forests

Private Woodlands

Native Broadleaved Woods
(the numbers correspond with those
listed in Chapter 6)

Caledonian Pinewoods

Miles

Kilometres

N

FIG.23

Chapter seventeen

WOODLANDS

To the casual observer the bulk of Sutherland must appear very much a virgin landscape to which trees have been introduced spasmodically by man in recent times. Consequently, at first glance their history holds little interest. Nothing could be farther from the truth. For centuries there has been some knowledge of the forests of past ages in Scotland from their remains entombed in peat bogs — of which Sutherland has its fair share. The *Old Statistical Account* mentions oak, pine and less frequently birch, hazel, alder, mountain ash, willow and juniper. This has been substantiated by our present day knowledge and use of pollen analysis.

Therefore, to understand the history of forestry in Sutherland it is necessary to study past ages, to follow the development of man from his early beginnings and to see how he has affected his environment.

Impact of Man on Forests in Prehistoric Times

After the last Ice Age we know that birch first spread over the Sutherland tundra followed by pine in the north and east. Oak and alder, while increasing, never replaced birch and pine as the major species.

The needs of Mesolithic man (perhaps the first inhabitant of Sutherland) for timber, whether for huts or fuel, must have been small. Clarke (1952) depicts the landscape thus: "If one could have flown over Northern Europe during Mesolithic times, it is doubtful whether more than the occasional wisp of smoke from some camp fire, or maybe a small cluster of huts or shelters by a river bank or old lake bed, would have advertised the presence of man: in all essentials the forest would have stretched unbroken save only by mountain, swamp and water, to the margins of the sea".

The forest first came under the threat of destruction when man turned from fishing and hunting to the growing of crops and the domestication of grazing animals during the succeeding Neolithic or New Stone Age (see Chapter 8).

With the coming of Bronze Age peoples and their metal technology an acceleration of forest clearances was very likely. It was probably the mixed deciduous forests in the lowlands and valleys that suffered rather than the pinewoods of the Highlands. Before the end of the Bronze Age however the climate began to change; it became cooler and wetter and with increased cutting, a combination of human and climatic agencies began to have their effect on the woodland cover. The displacement of bronze by iron for making cutting tools marked an important advance, because iron ores, although poor, were widely distributed. During this period much larger quantities of wood than hitherto were used for constructional purposes: the forests shrank, especially round places of settlement where the timber was used and it would be there also that grazing was most intensive. The deteriorating climate of the time accentuated the destructive effect of man's activities. Indeed the shrinkage of upland woodlands of pine and birch was due largely to the renewed growth of bogs, a climatological change and not basically due to the activities of man.

IMPACT OF MAN ON FORESTS IN HISTORIC TIMES

Other than a cursory glance by the Roman fleet, which encircled Scotland after its victory at the Battle of Mons Graupius in 84 AD, the Romans had no direct effect on the woodlands of the north, but, indirectly, the driving of the tribes from the southern and eastern plains may have led to the extension of cultivation and grazing in the Highland region.

From the end of the 8th century for a period of over four hundred years, Northern and Western Sutherland suffered from raids and, in due course, settlement by Norsemen. Brogger (1929) suggests that one of the many reasons why the Norsemen were attracted to Scotland was its timber wealth.

In mediaeval Scotland timber was required in ever-increasing quantities for building and for the smelting of iron. Sir Robert Gordon (1630), writing of Sutherland, says "In divers parts of this cuntrie ther is abundance of iron ore wherewith the inhabitants made good iron". This is corroborated by the multitude of known smelting sites throughout the District and further substantiated by Blaeu (1662). These long and constant attacks upon the forests for smelting fuel more than any other factor to date bore heavily upon the remaining areas of woodland. Alarmed by this decimation the Scottish Parliament passed an Act in 1609 prohibiting the use of timber for smelting. Woodland devastation had been recognised before but it was not until the latter part of the 17th century that some tentative repair work was done and native pine seed sown.

The 18th century saw sweeping changes: the failure of the Jacobite Rebellions altered the living styles of the Highland landowners who adopted those of their English counterparts. The need for money grew and to overcome this problem owners resorted to clearing the people from the land to make way for sheep, to leasing and in some cases selling their land to wealthy sheep farmers and industrialists from the south (see Chapters 13 and 15). Whatever the method used the outcome was the same, the sheep had arrived and, with the farming of Black Faced and Cheviot flocks, the numbers of both cattle and goats declined. Nevertheless, the native woodlands of Sutherland might still have remained far more widespread, in spite of the sheep flocks, but for muirburning, which was used extensively to increase the sheep pastures.

CALEDONIAN PINEWOODS

As previously noted, of all the species which survived since prehistoric times the most commonly mentioned in the *Old Statistical Account* are oak and pine. Oak predominated in the lowland bogs with pine in the upland (Geikie 1866); hence in Sutherland the latter was by far the most widespread. Unfortunately, there remain (in Strath Carron and Strath Oykel respectively), only two areas, Amat and Einig, which can be considered genuine native pinewoods (Steven and Carlisle, 1959).

There are other areas locally regarded as "Old Caledonian" woodlands which Steven and Carlisle studied but rejected for one reason or another. First of these are the Scots pine groups on the islands and shore of Loch Assynt (NC 212250). If they are genuine they would be the most northerly. They could be of native origin, but it is unlikely that planting would have been done on the rocky islands. On the other hand they are all less than 100 years old and there are no older mature trees in the vicinity. This is confirmed in the *Old Statistical Account* for the parish of Assynt which only mentions natural birch. Secondly, there is the remnant of a pinewood over 150 years old, immediately to the west of Rosehall (NC

455107) on the southern slopes of Sron na Croiche. In recent times this has been considered to be native but Macfarlane's *Geographical Collections* relating to Scotland (1905) state categorically "there are no firrs in the parish" (Creich). This statement was probably written about 1726. Oak and birch are recorded but the only reference to pine was to extensive plantations which were first laid down about 1750 on Rosehall Estate. The pine is therefore likely to be a survivor of this 18th century planting.

Blaeu's Atlas (1662) shows forests farther north in Strath Naver, by Lochs Loyal and Craggie and in Strath More; none was of native pine however but of birch and oak.

AMAT WOOD

Let us examine in more detail the history and importance of this wood. It is the largest of the two Caledonian pinewoods and as such holds a unique silvicultural place in the flora of Scotland. Owned by Lady Robson it lies at the western extremity of Strath Carron and at the confluence of the River Carron and the Black Water. Small groups are said to be found nearby in the tributary valleys which run to the south and west from the main wood. These are the property of Benmore Estates.

In a 16th century manuscript Timothy Pont wrote, " The head of Strath Carron is 30 myl from Tongue west north west, 2 myl thence Amad, a myl thence Amad na heglisse with gryt firr woods". An interesting aside is that the church referred to (Gaelic — eagllais, a church) is undoubtedly Croick which is still used and where, to this day scratched on the east window, can be seen the signatures and remarks of those unfortunates who were cleared in 1845 from their ancestral lands in Glencalvie and who spent the night of 24th May in the churchyard, being forbidden the use of the church itself. Half a century later another traveller, believed to be Robert Gordon of Straloch, described Strath Carron as a tract for the most part wooded and clothed with particularly tall firs, supplying neighbouring and distant places with timber (Macfarlane 1908). In 1767, while making a survey of the Highlands for the Commissioners of the Forfeited Estates James Robertson recorded: "In a glen at Dybdol (Diebidale) and in Glenmore there is a considerable quantity of natural fir and birch. The fir is the finest I have seen in Scotland. One tree, rearing a straight uninterrupted trunk to a height of 30 or 40 feet (9 or 12m) measures in circumference $8\frac{1}{2}$ feet (2.5m).

The stump of another measured $3\frac{3}{4}$ feet (1.1m) in diameter. The timber of these trees is as red and good as any bought from Norway". There is a local tradition that until about a hundred years ago there was a large pinewood at Diebidale which supplied timber both for local building and other uses and for export, the timber being carried by ponies along a rough hill track via Strath Rusdale to the Cromarty Firth. During the 1914-18 War some felling took place, and again in recent years. Today the woodland has a high proportion of birch and is classified as a Special Site of Scientific Interest (S.S.S.I.).

The nearby Einig wood of which nothing is known historically is little more than a few scattered remnants of Old Caledonian Pine, which the owners, the Forestry Commission, are retaining as long as possible; seed is collected so that the strain might be perpetuated.

NATIVE BROADLEAVED WOODS

Oak woods are part of one of the climatic formations of Europe, the Deciduous Forest, while the natural pinewoods and birchwoods are communities of the Northern Coniferous Forest (Tansley 1949). The birchwoods, however, are by far the most extensive of the three main natural communities in the Highlands of Scotland, and, as birches are rarely planted, their origin is not in doubt.

The coming of the sheep brought muirburning which comprehensively destroyed large tracts of these communities. Fortunately, as with the pine, inaccessibility provided a refuge for their survival.

Some of the more important remnants of these native broadleaves are discussed below:—

1. Eilean na Gartaig, Cam Loch (NC 218124), 3 hectares (7.4 acres).

Eilean na Gartaig, an island on Cam Loch in West Sutherland, is a good example of an area which has remained immune from burning and grazing. Partly wooded and lying close to the south end of the loch it consists of a mixture of birch, rowan, holly and willow below which is found a rich and varied herbaceous field layer of at least 60 different plant species. Part of the island was walled to keep out cattle which used to wade over and crop the herbage, including garlic, thereby tainting their milk. This island is interesting in that it is one of the few examples of woodland on base rich soils in the Northern Highlands and indicates what the vegetation would have been like in ancient times on similar sites that have today been changed by other useage.

2. Strathbeag (NC 380505), 70 hectares (173 acres).

Situated some 3.2km (2 miles) south of Loch Eriboll, this wood covers a steep north-west facing slope in a sheltered and shady position. It is the most northern birchwood of note with an unusual abundance of rowan. Growth is good reaching 9m to 12m (29ft to 39ft) in height.

3. Loch a' Mhullin Wood, Scourie (NC 195295), 25 hectares (62 acres).

This wood lies close to the sea and rises from sea level to 36m (117ft). Most of the trees are under 12m (39ft) and besides the dominant birch there are scattered oaks, rowans, aspens, hazels and willows. The oaks are of special interest, not only as they are at the virtual northern limit for this tree in Britain but also in being predominantly pedunculate oak, a situation comparable with the upland oaks of southern England! From their girths the oaks are much older than the other trees and the birch appears mostly to have invaded strongly over a limited and relatively recent period. The woods are grazed throughout so that herbaceous plants form only a low growth and tall species are cropped to dwarf forms — a further example of grazing damage and pressures.

4. Ledmore Wood, Spinningdale (NH 660891), 85 hectares (210 acres).

To include this wood under the heading of "Native Broadleaves" could be a misnomer as there is the possibility that it may have been planted. It is one of the most northerly oak woods in Britain and shows many features more characteristic of a native pinewood. Although hazel, holly, hawthorn and birch occur throughout, the ground vegetation of heather, heath and blaeberry is that of pine.

Historical records are sparse but of these woods Sinclair (1793) said: "There is a great quantity of natural wood in this parish consisting chiefly of oak and birch; but there is every probability that there was much more formerly. Several oakwoods have been cut down within these 30 years, some of them about ten years ago, and have yielded large quantities of excellent bark. Some old oakwoods have been cut down and no undergrowths have sprung up in their stead; but several young woods have been cut lately and are growing again in a thriving state".

There is every likelihood that the even canopy and regular size classes of today, which give the wood its even, aged, planted appearance could have been the result of regrowth from an old clearfell.

5. Mound Alderwoods (NH 765990).

Draining, cutting and subsequent cultivation have taken their toll on alderwoods countrywide and there no longer exists any large woodland area of that species other than here in Sutherland at the head of Loch Fleet. Extending to 265 hectares (655 acres) it is the most extensive alder carr in Scotland, yet it is of relatively recent vintage.

In 1813 Telford bridged the Kyle of Sutherland at Bonar and three years later constructed an embankment, the 'Mound', across the head of Loch Fleet to facilitate access to the north. A secondary purpose was to reclaim the 160 hectares (400 acres) of upper Loch Fleet which was now cut off from the sea, but this proved abortive. By 1845 the *New Statistical Account* read: "About 400 acres (160 hectares) of beach which may in time become arable, are gradually assuming a coating partly of herbage and partly of alder trees".

Gradually, since the mid 19th century to the present day, the sealed-off area has become colonised by alder and willow. The few ridges, which have probably always stood above the highest tides have an open growth of Scots pine and, apart from a few cattle and deer, little disturbance occurs. Scheduled as an S.S.S.I. the whole area was subsequently declared a National Nature Reserve.

There are many other woods of native broadleaves still in existence but in general they are for the most part degenerate and non-regenerant. The woods aforementioned however have all been taken under the wing of the Nature Conservancy and scheduled as S.S.S.I.'s; hopefully these remnants of past ages can now be saved if only to give future generations a glimpse of the past.

AFFORESTATION AND REAFFORESTATION

As previously mentioned the mid 18th century saw some tentative woodland rehabilitation but it was not until the beginning of the 19th century that more serious attempts were being made to make good some of the destruction of earlier periods. Anderson gives some interesting facts. In his *History of Scottish Forestry* he records Henderson (1812) finding some 378 hectares (936 acres) of plantations at Dunrobin, Uppat and Gordonbush, and about 325 hectares (800 acres) along the north side of the Dornoch Firth; also at Rosehall he mentions 472 hectares (1170 statute acres) of woodland.

In the five years from 1838 to 1845 under the management of James Loch there was a further burst of afforestation on the estates

TABLE 15 – DISTRIBUTION AND OWNERSHIP OF FOREST AREAS

Census	PRIVATE OWNERSHIP		STATE OWNERSHIP		TOTAL	
	High Forest	Percentage of total forest area	High Forest	Percentage of total forest area	High Forest	Percentage of land area of Sutherland
1947–49	2,908 Hectares (7,184 Acres)	80.7%	695 Hectares (1,717 Acres)	19.3%	3,603 Hectares (8,901 Acres)	0.8%
1965–67	4,151 Hectares (10,254 Acres)	35.7%	7,488 Hectares (18,496 Acres)	64.3%	11,639 Hectares (28,750 Acres)	2.5%
1977*	6,149 Hectares (15,188 Acres)	20.7%	23,577 Hectares (58,235 Acres)	79.3%	29,726 Hectares (73,423 Acres)	6.6%

* Figures extracted from Forestry Commission Annual Report

TABLE 16 – AFFORESTATION AND FOREST POTENTIAL

High Forest 1977	PLANTABLE RESERVE		Scrub (Estimated)	Total Forest Potential (as at 1982)	Percentage of Land Area of Sutherland (as at 1982)
	Private	State			
29,726 Hectares (73,423 Acres)	155 Hectares (383 Acres)	5,627 Hectares (13,899 Acres)	3,000 Hectares (7,410 Acres)	38,508 Hectares (95,115 Acres)	8.5%

of the Duke of Sutherland. Out of a total area of 846 hectares (2091 acres) of plantations, 732 hectares (1859 acres) were planted in that period, in several blocks, in one case to a height of 305m (1000 ft).

The New Statistical Account also makes references to 1010 hectares (2500 acres) having been planted in the Parish of Dornoch, 607 hectares (1500 acres) in Creich Parish, 'small areas' in the Parishes of Rogart and Scourie, and 80 hectares (200 acres) in each of Brora and Tongue Parishes.

This truly remarkable wave of tree planting gradually waned and was not maintained into the 20th century. There were a number of reasons for this, not the least being the enhanced returns which landowners got from developing their land as deer forests or grouse moors, or for sheep grazing. All these brought an immediate return, while trees took a long time to grow, and timber was easily and cheaply imported.

Before the outbreak of the First World War, however, there were some Highland landowners, notably Lord Novar and Lord Lovat, who could foresee a time when imported timber prices would rise and when the United Kingdom might suffer a shortage. Their foresight, and the need to replace the larger acreage of timber felled for war purposes and to ensure that Britain would never again be dependent on foreign timber, led to the setting up of a State Forest Authority — The Forestry Commission — to undertake a large afforestation programme. Fittingly, Lord Lovat became its first chairman.

Two years prior to the setting up of this Commission the Board of Agriculture acquired the estate of Borgie, as a gift from the Duke of Sutherland, to provide work and small holdings for home coming servicemen. Part of this area was leased to the Forestry Commission and it is interesting to note that this was their first acquisition in Scotland. Since that time there has been a steady and continuing state of afforestation programme in Sutherland in spite of the interruption of the Second World War.

An indication of the forestry programme since 1919 is given in Table 15 opposite.

In addition to these man-made plantations there are the remnants of degenerate broadleaved woodland which can be termed 'Scrub', but which in the main represent areas of former natural forest. The present area and immediate forest potential can therefore be represented as in Table 16 opposite.

One of the features of afforestation by the Forestry Commission
in recent years has been the gradual introduction of exotic conifers
from North America which are capable of withstanding exposure
and growing successfully on poor degraded peats. This is not to
say that native trees have been rejected. On the contrary, they are
planted whenever possible, but the less demanding Lodgepole pine
(Pinus Contorta) has the ability to grow on land previously deemed
unplantable. This adaptability has widened standards and been in-
strumental in pushing Sutherland to the top of the 'afforestation
league'. Currently Shin Forest, which encompasses Loch Shin and
Strath Oykel, is the fastest growing State Forest in the U.K. and is
the largest in Scotland. It forms, with the forests of Strath Naver,
Helmsdale and Dornoch, a substantial national investment which in
the future will play an increasingly important part in the nation's
economy. Much has still to be done, nonetheless, in comparison
with other regions and countries as is demonstrated by the following Table.

TABLE 17 – WOODLANDS AS PERCENTAGES OF TOTAL AREAS – 1977

REGION	Woodland as a % age of Total Area	COUNTRY	Woodland as a % age of Total Area
Sutherland	7.2%	Scotland	10%
Highland	9%	United Kingdom	8%
Dumfries & Galloway	16%	Belgium	20% †
Borders	11%	France	24% †
Strathclyde	12%	Germany	30% †
Central	13%	Holland	8%
Fife	12%	Italy	21%
Grampian	15%	† *EEC Average* –	20%

CONCLUSION

Although past abuse and mismanagement have left us with but little of our woodland heritage, a fuller realisation of its benefits is now recognised. Consequently a better understanding and tradition is growing with the formation of these young Sutherland Forests, not only concerning their commercial value, but of the less tangible advantages which go with shelter, amenity, recreation and sport.

The land area under forestry (Fig. 23) may be low in comparison with other areas of Scotland but it is to be hoped that, having rediscovered itself, man's love for trees will endure in Sutherland to the benefit of all.

Chapter eighteen

PLACE NAMES

The District of Sutherland encompasses an area of very considerable size, which contains within it a vast number of named localities. To discuss the given names in detail would require not a short chapter but a large volume to itself. Our coverage here, then, must necessarily be partial, and so what we have to attempt to do is to provide a reasonable overall general picture of the nomenclature of the area.

In order to do this it is necessary to look at different kinds of sources. In the first place we have, of course, to consult the Ordnance Survey (henceforth OS) maps of the area, which provide our basic data. We must always remember, at the same time, that OS names themselves are only a selection of the names in everyday use by local inhabitants, and it is always advisable to consult local knowledge for confirmation or name forms; it is not unknown for errors of form and even location to occur in OS materials.

It is also the case that the toponymy of Sutherland, like that of other parts of Scotland, is a complex phenomenon. The names were given, and subsequently used, by people speaking different languages and having different cultures. For such reasons it is not always easy to determine the origin of names or what they mean. It is often necessary for us to consult earlier documents in which the names occur in order to recover the historical dimension necessary for their elucidation. These sources may be early maps, charters to land, accounts of financial transactions (especially having to do with the church), accounts of historical occurrences and tales concerning events from the past. All of these have their contribution to make to the study and elucidation of placenames.

The earliest cartographer to take an interest in Scotland, whose work survives, was Ptolemy of Alexandria. His sources date from the 1st century AD. At least two places named by him (though somewhat displaced on his map, perhaps) still carry the names he gives for them; these are the two rivers which he called *Nabarus* and *Ila.* They are the river *Naver,* in Gaelic *Nabhair,* and the Helmsdale river, in Gaelic called *Ilidh.* The tribal names he cites in the area have left no certain sign of their presence, though W. J. Watson in *The History of the Celtic Placenames of Scotland* cites a *Carn Smeart* in the ridge between Strath Carron and Strath Oykel, and Ptolemy places a tribe called the Smertae in the Oykel basin. The other tribes, as a matter of interest, were, in the north, the Cornavii ("the people of the horn or promontory": cf. Cornwall), the Caereni in the north-west, and the Lugi in the east. These names appear to be Celtic though there is no clear evidence that they were all necessarily so in origin.

Certainly the first language that we can recognise and place in this area was a Celtic one spoken among the Picts. This language, which was akin to Welsh rather than Gaelic, is identified in its distribution in Scotland by the occurrence of certain placename elements. The most notable of these are the elements *pit-* or *pet-,* meaning a "settlement", or more generally a "portion of land used for a specific purpose", and the element *aber-,* meaning a "confluence". Both of these elements are to be found in Sutherland though there are only a few of them. The occurrences of names with *pit-* are *Pitfour, Pitmean, Pitarxie, Pittentrail,* and *Pitgrudy. Pitfour,* in Gaelic called also Baile *Phùir,* means in all probability "pasture town". Pór (genitive is pùir) means "pasture" and is a Gaelic borrowing from Pictish (cf. Welsh *pawr*). *Pitmean* probably represents *pit-meadhon,* "mid-town"; *Pitgrudy* probably stands for *pit-grùdich,* the "settlement by the dreg-filled or gravelly water" (probably a stream name). The earliest version I can find for *Pitarxie* is 16th century *Pettakarsie,* but the second element is obscure to me. *Pit-* names, generally, have Gaelic second elements.

There is only one *aber-* name on the OS map: *Aberscross.* This name presents problems as its earlier forms indicate *Aberscor* and the present pronunciation indicates *Aberscaig.* I venture no the Norse probably thought the same: cf. *Ekkjalsbakki* in eg. *Ork-* explanation of the second element.

Another Pictish (in all probability) placename is *Oykel* with the meaning "high territory" (cf. Welsh *uchel,* "high"). The present impression is that the river name is the basic one and other names with Oykel derive from it, and in a late Gaelic context (and indeed *neyinga Saga*) this was probably the case. It is, however, not unon for names to transfer from one topographic feature to another nearby, once this meaning in the original language is obscured. This element is found in other Scottish names, for example *Ochiltree* which means "high settlement". *Doll* looks as if it derives from *dol*, "a field" (as in Welsh); and the Picts are commemorated in names such as *Clais nan Cruithneach*, "the ditch of the Picts" (*Cruithneach* being the Gaelic for Pict).

The question of what language followed that (or those) of the Picts in Sutherland is one of some interest. Some would hold that by the time the Norse settled on the northern coast Pictish had already been superseded by Gaelic. Others would hold that Gaelic had not had time to penetrate the whole of the area by that period. Unfortunately the evidence that placenames have to give on this question, here as in other parts of the north and west, is inconclusive. On balance one would, I think, say that in Sutherland (as distinct from Caithness where the toponomy is much more thoroughly Norse, and there is little evidence for Gaelic in the eastern parts) the likelihood is that the two tongues co-existed side by side into the Norse period. The scarcity of Pictish names reflects the growing ascendancy of Gaelic on the one hand and Norse, in certain areas at least, on the other. Pictish lost out in a multilingual situation, its nomenclature being eclipsed by not one but two competing tongues.

The vast majority of names in Sutherland that we are able to elucidate — indeed all except the few Pictish names we have looked at and a handful of English names — derive from one or other of those tongues, Gaelic or Norse. This is, I think, nicely reflected in the names of the District itself. In English it is Sutherland. This reflects Norse *suthrland*, "southland", the name given by the Norse to the southern part of the mainland of Northern Scotland under their sway. The Ord of Caithness was the dividing line between the two territories and this is reflected in mediaeval times in divisions such as "Catanesia cis et ultra montem", "Caithness on this side of and beyond the mountain". The general Gaelic name for Sutherland is *Cataibh*. This reflects a locative plural of the generalised tribal name of the inhabitants of this area, the *Catti* or "cat people", and is translatable literally as "among the cat people". The English name *Caithness* is to be related to Norse *Katanes*, "the promontory of the cat people", the name they gave the northern coastal area facing the Pentland Firth (Norse *Péttlandsfjördhr*, "Pictland's Firth"). The Gaelic name for this area, and for modern Caithness, is

Gallaibh, which is a locative plural form of *gall*, a "foreigner" — the foreigners in this case being the Norsemen.

In Gaelic, distinctions within Sutherland are made especially with reference to that part of the north called in English the "Reay country". The name *Reay* itself possibly derives from Celtic *rath*, a "fort". In Gaelic the territory is called *Dùthaich 'ic Aoidh*, "Mac-Kay's Country". The parish names are also, as many of them as we can decipher, of mixed Gaelic and Norse origin. The Gaelic ones are *Creich* which derives *from crìoch*, "boundary", and, indeed, forms part of the southern boundary of Sutherland; *Lairg* from Gaelic *lurg*, "shank"; *Dornoch* which probably derives from *dornach*, "place of the round stones"; *Clyne* which derives from *cluain*, "meadow"; *Eddrachilles* which represents *eadar-dà-chaolas*, "between two straits"; and *Kildonan* which is *cill Donnan*, "the church of St. Donnan".

The following are of Norse origin: *Tongue* which is from *tunga*, "tongue" (of land); *Durness* which represents *Dýrnes*, probably "deer promontory" (and is so found in *Orkneyinga Saga*); *Golspie* which is almost certainly a compound ending in a form of Norse *-býr*, "farm"; the first element is obscure.

This leaves us with the parishes of *Farr*, *Assynt*, *Rogart* and *Loth* for which no satisfactory explanation is available. *Assynt* might be from Norse *áss-endi*, "ridge end". The latter pair are probably Celtic. The earliest form of *Rogart* (from the 13th century) is *Rothe-gorthe;* the -g- is not pronounced in the Gaelic form of the name; it may represent *rath-ghort*, "fort -field".

In the remaining portion of this account we will look at a selection of names of Norse and Gaelic origin to establish the types and range of toponymic elements to be found in the area. Each name will have the name of the parish in which it is located given in brackets following its first citation. If we look first of all at the names of Norse origin, we find that they are most frequent on the coast and in coastal areas, but they are certainly not confined to this sort of locality for we find a fair number inland, particularly in the straths where Norse farmers would have established themselves during the period of settlement. The names are of different kinds and the basic elements give us a picture quite similar to that which we get in other areas of Norse settlement, especially in some areas in the Hebrides, but without the density of occurrence that is typical of, for example, the island of Lewis. We may compare the defining elements in the Norse names with those occurring in the Gaelic names further on.

The main elements that indicate settlement in this area are -*bólstadhr* and -*setr*, both of which mean " settlement, farm ", and -*ból*, which means a " resting place for cattle, a steading, a farm ".

Containing -*bólstadhr* we have, for example :

SCRABSTER (Tongue) probably *Skárobólstadhr*, " Skari's farm ". (The name *Skári* in the Gaelic form *Sgàire* still surives as a personal name in Lewis.)

ULBSTER (Kildonan) probably *Ulftbólstadhr* (or possibly *Olafsból-stadhr*), " Ulf's (or Olaf's) farm ".

Containing -*setr* we have, for example :

BOWSETT (Farr) (cf. *Bosset* (*Creich*)) probably *bú-setr*, " cattle farm ".

CONESAID (Tongue) probably *konnasetr*, " woman steading ".

LINSIDE (Creich) (the earliest form is *Linsett* (16th century)) probably represents *lìn-setr*, " flax farm ".

(LOCH) STUAINISAIT (Farr) possibly *stùfsnes-setr*, " stump-point farm ". This interpretation is tentative.

Other settlement names are, with the element -*hús*:

BIGHOUSE (Farr) *bygdh-hús*, " village house "; and with the final element -*býr* 'farm', GOLSPIE, as we noted above.

There are a fair number of names in -*ból*, for example :

ARNABOLL (Durness) probably *Arnaból*, "Arni's steading ".

BORROBOL (Kildonan) *borgar-ból*, " fort steading ".

COLABOLL (Lairg) *kolla-ból*, " round hills steading ".

DIOBAL (Kildonan) probably *dý-ból*, " bog steading ".

ELDRABOL (Kildonan) probably *eldr-ból*, " beacon steading ".

EMBO (Dornoch); Earlier forms of the name are *Ethenbol*, *Eyndboll*, *Enbo* and *Inbol*, which might point to something like " Evyind's steading " but the derivation is very tentative. In modern Gaelic the pronunciation reflects '*Eribol*' (cf. below), but this is not original.

ERIBOL (Durness) probably *eyrar-ból*, " sandbank steading ".

KIRKIBOLL (Tongue) *kirkjuból*, " church steading ".

LEARABLE (Kildonan) probably *leir-ból*, " clay or mud steading ".

SKELBO (Dornoch) (earlier *Scelbol*) *skel-ból*, " shell steading ".

SKIBO (Dornoch); The 13th century form *Scithabol*, points to " Skíthi's steading ".

TORBOLL (Dornoch & Lairg); earlier forms in *Thorbol* suggests *Thorból*, " Thor's steading ".

MODSAIRIGH (Tongue) seems to represent *modserg*, " mud shieling ".

As well as these names denoting settlement there are many Norse names denoting topographic features. We can look briefly first at those referring to dry land and then to those referring to water and shore. We have first of all those with the element *-land* itself, eg.:

SUARDALAN (Assynt) *svardh-land*, " grassy land ".

(LOCH) BORRALAN (Assynt) *borgar-land*, " land of the fort ".

(LOCH) MERKLAND (Lairg) probably from *merki-land*, "boundary land".

Then we have a series of other elements such as *bakki, a "bank"* in, for example:

BACKIES (Golspie) *bakki* with an English plural added.

COLDBACKIE (Tongue); earlier forms give *Kubhac(k)* also; probably *kúla-bakki*, " bank with the bump ".

HYSBACKIE (Tongue) has the same final element but the initial one provides problems. It might be *hús-bakki*, " house bank ".

There are many names with the element *dalr*, " dale ". We can only deal with a few of these here, eg.:

ARMADALE (Farr) *armr + dalr*, " arm dale ".

ASTLE (Dornoch) (earlier *Askesdale, Askadail*) from *ask-dalr*, " ash dale ".

HALLADALE (Farr) (earlier *Helgadale*) probably *helgadalr*, " holy dale ".

HELMSDALE (Kildonan) in *Orkneyinga Saga 'Hjálmundálr'*, " Hjalmund's dale ".

LANGDALE (Farr) *langr-dalr*, " long dale ".

MIGDALE (Creich) *mugga-dalr*, " wet ground dale ".

NAVIDALE (Kildonan) probably *nafardalr*, " promontory dale ".

ORMADALE (Farr) *ormadalr*, " snake dale ".

OSDALE (Lairg) *ost-dalr*, " east dale ".

OSPISDALE (Dornoch) probably *Ospaksdalr*, " Ospak's dale ".

SPINNINGDALE (Creich) (15th century *Spanigdill*) possibly *spong-engi-dalr*, " round-shaped pasture dale ".

SWORDALE (Creich) *svardh-dalr*, " grassy dale ".

SLETDALE (Lairg) *slétta-dalr*, " flat(land) dale ".

TORRISDALE (Tongue) probably *Thorsdalr*, " Thor's dale ".

There are names in *-gil*, " ravine "; for example:

FRESGILL (Durness) possibly connected with *frasa*, " to gush ". *Fras-gil*, " gushing water ravine ".

ACHREISGILL (Eddrachilles). The first part is Gaelic *achadh* "field", and the remainder is probably *hris-gil*, " brushwood ravine " (or cf. Fresgill).

RIBIGILL (Tongue) possibly *ribbe-gil*, " ridge ravine ".

SUISGILL (Kildonan) possibly *sús-gil*, " noisy (water) ravine ".

TRALAGILL (Assynt) *trollagil*, " troll ravine ".

There are also names in *-fjall*, " hill ", such as:

ACHUTARFALE (Creich) possibly *útárfjall*, " out river hill ";
names in *-hóll*, " hill ", such as:

ARKLE (Eddrachilles) *ark-hóll*, " round top hill ";
names in *-hlíth*, " slope " such as:

SWORDLY (Farr) *svardh-hlíth*, " grassy slope ";
and names in *-vollr*, " field " such as:

ROSSAL (Creich) (earlier *Rosswell*) *hross-vollr*, " horse field ".

The names related to water and shore are reflected in elements such as *-á*, " river ", for example:

BRORA (Clyne) *brúar-á*, " river of the bridge ".

KINTROLLA (Kildonan) Gaelic *ceann*, " head " and *trolla-á*, " troll river ".

In *-øy*, " island ":

CALVA (Eddrachilles) *calf-øy*, " calf island ".

(EILEAN) CHRONA (Assynt). The second part is probably *hraun-oy*, " rocky island ". *Eilean* is Gaelic, " island ", and we note here the double occurrence of the same element in different languages.

OLDANY (Assynt) and BLANDA (Tongue). The first part is obscure to me in each case.

SOYEA (Assynt) *saudhr-øy*, " sheep island ".

SKERRY (Tongue) *sker-øy*, " sea rock island ".

In *-fjordhr*, " fiord " we have:

(LOCH) DIONARD (Durness). *Loch* is, of course, Gaelic. The first element of the second part is obscure.

LAXFORD (Edrachilles) *lax-fjordhr*, " salmon fiord ".

In *-gjó*, " *rift* on sea coast, geo ", we have:

LAMIGO (Tongue) *lambi-gjó*, " Lamb geo ".

SANGO (Durness) *sand-gjó*, " sand geo ".

In *-hóp*, " bay ":

(LOCH) HOPE (Durness) *hóp*, " bay ".

In *-nes*, " point ":

DURNESS is *dýr-ness*, " deer point ".

MELNESS (Tongue) is *mel-ness*, " bent grass point ".

SHINESS (Lairg) is the " point of Shin (obscure)".

In *-straumr*, " current ":

KYLESTROME (Eddrachilles), " the narrows of the current ".

In -*vatn*, " loch, water ":

UPPAT (Golspie) *upp-vatn* (probably) " rising (spring) water loch ".

(LOCH) SANDWOOD (Eddrachilles) (earlier *Sandwat*) *sand-vatn*, " sand loch ".

In -*vík*, " *creek* ":

(LOCH) ASCAIG (Kildonan) Loch *ask-vík*, " ash creek ".

CROICK (Farr) *kró-vík*, " nook (or sheep-fold) creek ".

KERWICK (Durness) *ker-vík*, " tub creek " (usually denoting a hollow depression or cave).

KIRKAIG (Assynt) *kirkjuvík*, " kirk creek ".

MELLAIG (Golspie) *mel-vík*, " bent grass creek ".

Many of the first or defining elements in these compound names are of considerable interest as a reflection of social and economic aspects of life at the time at which the names were given. Their comparison with Gaelic defining elements show a considerable degree of similarity and continuity between the two societies. There are some uncompounded names of Norse origin. The ' *Wrath* ' of *Cape Wrath*, for example, derives ultimately from Norse *hvarf*, " turning ". It is borrowed into Gaelic as *Parph* (*Carbh* in Lewis). *Stoer* point in Assynt is from Norse *Staurr*, " pole " used as a place-name for a mountain peak and sometimes a sea rock.

The largest number of names in Sutherland are of Gaelic origin. We will look at some of the main elements in these beginning again with those that refer to settlement.

The basic element here is *baile*, " farm settlement, village":

BAILENANALLTAN (Creich) *baile nan alltan*, " settlement of the streams ".

BALBLAIR (Creich and Golspie) *baile nam blàr*, " the settlement of the moors (or peat-mosses)".

BALCHARN (Lairg) *baile a' chairn*, " settlement of the cairn ".

BALCHLADICH (Assynt) *baile a' chladaich*, " settlement of the shore ".

BAILENACREIGE (Creich) *baile na creige*, " settlement of the cliff ".

BAILACHREAGAIN (Creich) *baile a' chreagain*, " settlement of the rocky hillock ".

BALACHNUIC (Dornoch) *baile a' chnuic*, " settlement of the hill ".

BALNAKEIL (Durness) *baile na cille*, " settlement of the church. (Same as Kirkton in English.)

BALLOAN (Dornoch and Lairg) *baile an lòin*, " settlement of the meadow ".

LEATHAD A' BHAILE FHOGHAIR (Assynt) "slope of the autumn (i.e. harvest) town ".

SEANNABHAILE (Creich) *seanbhaile,* " old settlement ". This is a common name all over the Highland and Island area.

We also have other settlement names in *tigh,* " house ", and in *croit,* " croft ", though some instances of the latter, for example *Croit an Easbuig,* " bishop's croft ", in Dornoch, are likely to refer to an apportionment of land rather than a settlement.

We have names related to land and animal husbandry. The most common element here is *achadh,* " field ". Some *achadh* names designate their function; some have descriptive rather than functional designations:

ACHNACORACH (Dornoch) *achadh na caorach,* " field of the sheep ".

ACHINDUICH (Creich). This may be *achadh an dabhaich,* " field of the davoch (a land measure)" or, more likely, *achadh an dubhaich,* ' field of the black earth " (which was used for making black dye).

ACHLEY (Dornoch) *achadh an laoigh,* " calf field ".

ACHCORK (Rogart) *achadh a' choirce,* " oat field ".

ACHMOLTARAICH (Tongue) *achadh a' mholltairich,* " field of the multure, or miller's dues ".

ACHVAICH (Dornoch) *achadh a' bhàthaich,* " field of the byre ".

ACHADH A' BHRAOIL (Rogart) *achadh a' bhraoil,* " field of the fissure ".

ACHANEAS (Creich) *achadh an eas,* " field of the waterfall ".

ACHADH AN INBHIR (Tongue) *achadh an inbhir,* " field of the confluence ".

ACHADHAPHRIS (Lairg) *achadh a' phris,* " field of the bush ".

SALACHADH (Lairg) probably " willow field ".

Other elements that denote husbandry are:

BARD NA BEINNE (Creich), " the field of the peak ".

CAPULAICH (Lairg), " the place of the horses, or stallions ".

DABHACHBEAG (Rogart) *dabhach beag,* " little davoch ".

DAVOCHIFIN (Dornoch) *dabhach fionn,* " white davoch ".

FANAGMORE (Eddrachilles) *feannag mhór,* " large plot or lazy-bed ".

FLEUCHARY (Dornoch) *fliuch-airigh,* " wet shieling ".

SINAIRIDH (Eddrachilles) *sean-airigh,* " old shieling ".

INNISNANCEAP (Rogart) " pasture of the sods " (probably referring to the cutting of sods for building walls).

LONBUIDHE (Creich) *lòn buidhe,* " yellow meadow ".

SHENLONE (Rogart) *sean-lòn,* " old meadow ".

CYLNELISH (Clyne) *cluan-leis,* " meadow enclosures ".

There are a fair number of names that have religious or church connotations. We have already seen some Norse names containing the element *kirk-*, " church ", and indeed we have Thor's name used on a number of occasions. The main Gaelic element denoting church is *cill-*, and there are a number of occurrences in the area:

KILBRORA (Clyne) " the church of Brora ".

KILCOLMKIL (Clyne) " Colmcille's or St. Columba's church ".

KILDONAN (Kildonan) *cill Donnain*, " St. Donnan's church ".

KILLEAN (Clyne) *cill Eóin*, " St. John's church ".

KILEARNAN (Kildonan) *cill Earnáin*, " St. Earnan's church ".

KILMOTE (Loth) *cill ... ...* , (the second element is obscure to me).

KILPHEDIR (Kildonan) *cill Pheadair*, " St. Peter's church ".

KILMAIN (Clyne) *cill meadhon*, " mid church ".

CULMAILY (Golspie) *cill Mhàillidh*, " St. Mallie's church ", or perhaps *cùil Mhàillidh*, " St. Mallie's retreat ".

BALNAKEIL (Durness) *baile na cille*, " church town ", with *cill as a* defining element.

Other names have defining elements in them that refer to church dignitaries or church officers, for example:

ACHINCHANTER (Dornoch) *achadh a' chantair*, " the precentor's field ".

ACHINTREASURICH (Dornoch) *achadh an treasuraich*, " the treasurer's field ".

CROIT AN EASBUIG (Dornoch) " the bishop's croft ".

EILEAN NAN NAOIMH (Tongue) *eilean an naoimh*, " the saint's island ".

LOCHANABB (Kildonan) *loch an ab*, " the abbot's loch ".

LOCH A' MHANAICH (Assynt) " the monk's loch ".

LOCH A' VICAIR (Golspie) *loch a' bhiocair*, " the vicar's loch ".

There is a wide range of Gaelic-based elements referring to topopraphic features. We may first look at those that refer to dry land, beginning with high ground and going on to low ground. The general word in Gaelic for " mountain " or " peak " is *beinn*. In my opinion the names of Sutherland mountains in general present problems of interpretation which are too complicated to enter into here.

Some of them, however, seem reasonably clear:

BEN MOR (Assynt) is Gaelic *beinn mór*, " large, high mountain ".

BEN HOPE (Durness) takes its name from the bay, Norse *hóp*, in front of it.

BEN STACK (Eddrachilles) *beinn an staca*, " mountain with the stack (from Norse *stakkr*, ' stack ') ".

Others are less clear:

BEN KLIBRECK (Tongue) is probably also of Norse origin — the
"mountain of the hillside slope", in Norse *hlíth-brekka*.
BEN ARMINE (Rogart). The second element is obscure.

The Gaelic word for hill is *cnoc* as in, for example:
CNOC DUBH (Lairg) "black hill".
KNOCKGLAS (Dornoch) *cnoc glas*, "green (or grassy) hill".
AN CNOC REIDH (Farr) "the smooth hill".

Meall means "lump" and is applied to peaks or protuberances
on ridges:
MEALL CHALUIM (Tongue) "Calum's peak".
MEALL MEADHONACH (Durness) "middle peak".

Druim means "ridge":
DRUIMBAN (Assynt) *druim bàn*, "white ridge".
DRUIMLIATH (Assynt) *druim liath*, "grey slope".

Leathad means "slope" and this is represented uncompounded
in LAID (Durness). We also get it in compounds, for example:
LEDSAURICH (Creich) *leathad sòbhraich*, "primrose slope".
LEDNASHERMAG (Dornoch) *leathad na seamrag*, "clover slope".

Another word for slope very common in Sutherland, especially
in the east, is *ruighe*. This we get in the plural in RHIAN (Dornoch)
"the slopes" and in the singular in:
REARQUHAR (Dornoch) *ruighe Fhearchair*, "Farquar's slope".
RIDARROCH (Dornoch) *ruighe daraich*, "oak slope".
RHISTOCACH (Dornoch) *ruighe stocach*, "slope of the tree stumps".
RUIGH NAN COPAG (Farr) "slope of the dockens".
RHIAN BRECK (Lairg) *ruighean breac*, "little speckled slope" (with
the diminutive form of *ruighe*).

Leiter means "stony slope", for example:
LETTERESSIE (Assynt) *leitir easach*, "waterfall slope".

Bad has a generalised and a particular meaning: it means both
"place" and "clump":
BAD A' CHRASGAIDH (Rogart) "the place of the crossing".
BAD BEITHE (Creich) "birch clump".
BADCALL (Assynt) "hazel clump".
BAD NA MUIRCHINN (Assynt) "ankle (shaped) clump".

Dail is a borrowing from Norse *dalr* and means a "dale" or
"valley":
DAILCHAIRN (Tongue) *dail a' chairn*, "cairn valley".
DAIL ARAILT (Farr) "Harold's dale".
DAILABHRAIGHEID (Tongue) *dail a' bhraghad* "neck dale".

Basic elements dealing with wet ground and water are as follows:

Allta, " stream ", as in:

ALLTA BREAC (Lairg) " speckled stream ".

Bog, " bog ", as in:

BOGAN BUIDH (Assynt) *bogan buidhe,* " yellow bog ".

Clais, " ditch ":

CLAISEAN GLAS (Assynt) " green (grassy) ditches ".

CLAIS BHUIDH NAN FUARAN (Creich) " yellow ditch of the springs ".

CLASHNAGRAVE (Dornoch) *clais nan cnàmh,* " ditch of the bones ".

Eilean, " island ":

EILEAN NAN RON (Tongue) " island of the seals ".

EILEAN DHOMNAILL (Lairg) " Donald's island ".

EILEAN A' GHAMHNA (Assynt) " heifer island ".

Forsa, " waterfall ", borrowed from Norse *fors:*

FORSINARD (Farr) forsa an aird, " waterfall on high ground ".

FORSINAIN (Farr) *forsa an fhàine,* " waterfall on low ground ".

Inbhir, " confluence ", as in *Inbhir* (Assynt):

INBHIR NAN ALLT (Creich) " confluence of the streams ".

INVERCASSLEY (Creich) *inbhir caislich,* " confluence of the swift or turbulent water ".

Poll, " pool, hole ":

POLNAHAIRDE (Creich) " promontory pool ".

POLL AN DROIGHINN (Assynt) " blackthorn hole ".

Loch is, of course, one of the basic elements referring to water. There are a great many lochs in Sutherland and a study of a selection of the defining elements that occur with *loch* gives us a good idea of the different categories of defining elements found in the area. We can conveniently exemplify those under the headings of persons functions (in relation to human beings), animals, vegetation, nature of the ground, shape, colour and size.

Persons. This may refer to individuals, professions or classes:

LOCH CHALUIM (Tongue) " Calum's loch ".

LOCH CHORMAIC (Tongue) " Cormac's loch ".

LOCHAN IAIN BHUIDE (Rogart) " Yellow John's little loch ".

LOCH AN ABB (Kildonan) " abbot's loch ".

LOCH A' CHLEIRECH (Farr) " cleric's loch ".

LOCH A' MHANAICH (Assynt) " monk's loch ".

LOCH NAN GALL (Farr) " loch of the foreigners ".

LOCH NA GRUAGAICH (Assynt) " loch of supernatural person ".

The personal designation may be secondary (i.e. define the defining term) as in:

LOCH POLL DÀIDH (Assynt) " the loch of David's pool ".

LOCH BAD MHÀRTEIN (Tongue) " the loch of Martin's clump ".

Functions:

LOCH NA CEARDAICH (Farr) " loch of the smithy ".

LOCH A' CHROISG (Assynt) " loch of the crossing ".

LOCH A' MHÒID (Farr) " loch of the meeting ".

LOCH A' MHUILINN (Assynt) " loch of the mill ".

LOCH AN T-SABHAIL (Assynt) " loch of the barn ".

LOCH AN TAIGH-CHOIMHEAD (Tongue) " loch of the watchhouse ".

LOCH NA H-AIRIGH BIGE (Assynt) " loch of the little shieling ".

Functional elements may also occur in secondary relationship as in:

LOCH POLL AN NIGHEIDH (Assynt) " loch of the washing pool ".

LOCH AN RÉIDHLEIN EÒRNA (Farr) " loch of the barley field ".

Animals:

(a) Domestic

LOCH NAN CAORACH (Farr) " loch of the sheep ".

LOCH NAN GOBHAR (Assynt) " loch of the goats ".

LOC AN LAOIGH (Dornoch) " loch of the calf ".

LOCH AN TUIRC (Assynt) " loch of the boar ".

(b) Wild

LOCH NA BÉISTE (Tongue) " loch of the otter ". This could also mean " loch of the monster "!

LOCH A' MHADAIDH RUAIDH (Tongue) " loch of the fox ".

LOCH BAD NA H-EARBA (Durness) " loch of the hind's clump ".

(c) Supernatural or legendary?

LOCH NAM BÓ-ODHARA (Farr) " loch of the dun cows ".

LOCH NAN CON-DONNA (Farr) " loch of the brown dogs ".

(d) Birds

LOCH NA CIRCE (Assynt) " loch of the hen ".

LOCH NAN GÈADH (Farr) " loch of the geese ".

LOCH NAN EALACHAN (Tongue) " loch of the swans ".

(e) Fish

LOC NAM BREAC BEAGA (Rogart) " loch of the little trout ".

Vegetation:

LOC A' CHAORAINN (Tongue and Assynt) " loch of the mountain ash ".

Loch na Cuilce (Durness) "loch of the reeds ".

Loch an Daraich (Assynt) "loch of the oak ".

Lochan Feàrna (Assynt) *loch na feàrna,* "loch of the alder ".

Loch an Fheòir (Farr and Lairg) "loch of the grass ".

Loch a' Ghiubhais (Rogart) "loch of the pine ".

    With secondary designation

Loch Ruighean an Aitinn (Assynt) "loch of the little slope of the juniper ".

Loch a' Phollain Bheithe (Assynt) "loch of the little pool of the the birch ".

Loch Preas na Sgithche (Rogart) "loch of the bush of the hawthorn ".

Nature of ground:

Loch Gainmhich (Lairg) " sand loch ".

Lochan na Gaoithe (Rogart) "little loch of the marsh ".

Loch Grùideach (Rogart) " dreggy or gravelly loch ".

Loch Mollach (Farr) " loch of the pebbly beaches ".

Loch na Saobhaidh (Rogart) "loch of the fissures ".

Loch nam Slugaide (Rogart) " loch of the quagmire ".

Loch nam Fuar-Leac (Lairg) " loch of the cold flagstones ".

Loch an Staing (Lairg) " loch of the ditch ".

Shape:

Loch Camasach (Farr) "loch of the bays ".

Loch nan Lùb (Assynt) "loch of the bends ".

Loch Sgiathanach (Farr) " winged loch ".

Loch Srònach (Farr) " loch of the promontories ".

Colour:

Loch Dubh (Farr) " black loch ".

Loch Riabhach (Durness) " brindled loch ".

Loch na Creice Léithe (Assynt) "loch of the grey cliff ".

Loch a' Coire Dheirg (Assynt) "loch of the red corrie ".

Size:

Loch Beag (Farr) " little loch ".

Loch Mór (Farr) " big loch ".

Loch Fada (Assynt) " long loch ".

Along with types of compound with a basic structure of common noun (+ article) + designating noun (genitive), and noun + adjective, we have names of another, close-compound, type, consisting of designating noun + basic noun, and adjective + noun. The following examples with *loch* add somewhat to the range of designations we have mentioned:

FEURLOCH (Assynt) " grass loch ".
GARBHLOCH (Assynt) " rough loch ".
CLÀRLOCH (Tongue) " broad loch ".
CAOL-LOCH (Tongue) " narrow loch ".
GLASLOCH (Rogart) " grey/green loch ".
GORMLOCH (Tongue) " blue/green loch ".

As was said at the beginning of this chapter, it has been possible here to look at only a small selection of Sutherland placenames. Nor do the examples above exhaust the range of elements that occur in these names. It is hoped that the selection, however, has been sufficiently representative to give a reasonable demonstration of the complexity and interest of the toponymy of this fascinating area.

Chapter nineteen

TALES AND LEGENDS

I hesitate to describe myself as a folklorist as at no time have I made a detailed study of beliefs and customs, but for over twenty years I have been a collector of stories, a hobby, for that is how it started, which has given me tremendous pleasure. And so I shall tell stories mainly from Sutherland showing why there are differences in lore and customs in this unique part of Scotland and how these differences came about.

I have never seen a ghost, I have never consciously spoken to a witch and I have never seen fairies dancing in the moonlight, but about all these manifestations of the supernatural I maintain an open mind, a kind of agnosticism and, indeed, I may experience any or all of them yet in my lifetime. I continually remind myself of those words from Hamlet, " There are more things in heaven and earth Horatio, than are dreamt of in your philosophy ".

Sutherland is an immense District lashed by the waves of the Minch in the west, where the legendary blue men ride the Atlantic waves ready to lure unwary sailors to their doom, by the cold North Sea where the Vikings of old landed their longships, in the north-east by the fertile lands of Caithness, in the south-east by the waters of the Moray Firth, while in the south Sutherland melts into the beauty of Ross. It is not easy to determine with any exactness where the people of Sutherland stand in the map of ethnic group-ings. They are a mixed bag of Celts, Scots, Picts, Vikings, and since the Clearances, with a not inconsiderable leavening of Low-landers brought in to look after the sheep. The lore and legend of the District bears traces of all those peoples. Wherever they came from, the low-lying mists, the dark lochs and tarns, the dreary moors and the towering mountains were bound to have added to the superstitions they already held and accentuated their fear of the unknown.

A belief that was prevalent from the beginnings of time in all parts of the country and, indeed, all over the world was witchcraft. It was the strange power, so it was said, that enabled some people to change into an animal, or bird or even fish, to perform evil deeds and sometimes murder.

THE HARE

While Celtic lore made the hare the favourite animal into which the witch changed, in Sutherland there were variations of this belief. Such an animal was known as a "familiar". According to the late Dennis Wheatley, an authority on the occult, the witch did not change into an animal but fed it with drops of her own blood. This ensured it would do her bidding, bringing misfortune to anyone to whom she sent it and to whom she bore some grudge. But if injury or death should befall the familiar, the same happened to the witch.

I shall begin with a hare story from the part of the country where I was born, just across the Kyle of Sutherland from Bonar Bridge. It involved a miller who grew suspicious of the antics of a hare in the vicinity of his byre where the cow was about to calve. In his small cottage the byre adjoined the house. One morning, when he went to the byre door, he saw a hare coming towards him. On seeing him the animal turned and fled. Although his cow had not been harmed the miller decided to take precautions and put silver in the milk pail to ward off evil. He went further. He melted down a silver shilling and loaded it into his gun. If the hare was what he believed it was, only a silver bullet would end its mischief. Next morning in the grey of dawn he went to the byre, armed with the gun, and to his amazement saw the hare emerge from the door, which according to the story, was closed. As the hare bolted away, the miller fired hitting the animal which tumbled over several times and then limped into the bushes out of sight. The cow had calved and to the miller's surprise, she seemed unharmed and gave milk freely. A day passed and everything seemed in order . . . In the nearby cottage of an old woman things were not so well. She had not been seen for some time, and her reputation as having the " evil eye " prevented neighbours from enquiring too closely. But a bold character, an old postman, decided to investigate. He got no answer to his knocking and at last forced the door. Sure enough the woman was in bed apparently seriously ill. A doctor was called and he found one of her legs badly injured, a circumstance she refused to explain. But when the doctor used his knife on the wound, he extracted the silver bullet that had been fired from the miller's gun. She survived but her alleged power was destroyed for ever.

FAIR WINDS

It should be understood, of course, that the term witch is applicable equally to men and women. The reason that witches are generally female is said to come from early Christian days when the church had little to offer women and to gain power, those evilly disposed, were in league with the Devil. But witches or warlocks could work for good as well as evil, provided their instructions were faithfully carried out. It was customary for fishermen on occasions to ask a witch for a fair wind to help them to their home port. Such a witch in Assynt was called Mor Bhan or Fair Sarah. When young she was extremely pretty and fell in love with a handsome young man from the district. But she had a rival and they fought each other for his favours . They tore each other's hair out and Sarah, throwing a bunch of her opponent's hair in the air, asked the Devil for his help. She failed to get her lover but she got the black power. She had fresh milk from her neighbours' cows which she could draw from the rafters of her house and she had fresh fish when nobody else had, and her fame as a witch spread over the west coast. On one occasion some fishermen from the north coast were in Assynt fishing when a great storm blew up preventing them from getting home. One of them called on Mor Bhan and asked her help. She went to the boat and taking a sheet rope put three knots in it and told them to hoist sail. If the wind continued too strong they could undo one of the knots and if still too strong another could be untied but on no account were they to touch the third knot until they were safely in harbour. They sailed towards home with a fair wind as advised by the witch. One of the fishermen, thinking that no harm would come to them, wondered what would happen if the third knot was undone. When almost in harbour, this man untied the last knot on the sheet rope and immediately the wind blew with renewed ferocity. It was with great difficulty the boat made port but the man who had disobeyed the witch's instructions fell victim to the wrath of Mor Bhan and was drowned.

THE DOG

Another story from Sutherland has a strange twist about the
behaviour of animals in the presence of evil. A shepherd tending
sheep on the hills in the west was overtaken by a storm and took
shelter in a small bothy. He had dogs with him, a male and a
female. While resting until the storm passed, a bird came down
the chimney, wet and bedraggled. It began to ruffle its feathers,
slowly changing into a woman and growing larger and larger. Suddenly the creature attacked the shepherd and strangely enough, the
bitch assisted the woman in her attack. The dog jumped on the
woman and she fled screaming into the storm with the animal's
teeth in her breast. Shortly after, the dog returned to the bothy
bloodstained and mangled and expired on the floor at its master's
feet. On returning to the township, the shepherd was informed that
a neighbour's wife was seriously ill and likely to die after being
found near her house with severe wounds to her head and breasts.
There are similar stories showing that a female animal will not come
to the assistance of a person attacked by a female witch.

ARDVRECK CASTLE

Witches and warlocks were believed to be in league with the
Devil, but the Prince of Darkness sometimes acted on his own.
Burns' " *Address to the Deil* ", that gem of literature, gives a vivid
description of the haunts and works of the Devil : -

> *I've heard my revern'd Grannie say,*
> *In lonely glens ye like to stray;*
> *Or where old ruined castles, gray,*
> *Nod to the moon,*
> *Ye fright the nightly wanderer's way,*
> *Wi' eldritch croon.*

There is one such castle in Sutherland — Ardvreck Castle in
Loch Assynt — the scene of a visit from the Devil. It followed the
tragedy of the Marquis of Montrose who was defeated at Carbisdale.
To escape capture he swam the Kyle of Sutherland and took to the
mountains, ultimately coming to Ardvreck, the seat of the Macleods
of Assynt, an impoverished branch of the Dunvegan Macleods. He
was treated with the usual Highland hospitality, but news soon
trickled though that there was a price on the head of the fugitive
and Macleod, desperate for money, betrayed him to the Government.

Montrose was arrested and hanged as a traitor in 1650. But Macleod never received the promised reward and his fortunes sank even lower.

One night an elegantly dressed gentleman called at Ardvreck and was entertained, meagre though the fare was. During the meal he disclosed his identity as the Devil and proposed that for the soul of Macleod he was prepared to reverse the fortunes of the family and make the crumbling castle of Ardvreck finer than Dunvegan itself. Macleod was afraid and declined. But the Devil was not to be outdone. Waiting at table was the beautiful young daughter of the house. She was impressed by the stranger and the interest he was taking in her. The association grew as the days passed. In the end the Devil proposed a new plan to Macleod. For the hand of the daughter he would restore the Macleod fortunes, just as if it was the soul of Macleod he had won. Macleod in his greed consented. The unsuspecting daughter was given in marriage to the stranger. The wedding celebrations were the grandest ever seen in the west. But just as the couple were leaving the castle after the wedding to sail to the shore, a violent thunderstorm broke out. The couple sailed into the darkness and were never seen again. Macleod received nothing of the fortune the Devil promised him and when he died his line expired. Today the castle stands in ruins on its island in Loch Assynt. On nights when thunder rolls in the surrounding hills and lightning plays on the dark loch, the screams of a woman can be heard and a figure in white is seen weeping on the stony beach by the ruined castle.

THE KILDONAN CAVE

The Devil could assume any shape, and here is a very different story, from the Strath of Kildonan, a beautiful place especially where the Suisgill Burn, joins the Helmsdale river. Close by there used to be a smithy and near it the entrance to a cave, one of many subterranean passages in the District. This cave was believed to pass underneath the river and come to an end under a township on the other side. One day two girls were herding cattle when they saw two black calves jumping and gambolling nearby before disappearing into the cave. Thinking the calves belonged to their herd, they followed. After some distance along the passage one of the girls suddenly realised that her companion and the calves had disappeared. Becoming terrified, she groped her way along the cave until she reached the end. To her surprise she found that its low

roof moved and pushing it up she found herself in the room of a
house. The occupants, startled by this invasion of their privacy,
fled in terror. The girl climbed into the room and followed the
occupants to reassure them of her harmlessness. When she told her
story the alleged truth came out. Her companion had been the
daughter of a woman believed to be a witch and she had promised
the soul of her daughter to the Devil, but changed her mind. The
Devil, changing into the playful black calves had enticed her into
the cave and neither she nor the calves were ever seen again. The
field where the girls were herding the cattle became known as Ach
nan Nighean — the Field of the Maidens.

GOLSPIE TOWER

Golspie Tower was the scene of another encounter with devils
and demons. Of Golspie Tower nothing now remains. Whether it was
a medieval keep of some sort or not is unknown but that it was
haunted by ghosts and devils is part of the old Golspie folklore.
It was not occupied at the time of the story but was in charge of
a villager who, because of its unsavoury history, seldom visited it.
One winter night during a snowstorm there was a knock at the
man's door and when he opened it there stood a monk looking for
a night's lodging. He was invited into the house and offered a chair
by the fire. The man asked his wife to prepare food while he went
to feed and stable the monk's horse. Supper over, the man explained
to the monk that while he had stabling for the horse, he had no
bed for him, but if he did not mind he could spend the night in the
Tower. The monk, glad of shelter, agreed although he was told in
advance about the ghosts and demons. Both men started for the
Tower through a narrow path overhung with thorns. They reached
the door of the Tower which was opened with much creaking, and
entered the hall. The rooms were examined, the monk chose his
bedroom and the caretaker departed, locking the huge door. The
monk felt fear overtaking him so he placed a lighted candle at each
end of the table, put his sword between them and seating himself on
a chair, put his Bible on his knees. At midnight he heard a great
commotion in the Tower and looking into the hall he saw that a
host of ghosts and demons had entered and there was a crashing of
pots and pans as if preparing for a feast. The monk retired to his
chair thinking his last moment had come. To his horror he heard
footsteps on the stairway and a knock at his door. The holy man
asked who was there and a strange voice said, " 'Tis I. My master

wishes you to join him at supper ". " I have eaten, sir, " replied the terrified monk. The caller left, but soon returned making more noise than ever but again the monk declined the invitation. Again the caller returned and this time the noise and clamour was so great, the Tower seemed to be shaking on its foundations. Fearing now to refuse, the monk, holding a candle, opened the door and facing him was a skeleton with long grey hair. The thing turned and beckoned the monk to follow. When they reached the great hall, there was a table around which sat a motley collection of demons, devils and skeletons. Trembling with fear the monk seated himself at the head of the table where he was invited to take his place. In the midst of the noise he placed his hands over his eyes and said aloud, " O blessed God, thou hast always supported me with thy providence. Permit me not now to feast with devils ". At once darkness descended on the place and the monk found himself in an empty hall with his candle spluttering in his hand. The unholy host had melted into the night at the sound of the Almighty's name. The monk returned to his room and enjoyed a sound sleep until awakened by the caretaker in the morning.

THE FAIRIES

Belief in fairies is perhaps the most intriguing of lore and legend. In his book *The Devil and all his Works* Dennis Wheatley has sugested that the " little people " may have been remnants of a race of small Neolithic men who continued in existence in uninhabited parts of these Islands until the 17th century. It seems that when Christianity came to this country, the little people never acknowledged the Christian God but continued their pagan customs and it was their tenuous association with ordinary Christian people that gave rise to the belief in their supernatural powers. It is said that fairies as envisaged by the modern mind were invented by Shakspeare in *A Midsummer Night's Dream*. For the first time they appeared as miniature people floating on gossamer wings and dancing on rings on the grass and heath. Strange were the beliefs about these fairy rings. If a person ran round a fairy ring nine times on a night of the full moon, the fairies could be heard laughing and making music underneath the ring. But it had to be in a clockwise direction, otherwise there was a danger of being spirited away and never seen again. Our Celtic forefathers, being of a romantic nature, revelled in the belief in fairies and stories of them abound all over the Highlands. There are fairy hills, fairy glens, fairy bridges and fairy hollows. One of the most intriguing stories is of the fairies of Ben Loyal and in the excellent book *The Highlands and their Legends,* Otto Swire refers to them as dwarfs. They were hammerers and this may be an example of Scandinavian influence on Sutherland lore. Thor, the Norse god, was the great hammerer and the ring of his hammer could be heard all over the world. The little people of Ben Loyal were smelters and the ring of their hammers could be heard in the silence of the night by those brave enough to be on the mountain. It was said that if a gift of silver was left on a certain stone along with a plan of some mechanical contrivance, the dwarfs would make it and leave it for collection on the mountain. Apparently the dwarfs were greatly excited when they heard the railway was coming to Sutherland and on an October morning in 1870 they crept unseen from Ben Loyal and hid along the railway line at Golspie to witness the opening of the Duke of Sutherland's railway. They were amazed at the new mechanical monster, but when it suddenly let off steam they were so terrified that they disappeared behind Ben Bhraggie and were never seen again.

People who were spirited into fairyland were said to lose all trace of time. A year was like a day. There was a man in the Lairg district whose wife had just had a child and he set off with a friend to Lairg to have the baby's birth and name entered in the Church records, and to buy some whisky for the celebrations and baptism. As they were returning and somewhat weary they sat down to rest at the foot of a hill. Nearby was an entrance to a cave and the men were astonished to hear coming from it the sound of piping and dancing. The father of the baby went to investigate and disappeared. The friend waited and waited and when weeks passed and the baptism was over people began to allege that murder had taken place. The friend repeated the tale of the father's disappearance and having belief in fairies begged for a year and a day to prove his story. Often he would visit the spot, call at the cave mouth and pray for the return of his friend. When the term had but one day to run, he was sitting at the cave mouth when he thought he saw the missing father within it. He went inside to make sure and to his astonishment found him dancing merrily with the fairies. He caught him and took him out into the open. The father asked why he would not let him finish the dance. "Dance!" said his friend, "surely you have had enough dancing this last year". The father would not believe him and it was not until he got home and found his wife with their year-old child in her arms that he realised he had been a 12-month with the fairies.

But my favourite fairy story is one with a moral. It is about two men, Donald and Angus. Donald was a good man but he was unfortunate enough to have a hump on one of his shoulders. On a New Year's eve he left his cottage to go to the nearby village to buy his stores for the New Year festivities. His path lay near a knoll believed to be the haunt of fairies. It was a sunny, frosty day and suddenly he heard music and to his astonishment there were the little people dancing on the knoll. The tune was to a rhyme about the days of the week and Donald noticed there was something wrong with the measure. It was out of time and he realised they were leaving Wednesday out, and this was putting the dance all wrong. So at the proper moment, Donald shouted " Wednesday " and the fairies, responding to the correction, finished their dance with joy and gusto. And not only that, they invited Donald to join them and they all disappeared into the knoll. There they kept him for a year and a day, sending him back to the world of humans with his back as straight as a ramrod. Now Donald's neighbour, Angus, on hearing of this and being envious of the success it produced decided he would have a try. As it happened Angus also had a hump on one of his shoulders and this deformity embittered him. So, he went to the fairy knoll and sure enough there were the fairies dancing just as Donald had seen them and going wrong in the dance just as before. But Angus in his anxiety to benefit from his lucky encounter forgot what Donald had told him and shouted " Thursday " instead of Wednesday. The fairies were in complete confusion. However, they took Angus with them into the hill but instead of keeping him for a year and a day to share their enjoyment, they pushed him out the next day and alas, not only was his own hump still on one shoulder, but he had Donald's hump on the other! It was the punishment the fairies had meted out to a man who was jealous, bitter and lacking in goodwill at New Year.

THE WATER HORSE

Of all the supernatural creatures flitting through the pages of folklore none was so feared as the water horse, in Gaelic, Each Uisge. Sometimes it was a water bull, Tarbh Uisge. In my own childhood we were forbidden to go near certain lochs which were dark and dangerous because they were said to be the haunts of waterhorses.

The worship of water power was prevalent among the Celtic peoples, but like the power of fire, water could be looked upon as malignant or beneficial. In the Highlands with stormy seas, wave-lashed islands, short and rushing rivers and deep dark lochs, water power was feared and looked upon as malignant. This malignancy often took the form of a horse that could change shape into a handsome young man, or even an old woman. Indeed the water-horse or kelpie as it was sometimes called could change form at will to lure its victims to their deaths. The Highlands abound in stories of these monsters: every river, loch and whirlpool, sandbar or rocky reef had its spirit of evil ready to take the life of human beings. In the Farr district there is a loch known as Lochan Na Cloinne — the Loch of the Children. It is so named because once a number of children were playing on the shore on a Sunday when a beautiful yellow horse came out of the loch. The children were attracted by it and had no difficulty mounting it, all but one who did not like riding. But he liked the sleek coat of the beast and placed his finger on its shoulder. To his horror he found he could not take his finger away. It was stuck fast. Drawing a knife from his belt he cut off his own finger just as the horse was moving away. It was well that he did for the beast rode right into the loch with the children and disappeared. When the people heard about this they rushed to the loch but all they found were parts of the bodies of the children floating on the surface.

Another Sutherland story is about thirteen men who had been on a fishing expedition in a deep loch in the mountains and were on their way home when they decided to rest at an old bothy to have some food. One of the men was a piper and having his instrument with him remarked it was a pity there were no women about so that they could have a dance. No sooner had he uttered the words than to their astonishment, they were joined by a number of young women. The piper blew up and a dance began. The piper, saw to his horror that each female had hoofs instead of feet. He well understood the danger they were all in but was unable to warn his friends who were having a wonderful time. When the dance finished, the piper said he wanted to go out but the woman who had taken him for a partner would not allow him. He removed his belt and offered to let her hold one end while he would hold the other outside the door. She agreed and he was able to hang the buckled end to a nail in the door. He fled for his life. Coming on some horses he mounted one but was immediately thrown. It was a mare. He mounted a second one but was thrown again. It, too, was a mare. The third one was a male and it carried him from the scene at full gallop. Next day when men sent to investigate arrived at the bothy they found to their horror the dead and mutilated bodies of the twelve fishermen. The monster of the loch had had its revenge. In this story we have another example of the strange reluctance of female animals assisting in any way when monsters in female form attacked anyone.

I have a favourite waterhorse story. Near the south end of Loch Shin before the days when it became affected by the Hydro Electric scheme, there was a small island where it is believed once lived a hermit of the ancient Celtic church. The island known as St.Murie's and dedicated to St. Maelrubha was always held in veneration by the people of the area and in fear too as it was believed to be the haunt of the dreaded waterhorse of the loch. A Mr. John Mackay was the first Presbyterian minister of the church at Lairg and on his induction to the charge in 1714 he found great difficulty in persuading the people to come to his church. It seems the people of Lairg were keener on sport on Sundays than church and they paid little heed to the new minister. But the Rev. Mackay was a man of mettle. Unlike many of his contemparies, he was a man of deep learning, of great physical strength and courage, to say nothing of determination. For all that he was making little headway with his rebellious flock. He always carried round with him a stout wood cudgel and if his flock did not respect him for what they called his new fangled doctrines, they certainly respected his strength and the way he could use the cudgel. On one particular Sunday morning, the young men of Lairg were playing the Club, a name for shinty, round the church when the minister, wielding his cudgel to effect, drove them all into the building. After several instances of this kind he at last convinced them to desist from desecrating the Sabbath and to attend divine worship instead. It happened that a little shoemaker appeared before the kirk session charged with assault, insobriety and profanity. He did not deny the charge but disputed the authority of the kirk session to punish him and refused to pay any penalty. Seeing it was useless to argue, the minister invited the shoemaker to meet him at the side of the loch to discuss the matter. He agreed and when they met, the minister asked him if he could swim. On being told that he could not the minister grabbed him by the collar and plunging into the water swam the 55 m (60 yd) to St. Murie's island and left the shoemaker on the stony beach. The Minister told him he would leave him there until he changed his mind, and with that he swam back to the Lairg shore. When the shoemaker recovered from his immersion be began shouting his obstinacy at the minister on the shore saying he would complain to the Sheriff, the Earl of Sutherland, the Court of Session and the General Assembly, but he was never going to yield. As night began to fall and the shadows on the island lengthened into eerie shapes, the shoemaker's bravado began to weaken. Well he knew the story of the dreaded waterhorse and to pass a night on the island was a much more fearsome prospect than accepting the authority of the kirk session. At last the minister heard the terrified entreaties of the little man shouting to be taken off the island. He took no notice at first but fearing that a longer imprison-ment might affect the man's sanity, he launched a boat and rowed to St. Murie's. But before agreeing to take him back to Lairg, the minister made the shoemaker pledge his good behaviour and adherence to church dictates. It is said the man became one of Mr Mackay's most ardent disciples and the minister's supremacy in his parish was assured!

SECOND SIGHT

Second Sight, that strange ability to foresee events and objects invisible to ordinary people has been prevalent among Celtic peoples since the beginning of time. It is a dangerous and most feared gift and many are the strange beliefs surrounding it. It was believed that people who were mutes had what was called " a sight of both worlds " and although they could not speak, they had healing powers denied to others.

The day of the week on which babies were born was said to have an effect on the character. Those born at midnight and during the hour before or after that time, were said to have the power to see ghosts and to have the second sight. Some children are born with a thin membrane, known as a caul, covering the head and provided the caul is preserved the person will, according to legend, never be drowned, will be free from the power of witches and fairies and have the second sight. I was discussing this very subject with a prominent Brora lady recently and to my amazement she pro-duced from her handbag a small leather purse which contained the very caul with which she had been born. She would not part with it for anything. I cannot say if this good lady has the gift of second sight, or whether she has had any visions, but the possibility would not surprise me. In the 18th century, cauls were much sought after by sailors to protect them from drowning as the power was said to pass to the new owner and many an unscrupulous midwife indulged in the nefarious practice of selling them for profit. But it was dangerous, for unless the caul was buried with the rightful owner, the dead would not rest in the grave and the ghost would haunt the person to whom the caul had been given or sold. Great too was the power believed vested in the seventh son of a seventh son. Not only were they said to have second sight but had strange healing powers and to this day are thought to make excellent doctors. But the power of second sight was a painful quality over which the possessor had no control. The visions or sightings were usually of death or some such manifestation that foretold death and it is this strange association which has puzzled researchers.

Two Sutherland stories in this context come to mind. In one a woman had a vision of her son falling over a cliff. Soon afterwards, he was herding sheep at the cliffs near his home and on trying to rescue a lamb that had fallen on to a ledge, he fell to his death. In another case, a fisherman's wife in a vision saw her husband who was at sea at the time enter the house in dripping oilskins, remove a stone from the fireplace and take it away. Next day news was received that a fishing boat had foundered in a storm and all hands were lost, including the husband of the woman who had the vision. But the strange thing about this story is that when the woman examined the cavity left by the stone the vision had removed there was her husband's life savings revealed for her use. Another example involves a Brora woman who, having had occasion to go from Brora to the Manse at Lothbeg, observed a funeral procession going along the road in front of her. Overtaking it, she spoke to some of the men she recognised in the rear of the cortege. She asked whose funeral it was but got no reply. She followed them into the churchyard near the manse and distinctly heard the men speaking among themselves. Standing not far from the grave she actually saw the coffin lowered into it and the earth filled in. The funeral party vanished out of sight the moment the interment was completed and the woman knew she had seen a phantom funeral. She related her experience to friends at the Manse. A few days afterwards a real funeral cortege came to the churchyard attended by the very people mentioned by the woman, the grave being dug and the coffin placed in it at the very spot she saw the spectre burial taking place. The woman, after seeing the phantom funeral, suffered a severe mental collapse and spent several weeks in bed.

Perhaps the greatest of all possessors of second sight was Coinneach Odhar, the Brahan Seer. There are few instances of predictions about Sutherland but one which is alleged to have come true is of interest. He foretold the Clachtoll in the Stoer peninsula, that natural arch, would fall with a crash so loud that the Laird of Ledmore's cattle, 32km (20 miles) away, would be so terrified that they would break their tethers and flee. The prophecy was fulfilled in 1841 when Ledmore cattle strayed north into Stoer and when the arch fell with a resounding crash the cattle fled home in panic, tearing everything before them.

It is said that some people who have the gift of second sight can also see ghosts. According to legend, Celtic ghosts are the spirits of the unhappy departed dead. No ghost returns to earth if happy among the blessed, except in rare cases of revenge. But if a man or woman dies without confessing or repairing some wrong done to anyone in lifetime, the ghost returns and haunts the place where he or she lived until it is spoken to. It then reveals the secret and disappears for ever . . . . A crofter from the Stoer area died and the very night after the funeral his ghost returned to his house and sat in his familiar chair. His little grandchild on seeing him and not understanding about death went and sat between his knees. His relatives were terrified. He disappeared in the early hours of the morning but returned again in the evening, and this behaviour persisted until he became most unwelcome in the house. So the relatives decided to send for a holy man they thought would speak to the ghost. Next time the ghost arrived the holy man blessed himself, made a chalk circle round himself on the floor and asked the ghost why he was back on earth and annoying his people. The reply was remarkable. It seemed he was troubled by a dishonest act he had committed before dying and had to confess it to the living. He had stolen a cow and the owner had taken him to court but he had given false evidence on oath and got away with the crime. He now wished the man to be given a cow and he would disappear and worry no one again. His story was checked and found to be true. The beast was handed over and the ghost was never seen again. Another Sutherland story is about a north coast merchant who died and not long after his death his ghost returned but the relatives were too afraid to speak. At last a bold servant girl plucked up courage and asked the ghost why he was haunting the place and terrifying people. He said that during his lifetime as a merchant he had used false weights and measures. He had cheated his customers and even his servants and to make amends he said his son must destroy the false measures, marry the girl who had been brave enough to speak to him and he would disappear and live in peace among the spirits. The wishes of the ghost were carried out and the family were left in peace, and, according to the story, prosperity.

FUNERALS AND FUNERAL RITES

From ghosts and coffins to funerals! A sensation of horror spread throughout the country following the trial in Edinburgh of a man Burke who with Helen Macdougall was tried for sixteen murders in the West Port area of the city. The bodies, it was alleged, had been sold to anatomists for medical experiments. And to provide more bodies, grave robberies became the order of the day to such an extent that vigilantes were set up to guard graveyards. Even in the Highlands, graveyard watching became an important part of funeral arrangements and watching bothies were erected in most graveyards to prevent desecration by body snatchers or resurrectionists as they were called. It became the duty of friends of the last person buried to hold watch till the next burial took place when the friends of the new deceased took up the vigil. It is said that Fascally House in Brora near the old coal pit had a haunted room where a doctor of the late 18th century carried out anatomical experiments on bodies taken from the old Clynekirkton cemetery. Despite the seriousness of the situation some amusing incidents took place, especially when two funerals were arranged for the same day, as this story from West Sutherland will illustrate. The funerals approached the graveyard from opposite directions and spies were posted to report progress. In those days coffins were transported on the shoulders of mourners, all taking turns at carrying. As they neared the cemetery, their speed increased until they were both running in a most ridiculous manner considering the solemnity of the occasion. When almost at the graveyard it was obvious that one party would be inside first as the gate was nearest to it, while the other party had to go round the cemetery wall to reach the entrance. When passing the wall and fearing they would be beaten in the race one of the coffin bearers shouted, "Over the wall with the cailleach", and the coffin was unceremoniously pitched over. The deceased's little grandchild was among the mourners and evidently enjoyed what seemed great fun for him and was heard to say, in Gaelic "Isn't my granny the boy? She never liked to be left behind!" Needless to say, by this stratagem, the graveyard watching fell to to be carried out by the friends of the other deceased who just failed to make the graveyard in time. In olden days there were some strange customs in connection with burial grounds and funerals. In some places a new cemetery would remain empty until a tramp died and was buried there before it came into general use. There is an old rhyme which says,

> " *Happy is the bride the sun shines on;*
> *Happy is the corpse that the rain rains on.*"

And so it was considered unlucky to have a funeral on a sunny day.

The placing of flowers on the grave is thought to be a remnant of the old pagan custom of making offerings to the dead or burying personal belongings with the corpse. It used to be the custom to hold watches or wakes over the dead as it was believed the soul of the departed remained with the corpse until it was actually placed in the grave. And often these wakes were far from being sober affairs. Drink flowed freely and relatives might fall out and come to blows. No longer do we see the long slow processions of mourners, all in deep black and all taking a hand carrying the coffin to the graveyard. Even in my own childhood it was the custom for whisky, biscuits and cheese to be handed round at the graveside after the coffin was lowered and the earth filled in. In some cases it was a welcome re-past after the long miles of carrying a coffin. But still today, it is customary for the women folks to remain at home and prepare a large meal for the returning mourners, provided they do not retire to the nearest hostelry for drinks and stay too long.

I am indebted to Mr Hugh Campbell, a crofter pensioner, until recently resident in that delightful crofting township, the Doll at Brora, for this story about funerals. It happened about the turn of the century that an English visitor was fishing the River Brora where it skirts the Doll when he saw emerging from nearly every cottage, men in deep black, with solemn faces, slow tread and each with a bowler or, as they were called, "half-milestone" hat. He enquired from one man what meeting was in progress and was told they were all going to a funeral. The visitor was satisfied with the explanation, but some four hours later he was given a surprise. Wafting towards the Doll came the the sound of singing and merriment and to his amaze-ment the sombre attired crofters were returning in jolly groups, indulging in horse play, dancing, and throwing the black hats in the air. On returning to his hotel and relating his experience, he was heard to remark, " Well, I don't know what sort of place the Doll of Brora is to live in, but it certainly seems a happy place to die!"

THE SALMON

In this small contribution, I have touched on the richness of lore and legend in Sutherland. I have had to leave out many "old wives' tales", many customs, strange cures and stories of marriage, divination and luck but I would like to conclude with two delightful stories from Otto Swire's "The Highlands and their Legends". Salmon fry are not so well behaved as the elegant salmon and the River Helmsdale abounds in both. It seems that when the Devil was cast from Heaven, he found himself for some strange reason on the banks of the river at Helmsdale, and the salmon fry jumping in their dozens out of the water kept mocking him and calling "Sooty nose" and making other rude remarks. So the Devil, sore and angry at this treatment, roundly cursed the fish. And that is why every tenth fry hatched in the river has two heads, two tails or some other deformity which results in them being eaten by their cannibalistic brothers and sisters. Some 64km (40 miles) from the Helmsdale is the Shin, a river with steep banks covered in birches, bracken and myriad moor flowers. With its dark pools and gleaming white waterfalls it is indeed lovely. So it is said, Christ thought. Christ who loves all the world and particularly the Highland glens and brown peat rivers often visits them. He usually comes in winter when there are few human beings about and He can watch the fish and birds and beasts who come to greet Him. One clear winter night, bright almost as day with the moon's light when every tree and grass blade sparkled with the silver frost Christ came to the River Shin and rejoiced in the beauty of it. Then He noticed the fish, heavy, busy and preoccupied, obviously in trouble. He called a large salmon to Him and asked what was wrong in so beautiful a world. "Oh, yes, it may be beautiful" said the salmon impatiently, "but it isn't going to last. We can smell a real freeze coming, real black frost and then the river may freeze too. That is the one danger against which we are helpless." And Christ had pity on the salmon. He stretched out His hand and blessed the River Shin and said to the salmon, " You need no longer be afraid. The waters of this river will never freeze again." And they never have.

Bibliography

Adam, R. J. (Ed.)	"John Home's Survey of Assynt"	Edinburgh	1960
Adam, R. J. (Ed.)	"Papers on Sutherland Estate Management" — 2 volumes	Edinburgh	1972
Adam & Rankin	"Survey of Parishes of Assynt and Eddrachilles"	Inverness	1964
Akroyd, C. H.	"A Veteran Sportsman's Diary"	Inverness	1926
Anderson, A. O. & Anderson, M. O.	"Adomnan's Life of St. Columba"	Edinburgh	1961
Anderson, J.	"The Orkneyinga Saga"	Edmonston & Douglas Thin (repr. 1973)	1873
Anderson, M. L.	"A History of Scottish Forestry"	Nelson	1967
Anon.	"A Nature Conservancy Review"	C.U.P.	1977
Answers made by Schoolmasters in Scotland to queries circulated in 1838		House of Commons	1841
Auld, A.	"Ministers and Men in the Far North"	Edinburgh	1891
Barber, A. J. et alia	The Lewisian and Torridonian Rocks of North-West Scotland Geologists' Association Guide No. 21	The Geologists' Association, London	1978
Beaton, D.	"Noted Ministers of the Northern Highlands"	Inverness	1929
Beaton, D. (Ed.)	"Notes on the Tongue Presbytery Records"	in Old Lore Miscellany Vol. VII Vol. VIII	1914 1920
Bentinck, C. D.	"Dornoch Cathedral and Parish"	Inverness	1926
Birse, E. L. & Dry, F. T.	"Assessments of Climatic Conditions in Scotland"	Macaulay Institute, Soil Survey of Scotland	1970
Blaeu, J.	"Atlas: Scotia quae est European"	Amsterdam	1662
Brichan, J.	"Origines Parochiales Scotiae. The Antiquities Ecclesiastical and Territorial of the Parishes of Scotland" (2 volumes)	Lizars	1855
Brøgger, A. W.	"Ancient Emigrants"	Oxford	1929
Burl, A.	"The Stone Circles of Scotland"	Yale University	1976
Burnett, G. & Mackay, A. J. G. (Eds.)	"The Exchequer Rolls of Scotland" — Vol. 13	Edinburgh	1891
Burnett, J. M. (Ed.)	"The Vegetation of Scotland"	Oliver & Boyd	1964
Campbell, H. P.	"Notes on the County of Sutherland in the Eighteenth Century"	Trans. of Gael. Soc. Inv. Vol. XXVI	1907
Clarke, J. G. D.	"Prehistoric Europe: The Economic Basis"	London	1952
Coles, J.	"Scottish Early Bronze Age Metalwork"	Proc. Soc. Antiq. Scot. 101, 1-110	1968-9

Coles, J.	"Scottish Middle Bronze Age Metalwork"	Proc. Soc. Antiq. Scot. 97, 82-156	1963-4
Coles, J.	"Scottish Late Bronze Age Metalwork" Typology, Distributors and Chronology"	Proc. Soc. Antiq. Scot. 93, 16-134	1959-60
Commissioners of the British Fisheries	"Annual Report"		1855-56
Commissioners Report on the Employment of Children, Young Persons and Women in Agriculture	Appendix Part II		1869
Corbet, G. B. & Southern, H. N.	"The Handbook of British Mammals" (2nd edition)	Oxford	1977
Craig, G. Y. (Ed.)	"The Geology of Scotland"	Edinburgh	1965
Crawford, B. E.	"The Earldom of Caithness and the Kingdom of Scotland"	Northern Scotland Vol. 2 No. 2	1977
Curle, A. O.	"Exploration of a Chambered Cairn at Achaidh"	Proc. Soc. Antiq. Scot. No. 44, 104-11	1910
Davidson, J. M.	"A Miscellany of Antiquities in Easter Ross and Sutherland"	Proc. Soc. Antiq. Scot. No. 80, 25-33	1948
Day, J. P.	"Public Administration in the Highlands and Islands of Scotland"	Univ. of London Press	1918
Education Enquiry (Scotland): Abstract of answers made in 1834		House of Commons	1838
Fairhurst, H. & Taylor, D. B.	"A Hut-circle Settlement at Kilphedir, Sutherland"	Proc. Soc. Antiq. Scot. Vol. 103, 65-99	1971
Fanaticism in the North by "Investigator"		Blackwood	1852
Feachem, R.	"Prehistoric Scotland"	Batsford	1963
Fishery Board for Scotland	"Annual Report, 1886, 1900 & 1913"		
Flinn, M. (Ed.)	"Scottish Population History"	C.U.P.	1977
Forbes, D. (Ed.)	"The Sutherland Clearances, 1806-1820: a documentary survey"	Craigie College, Ayr	1977
Ford, T. D.	"The Sutherland Caves"	Cave Research Group (GB) Vol. 5 No. 2	1959
Fraser, Sir W.	"The Sutherland Book" (3 Vols.)	Edinburgh	1892
Geikie, J.	"Trans, Roy. Soc. Edin."	Vol. 24	1866
George, T. N.	"Geomorphic Evolution in Hebridean Scotland"	Soc. J. Geol. 2(1)	1966
Godard, A.	"Recherches de geomorphologie en Ecosse du Nord-Ouest"	Paris	1965
Gordon, Sir R.	"A Genealogical History of the Earldom of Sutherland from its origin to the year 1630"	Edinburgh	1813

Grant, M. W.	"The Parish of Golspie in the Shire of Sutherland, 850AD-1850AD"	M. W. Grant, Golspie	1977
Gray, J.	"Sutherland and Caithness in Saga Time"	Oliver & Boyd	1922
Gray, J. M. & Lowe, J. J. (Eds.)	"The Scottish Late-glacial Environment"	Edinburgh	1977
Gray, M.	"Crofting and Fishing in the North-West Highlands, 1890-1914"	in Northern Scotland Vol. 1 No. 1	1973
Gray, M.	"The Highland Economy 1750-1850"	Oliver & Boyd	1957
Grieg, S.	"Viking Antiquities in Scotland in Shetelig, H. "Viking Antiquities in Great Britain and Ireland"	Oslo	1940
Grimble, I.	"Chief of MacKay"	London	1965
Grimble, I.	"The Trial of Patrick Sellar"	London	1962
Gunn, the Rev. A. with MacKay, J.	"Sutherland and the Reay Country"	Glasgow	1897
Harting, J. E.	"British Animals Extinct within Historic Times"	London	1880
Harvie-Brown, J. A. & Buckley, T. E.	"A Vertebrate Fauna of Sutherland, Caithness and West Cromarty"	Edinburgh	1887
Harvie-Brown, J. A. & Buckley, T. E.	"A Fauna of the Moray Basin"	Edinburgh	1895
Harvie-Brown, J. A. & Macpherson, H. A.	"A Fauna of the North-West Highlands and Skye"	Edinburgh	1904
Henderson, I.	"The Picts"	Thames & Hudson	1967
Henderson, I.	"The Meaning of the Pictish Symbol Stones" in Meldrum, E. "The Dark Ages in the Highlands"	Inverness Field Club, 53-67	1971
Henderson, J.	"General View of Agriculture of Sutherland"	Board of Agriculture	1815
Henshall, A. S.	"The Chambered Tombs of Scotland" (2 Vols.)	Edinburgh	1963 1972
Henshall, A. S. & Wallace, J. C.	"The Excavation of a Chambered Cairn at Embo, Sutherland"	Proc. Soc. Antiq. Scot. Vol. 96, 9-36	1965
Hunter, J.	"The Making of the Crofting Community"	John Donald	1976
Hunter, J.	"Sheep and deer: Highland sheep farming, 1850-1900"	Northern Scotland (i)	1973
Huxtable, J. et. al.	"Dating a settlement pattern by thermoluminescence: the burnt mounds of Orkney"	Archaeometry Vol. 18 No. 1	1976
Inventory of Ancient Monuments and Constructions in Sutherland		HMSO	1911
Iona Club	"Collectanea de Resus Albanicus, Original Papers and Documents relating to the History of the Highlands and Islands"	Edinburgh	1847
Johnston, M. R. W. & Parsons, I.	"Macgregor and Phemister's Geological Excursion Guide to the Assynt District of Sutherland"	Edinburgh Geological Society	1979

Jowsey, P. C.	"Peatlands" in "The Organic Resources of Scotland" (ed. Joy Tivy)	Oliver & Boyd	1973
Kenworthy, J. B.	"John Anthony's Flora of Sutherland"	Bot. Soc. Edinburgh	1976
Lamb, R. G.	"Coastal Settlements of the North"	Scot. Archaeol. Forum 5	1973
Lightfoot, J.	"Flora Scotica"	London	1777
Loch, J.	"An Account of the Improvements on the Estates of the Marquess of Stafford"	London	1820
Macalister, R. A. S.	"The Memorial Slabs of Clonmacnoise"		1909
Macdonald, A.	"On 'Papar' Names in N. & W. Scotland"	Northern Studies 9, 25-30	1977
Macdonald, J.	"Agriculture of Sutherland"	Blackwood	1880
Macfarlane, W.	"Geographical Collections relating to Scotland"	Scot. Hist. Soc. (Edinburgh)	1908
Macgregor, M. & Phemister, J.	"Geological Excursion Guide to the Assynt district of Sutherland" (3rd Edition)	Geol. Soc. Edin.	1972
MacInnes, J.	"The Evangelical Movement in the Highlands of Scotland 1688-1800"	Aberdeen U.P.	1951
Mackenzie, A.	"The History of the Highland Clearances"	Maclaren	1883, 1946
Macleod, D.	"Gloomy Memories in the Highlands of Scotland"	Canadian Edition	1857
Macleod, J.	"Bypaths of Highland Church History"	Knox Press	1965
Mackay, A.	"Sketches of Sutherland"	Edinburgh	1889
Mackay, A.	"The Book of Mackay"	Edinburgh	1906
Mackay, A.	"The History of the Province of Cat"	Wick	1914
Mackay, R.	"History of the House and Clan of Mackay"	Edinburgh	1829
Mackie, E. W.	"English Migrants and Scottish Brochs"	Glasgow Archaeol. Journal 39-71, Vol.2	1971
Mackie, E. W.	Scotland: An Archaeological Guide"	Faber	1975
MacWhite, E.	"A new View on Irish Bronze Age Rock-Scribings"	J.R.S.A.I. 76, 59-80	1946
Matheson, W.	"The Pape Riot and its Sequel in Lewis"	Trans. Gael. Soc. Inverness Vol. 48	1973
McNeill, P. & Nicholson, R. (Eds.)	"An Historical Atlas of Scotland c. 400 - c. 1600"	Confer. Scot. Medievalists	1975
McVean, D. N. & Lockie, J. D.	"Ecology and Land Use in Upland Scotland"	E.U.P.	1969

Memoirs of the Geological Survey of Great Britain	"The Geological Structure of the North-West Highlands of Scotland"	1907
	"The Geology of Ben Wyvis, Carn Chuinneag, Inchbae and the surrounding country"	1912
	"The Geology of Strath Oykel and Lower Loch Shin"	1926
	"The Geology of the country round Golspie, Sutherland"	1925
	"The Geology of Central Sutherland"	1931
Meteorological Office	"Monthly Weather Report"	
	"Maps of mean and extreme temps. over the UK 1941-70"	Climat. Memo. 73	1975
	"Maps of mean number of days of snow over the UK 1941-70"	Climat. Mem. 74	1975
	"Averages of Temperature for the UK, 1941-70"	Met. Office 883	1976
Millais, J. G.	"The Mammals of Great Britain and Ireland"	London	1904
Miller, H.	"Sutherland as it was and is"	Myles Macphail	1844
Mitchell, J.	"Remininscences of my life in the Highlands" — 2 Vols.	David & Charles	1883 (repr.1971)
Mitchell, ME. C.	"A New Analysis of the Early Bronze Age Beaker Pottery of Scotland"	Proc. Soc. Antiq. Scot. 68, 132-189	1933-4
Morris, R. W.	"The Cup-and-Ring Marks and Similar Sculptures of Scotland: A survey of the Southern Counties, Part II"	Proc. Soc. Antiq. Scot. 100, 47-48	1967-8
Moss, R.	"A Comparison of Red Grouse Stocks with the Production and Nutritive Value of Heather"	Journ. Anim. Ecol. Vol. 38, 103-122	1969
Murray, A.	"The Northern Flora"	Edinburgh	1836
Neves, R. & Selley, R. C.	"A Review of the Jurassic Rocks of Sutherland" in Finsted, K. and Selley, R. C. (Eds.)	Proc. of Jurassic North Sea Symposium Norwegian Petroleum Soc.	1975
New Statistical Account for Scotland (N.S.A.)		Edinburgh	1936
Nicolaisen, W. F. H.	"Gaelic Place-Names" in McNeill, P. and Nicholson, R. (Ed.)	Confer. Scot.	1975
Nicolaisen, W. F. H.	"Scottish Place Names"	Batsford	1976
O'Dell, A. C. & Walton, K.	"The Highlands and Islands of Scotland"	Edinburgh	1962
Ogilvie, A. G.	"The Physiography of the Moray Firth Coast"	Trans. Roy. Soc. Edin. Vol. 53, pt. 2 (No. 19)	1923
O.S.A. (Old Statistical Account for Scotland)		Edinburgh 21 Vols.	1790-8

Palsson, H. & Edwards, P.	"The Orkneyinga Saga. The History of the Earls of Orkney"	London	1978
Peach, B. N.	"Proc. Roy. Soc. Edin. Vol. 37, 327"		1917
Pennant, T.	"A Tour in Scotland 1769"	Chester	1771
Pennington, W.	"The History of British Vegetation"	English UP	1969
Phemister, J.	"The Northern Highlands"	Brit. Reg. Geol. Scot. (6th impression) I.G.S.	1974
Prebble, J.	"The Highland Clearances"	Penguin Books	1963; 1970
Price, R. J.	"Highland Landforms"	Morrison & Gibb	1976
Raven, J. & Walters, M.	"Mountain Flowers"	Connins	1956
Reid, R. W. K. et. al.	"Prehistoric Settlement in Durness"	Proc. Soc. Antiq. Scot. 99, 21-53	1966-7
Report on the Department Comm. on Sea Fisheries in Sutherland and Caithness		1905	
Richards, E.	"Leviathan of Wealth: the Suther- land Fortune in the Industrial Revolution"	Routledge & Kegan Paul	1973
Ritchie, J.	"The Influence of Man on Animal Life in Scotland"	C.U.P.	1920
Ritchie, J.	"Scottish Naturalist: Cave- Hunting in Scotland"	97-102	1918
Ritchie, W. & Mather, A.	"The Beaches of Sutherland"	Univ. of Aberdeen	1969
Sage, D.	"Memorabilia Domestica, or Parish Life in the North of Scotland"	Albyn Press	1889; 1976
Saxon, J.	"Fossil Fishes of the North of Scotland"	Thurso	1975
Saxon, J.	"Kildonan Gold"	Golspie	1975
St John, C.	"A Tour in Sutherlandshire"	London	1849
Selby, P. J.	"On the Quadrupeds and Birds Inhabiting the County of Suther- land"	Trans. Nat. Hist. Soc. Northern Scotland Vol. 2 (2), 288-303	1838
Selley, R. C.	"The Habitat of North Sea Oil"	Proc. Geol. Assoc. 87(4), 359-87	1975
Sinclair, Sir J.	"The Statistical Account of Scotland (21 Vols.)"	Creech	1790-98
Sissons, J. B.	"The Evolution of Scotland's Scenery"	Oliver & Boyd	1967
Sissons, J. B.	"The Geomorphology of the British Isles: Scotland"	Methuen	1976
Smith, J. & Mather, A.	"The Beaches of East Sutherland"	Univ. of Aberdeen	1973

Smout, T. C.	"The Highland Clearances"	Scottish International	1972
Spence, M.	"Flora Orcadensis"	Kirkwall	1914
Steer, K. A.	"The Early Iron Age Homestead at West Plean	Proc. Soc. Antiq. Scot. 89,227-251	1955-6
Steers, J. A.	"The Coastline of Scotland"	Cambridge	1973
Steven, H. M. & Carlisle, A.	"The Native Pinewoods of Scotland"	Cunningham & Sons	1959
Strang, T.	"SMC Guide: The Northern Highlands"		1975
Sutherland and the Sutherlanders, their religious and social conditions		Myles Macphail	1844
Swire, O. F.	"The Highlands and their Legends"	Oliver & Boyd	1963
Symon, J. A.	"Scottish Farming"	Oliver & Boyd	1959
Tait, L.	"Note on the Shell-mounds of Sutherland"	Proc. Soc. Antiq. Scot. Vol. 8, 63-4	1869
Tait, L.	Notes on the Shell-mounds, etc."	Proc. Soc. Antiq. Scot. Vol. 7, 525-32	1870
Tansley, A. G.	"The British Islands and their Vegetation"	Cambridge	1949
Taylor, A. B.	"The Orkneyinga Saga"	Edinburgh	1938
Thom, A.	"Megalithic Sites in Britain"	Clarendon Press	1967
Tranter, N.	"The Fortified House in Scotland"	Chambers Vol. 5	1970
Watson, J. A. S.	"The rise and development of the sheep industry in the Highlands"	Trans. of Highland Agric. Soc. of Scot. 5th ser. XLIV	1932
Wheatley, D.	"The Devil and All His Works"	Hutchison	1971
Wheeler, P. T.	"Landownership and the crofting system in Sutherland since 1800"	Agric. History Review XIV	1966
White, I. D. & Mottershead, D. N.	"Past and Present Vegetation in relation to solifluction on Ben Arkle, Sutherland"	Trans. Proc. Bot. Soc. Edin. Vol. 41, 475-89	1972
Whittington, G.	Placemanes and the Settlement Pattern of Dark-age Scotland	Proc. Soc. Antiq. Scot. Vol. 106 99-110	1974-75
Whittles, C. L.	"Heath Areas in Scotland"	Scottish Beekeeper 26	1950
Wilson, D. M.	"The Treasure" in A. Small (Ed.) St. Ninian's Isle and Its Treasure	Oxford	1973
Worsaae, J. J. A.	"An Account of the Danes and Norwegians in England, Scotland and Ireland"	London	1852

Index

Index